C000177143

DENIAL, DECE

DENIAL, DECEIT, DISCOVERY

J. James

© J. James, 2013

Published by Inkslingers Publishing

Disclaimer
In the interest of privacy, all names have been changed. Any resemblance to persons living or dead is purely coincidental.

A CIP catalogue record for this book is available from the British Library.

ISBN 978-0-9576403-0-6 (Paperback)
ISBN 978-0-9576403-1-3 (epub)
ISBN 978-0-9576403-2-0 (mobi)

Prepared and printed by:

York Publishing Services Ltd
64 Hallfield Road
Layerthorpe
York YO31 7ZQ

Tel: 01904 431213

Website: www.yps-publishing.co.uk

DEDICATION

Dedicated to the loving memory of Sheila and Jimbo – you always believed in my potential and unknowingly inspired me so much.

ACKNOWLEDGEMENTS

To my loving family whose love has always carried me through the difficult stages in my life.

To all my friends who read the book at every stage and provided support, encouragement and praise. I am so grateful for your help.

To Gary at Bubble Cow - thank you for your positive and constructive feedback. Oishi for your talented creative ideas and for producing a great cover. To all of the staff at York Publishing for their support – many thanks, especially to Clare.

Most importantly I would like to thank my amazing fiancé TS. Your love has provided me with the inspiration to write. I am truly blessed.

PROLOGUE

'**D**id you ever think of men when you masturbated?'
Sometimes I cannot believe I have arrived at this point. This is one of many direct and personal questions from the Catholic priest dealing with my annulment. I cannot help but sense his judgement of me, from his failure to hide his disgust to the way his sunken, weathered eyes glare at me as he waits for my sordid responses. I am sitting in a room that reminds me of a nursing home. It is bitterly cold, although I'm not sure if I am shivering from the cold or the depth of the questioning. Excessively floral wallpaper with clashing printed soft furnishings is never a good look. The mahogany, 70s-style furniture pieces mark the perimeter of the room while the over-sized portrait of God's beloved son hanging above the chimneybreast is particularly distracting. I do not feel comfortable discussing my love of cock with a priest, let alone with Jesus in the room!

Two years after our thirteen year relationship ended, I have been instructed by my now ex-wife to visit the priest to support her annulment application – a Catholic loophole that allows two Catholics to declare that their marriage never truly existed. We have to prove that I was incapable of willingly entering into the marriage due to my underlying, yet undiscovered, homosexuality. Personally I do not have the patience for this, but it is a small gift for my ex-wife that will enable her to one day remarry in the eyes of God.

In 2001 we married after seven happy years and we stayed married for another six, although maybe these were not as happy as the first seven. And why did I do it? Why did I marry a girl when the answer to the opening question was YES? Quite simply, because I loved her. When I stood there on the day of our wedding it never entered my mind that I was lying, or trying to cover up or trick anyone. I simply loved her and wanted to spend my entire life with her. On reflection, I guess I knew I was gay but I certainly did not want to live my life as a gay man. At that point I had never admitted to myself that I was indeed gay; something I have come to regret. It was not out of malice or false intentions, rather just total confusion and denial, born out of an upbringing in a straight, Catholic world. The signs were all there, but no one ever asked me the question and, therefore, I had no reason to even question it myself.

I have spent many a sleepless night trying to piece together the complex story of my sexuality and can now define three distinct periods in my life: one of denial, one of deceit and a final time of discovery. To some extent they are chronological but there are many overlaps between each phase of my life. When I finally declared my sexuality at the age of thirty-one, I ended the thirty-one years of denial – a pretty hefty sentence for anyone! To some extent I am still there now. But there have been many exciting and somewhat dangerous discoveries along the way; from early childhood fumbles with girls, mutual masturbation sessions with male friends as teenagers first discovering porn, to naïve visits to male prostitutes as a young man and random hook ups with strangers off the Internet as a married man. With some of these discoveries came webs of deceit shrouded in guilt, lies and more confusion. But it was these very experiences that have shaped the gay man I am today – one who has found true monogamous love.

Since accepting my homosexuality, many people have used the line, '*You had a choice...*' but to me it was anything but a choice. In fact, I would say I did everything possible to choose *not* to be gay and, despite my greatest efforts, to suppress who I really was; eventually it came and bit me on the arse anyway.

DENIAL

CHAPTER ONE

Around the age of ten I remember having my first 'gay' feelings. There were no positive role models around in the late-eighties and no one ever talked about being gay or gay feelings, or if they did it was always in a very derogatory way to belittle or mock someone. So I had no concept of the meaning of these feelings. My first vivid memory was when I saw my primary school teacher, Mr Simms, naked in the shower whilst at holiday camp. He was a young, fit and rather handsome guy. I remember being enticed by his hairy, thickset body and of course his penis, which I was mesmerised by. At the age of ten there did not seem to be anything sexual involved, just utter fascination. The image of his naked body still stays with me now.

This vision occurred on the first night of the trip. We were in the final year of primary school and had travelled to Cornwall on an adventure activities week. It was so much fun staying in a caravan with a group of your closest friends. There were about six pupils per caravan with one adult supervising in each. I remember my disappointment when our teacher announced who the responsible adult was in our caravan. I really wanted it to be Mr Simms but instead we got Rob, the older brother of one of my classmates. His girlfriend was also supervising one of the other caravans. Rob was a scrawny, lanky young guy covered in threatening tattoos; the perfect image for someone supervising primary aged pupils I am sure! Looking back now I guess he did have a cute face, although his mass of ginger hair made him less appealing. I remember when he arrived at school wearing grey jogging pants, that were certainly too tight in the crotch area, I noticed something nestling in there and I'm sure I was not the only one as I caught a few of the younger teaching assistants giggling.

Mr Simms had ordered us to take showers at six o'clock, after a long and lively bus ride from school earlier that day. Once showered, we were instructed to go back to the caravans and settle down before lights out at nine. I think Mr Simms had deliberately waited for us to be tucked up in bed before taking a shower himself, for the purpose of appropriateness. I had left my wash bag in the shower block so had crept back over to collect it. The path to the old shower room was really dark, but I could see a light in the distance and hear the sound of running water. As I gently opened the door I caught a glimpse of his hairy tight butt. I was frozen to the spot and waited until he turned around so I could see what was hanging between his legs. Mr Simms was covered top to toe in soap suds and his eyes were closed so he did not spot me staring. He turned back around and the hot soapy water ran down his muscular back and the crack of his arse. He was a rugby player at the weekends and so, although very short, he had very muscular, strong legs. I thought Rob would be looking for me soon so I grabbed my wash bag and, before leaving, took one last look at what would later come to be the type of man I would fantasise about fucking.

I'm not quite sure why the school allowed Rob and his girlfriend to act as 'responsible adults' because they were anything but responsible! I grew up in a very working-class area of South Wales with high unemployment and crime figures above the national average. Whilst I'm proud of my upbringing I certainly recognise the calibre of people my school had to choose from when organising this kind of trip. Rob was an unemployed nineteen-year-old former pupil at our Catholic School, and many of his siblings were still going through the education system. He was someone you would describe as 'dragged up' – six siblings, five different fathers.

On the third day Mr Simms had organised for us to go swimming at the pool, which was located on the caravan site. There were a number of lifeguards there so he had given the accompanying adults, including Rob and his girlfriend Julie, some much-needed time off. You can imagine how difficult it was to control a caravan full of pre-pubescent kids. I am sure the sleep deprivation was starting to take its toll on these volunteers.

After twenty minutes of swimming I needed the toilet, so I quickly ran back to my caravan with my close friend Michael. We came bounding into the caravan like two Labrador puppies to discover Julie holding the rather thick, long and very pink cock attached to Rob. We were frozen to the spot and, for the first time on the trip, speechless. Of course my beady eyes were transfixed by Rob's cock. This was the first time I had ever seen an erect dick. The veins were throbbing and the foreskin was fully retracted. It looked wet and slimy so I guessed Julie had been feasting on it. Julie was one of those girls who others assumed was a bit of a slut due to her weekly change of boyfriend, and she certainly dressed to earn herself that fine label. She looked like a cheap whore trying to make an impression, but it really wasn't working. I know it was the 1980s but was it ever appropriate to wear a tracksuit and stilettos? She was also sporting a mass of bleached blonde, poorly permed hair, tied back with a scrunchy. Well, regardless of my opinion, Rob seemed to be into her.

When I reflect now on the incident, what surprises me is how Rob was not shocked or embarrassed. He did not jump up and jam that snake back in his trousers. No, he just sat there, holding it and playing with it. I think he got some pleasure from his role in enlightening us! It felt like we had been standing there for hours, not seconds when finally he spoke as he stood up, the long, now semi-flaccid cock waving at the ground.

'What's up boys? Never seen a dick before? You pair of puffs!' This was the first time anyone had ever used a gay term against me. I only knew the meaning because I remember my grandfather shouting that at the TV when some sexy male celebrity was being interviewed. Michael and I never looked at each other or spoke to each other. We did not even take that much-needed piss we had been craving. We walked backwards out of the caravan, ran back to the pool and never mentioned a word to anyone!

Of course boys will be boys and later that day we had all dared each other to show our cocks under torchlight. Again, whilst being fascinated I do not remember being sexually aroused by this. Six ten-year-olds all sharing one double bed. One by one we had to go to the foot of the bed, lower our Y-fronts and wait for the torches to be shone on our shrimp-like penises. For some reason I was made to go first and I caused hysteria when showing my boyhood. I gingerly positioned by wafer thin body at the opposite end of the tiny and rather cramped room, pushed my black, thick-rimmed National Health glasses up my nose bridge and yanked down my red and black pants. I was mortified by the laughter, but later realised it was because I already had pubic hair and my balls were hanging rather low. It is hard to believe now, since I am a short, 5 foot 7 adult male, but I was the tallest in the class. Growing up and going through puberty is not easy for anyone, let alone someone who has the start of homosexual feelings. No one ever talks about puberty so you assume everyone else is the same. It seemed for now I was the man of the group, which would also lead to being the butt of many jokes to come when back at school.

During the final year of primary school, I would frequently stay over at another close friend's house. Nick and I would often wrestle with each other and 'accidentally' grab each other's cocks. Actually I hated staying at Nick's house because his gran was crazy, the place was freezing cold and they never fed you breakfast in the morning. But I loved my time with Nick. He was such a great friend who always made me laugh. I enjoyed the intimate moments too, although at the time we didn't see them as this. We never got hard, but I remember us vigorously rubbing ourselves on each other and it felt good. I do not think Nick was in the same place as me. I think he was a typical young boy exploring the world around him.

Nick's father was never around so I think he enjoyed the male company. He was much better looking than me and attracted a lot of attention from the girls in our class. We were both part Italian, but his part seemed to be working better for him in terms of looks and appeal. On many occasions he advised me on the clothes to wear and how best to style my hair. It was also because of him that I played football; well tried to at least! I am not sure if I joined the team because I genuinely wanted to or just so that I could spend more time with him. One time I made both the school rugby and football teams – a bid to impress my father and grandfather I think. The showers after the matches were crazy. The other lads, who were far more confident than me, would piss on each other, grab each other's cocks and once they even had a race to cum first! And it was me that they were calling homo! Although we never talked about it, I think it was a perfectly normal stage for boys to be intrigued by other boys. I have seen or been a part of so many incidents like this that it has to be normal. Either that or my hometown is full of raging homos in denial! So many of my friends wanted to fumble around, in primary school, high school and even as a young adult. And it seemed 'cocking around' was part of laddish behaviour.

What added to the confusion was that I also used to do the same thing with Joanna, a girl who lived a few doors away. Every Tuesday her mum would go to bingo with my Aunt Jess, and me and five lads would go to her house and take turns kissing her and feeling her breasts, even though she was the girlfriend of one of the lads! We were only eleven years old at the time. This progressed into dry humping and I remember the first time I came after vigorously rubbing myself on her. There was a brown leather bean bag behind the back of the sofa and whilst kissing her one time I pushed her back on the inviting over-sized cushion. The other boys seemed a little surprised or shocked by my actions and maybe this reaction contributed to the level of excitement I felt. At first it just felt like a more comfortable position but as I moved my hips in a rhythmic pattern I felt a new and unusual sensation. Nick and Michael were eagerly looking on and I guessed it was their sniggering I could hear. I didn't feel self-conscious at all. I certainly was not excited by Joanna but the angle of our bodies was causing the most incredible waves of indescribable pleasure that ended suddenly with waves of erratic spasms that made Michael laugh out loud. I had no comprehension about what had just happened and the small wet patch on the crotch of my beige chinos disturbed me somewhat.

'Haha, he has pissed himself!' sniggered Nick.

'Oh get lost!' I snapped back. I was so embarrassed at this point, and we were all so naïve and unaware that I had just had an orgasm for the first time in my life!

Joanna was not the most attractive of girls and on reflection she was quite manly aside from her over-sized breasts, but those Tuesdays were so exciting! I will never understand why our friend just stood there whilst we acted like testosterone-crazed baboons. Maybe he grew up to be a voyeur.

There must be something about the children of parents who play bingo because my first 'physical' experience involved a boy whose mother also played bingo every Tuesday. James and I had been friends since starting high school and now that Nick was attending a different school to me, I seemed to spend most of my time with my new best mate. James and Michael also didn't get along with each other and although I was still really fond of Michael, I preferred how much more fun James was. I remember looking up to James like some sort of role model in terms of fashion and charisma. He was not necessarily the most handsome boy at school but he was certainly popular on account of his humorous personality. My feelings towards him did not seem inappropriate at any time. I just really enjoyed being with him. James was the first person I knew who had Sky TV at home and we spent hours watching MTV into the early hours on the nights when I stayed over. After surfing through the endless channels we stumbled upon a number of adult channels that we were unable to view on account of the deliberate blurring to protect the innocent! We were both 13 years old and our hormones were racing. This teasing had flicked a switch and we both needed satisfying.

'My brother has some sexy films in his room. I remember hearing a girl moaning on the TV and he quickly turned it off when I ran into his room one time,' laughed James.

James' brother Gavin was much older and much hairier than his younger brother. I remember seeing him walking from the bathroom to his bedroom after a shower and being shocked by the amount of thick black hair on his back. After rigorously searching Gavin's room, we finally stumbled upon his straight porn collection. As a young teenager this was my first porn experience and I loved every moment. I remember being obsessed with the guy's cock, barely noticing the woman he was fucking. It was incredibly thick and the way the foreskin retracted in the woman's hand fascinated me. I couldn't get the image out of my head. The first two occasions we watched the film we just giggled and pretended to be disgusted by the on-screen action. We were too afraid of being caught by his brother to allow the moment of indulgence to continue. However, the need grew stronger and we couldn't contain our excitement each week when his mother finally left the house.

Gavin worked away from home now and so most weeks we knew we were unlikely to be disturbed for a few hours. James and I would talk about the size of the women's tits or how we couldn't wait to taste pussy. But of course, I was lying. I was thinking about anything but pussy. I was imagining holding the thick penis in my hand and kissing the guy. I would often run home and go straight into the bathroom where I would masturbate over the thought of touching the guy from the movies. The moment I came I hated myself. I felt dirty and confused and yet I still never considered this meant that I was gay.

After several weeks I felt a kind of obsession with the men in the movie and their dicks. The last time we enjoyed this viewing pleasure together I remember being aware of my erection as the woman simultaneously sucked on two big black cocks. I glanced over at James who was now masturbating inside his boxers. This increased my own excitement to another level. Taking a second glance, I saw that his penis was now in his hand with his jeans and oversized boxers half way down his skinny thighs. I edged myself a little closer to him with each glance until I suddenly reached across and placed his small penis inside my sweaty palm. It was certainly not comparable to the monster I had been perving over onscreen but it was the first cock aside from my own that I had played with. I had only stroked it a few times before he came without a single sound. It was thrilling yet terrifying at the same time. He simply stood, cleaned himself up and we never spoke of it again.

After failing to rewind the cassette to the same start point it was not difficult for Gavin to realise how we were spending our evenings together and after receiving a small beating, James promised he would never steal the tapes again. I never considered that these playful evenings were the start of many enticing encounters that were going to contribute to the total confusion and misery of the years to come.

CHAPTER TWO

As an openly gay adult, I frequently find myself entering into conversations around the whole 'nature versus nurture' gay debate. It is actually an argument I feel very strongly about because I feel with conviction that I was born this way and, for the vast majority of gays, I believe this to be the case too. I would agree that there are situations, circumstances, exposure to certain environments, that could lead someone to seek emotional or sexual gratification from someone of the same sex. I particularly believe this to be true of lesbians. Women are an incredibly sensitive species who enjoy the close contact, both physically and emotionally, of another person. They are capable of receiving this in the form of a male lover or a close female friend. Sometimes these close friendships develop into something more intimate. When a woman has been hurt very deeply by a man, she is sometimes unable to let another one ever get as close. Instead her needs are catered for in a fellow female. To what extent they enjoy a close physical relationship I would not know. But sexuality, especially for women, is not black or white but a whole spectrum of grey hues.

I have analysed my home life and upbringing in great detail, scrutinising every single moment and no doubt it is something my parents have also done. Born into a Catholic family, the middle of three children and the only son, I was certainly over-indulged in my mother's love and affection. Apparently firmly attached to her hip, I rarely left her side and she was besotted with me. I could not have wished for a more attentive upbringing from my mother. Strangely enough my relationship with my father was less successful and did not really improve until I finally admitted I was gay. Before this we seemed to misunderstand each other and could not find a common ground – something many other gay guys will be able to relate to. I always felt so much closer to my grandfather who seemed to understand me. Although he would enjoy teasing me, he always made so much effort to spend quality time with me and certainly provided great support during my studies. We would have the most dynamic conversations when we were hanging out, from discussing religion and science, to the size of women's breasts as we passed the unsuspecting ladies in the car. Of course I never joined in but it certainly made me laugh out loud.

Having two sisters, an overly attentive mother and a strained relationship with my father, I seem to be a prime candidate for being gay through nurture. But I was not the type who played with my sisters' dolls and dressed up in my mother's clothes. From a very young age my friends were all male and we spent hours playing cowboys and Indians or football, baseball or rat-a-tat ginger. Admittedly, I have always been very sensitive and maybe *this* is a result of my upbringing, but there was nothing different in my first ten years as compared to my best male friends who have all turned out to be straight.

I did not spend much time with my older sister, though she was very protective of me. We frequently fought and she constantly teased and tortured me, much to my mother's misery at times. Sophia was five years older than me and once she hit puberty she did not want anything to do with me, unless it was to give me a sly slap for breathing too heavy whilst eating my cereal! But despite this, she would never let anyone else give me a tough time. I chose to spend many of my weekends with my Aunt Jess and her husband Sam. They didn't have any children when I was growing up and so I received their undivided attention. My relationship with my younger sister Adela was completely different and this difference has continued into adulthood. We were inseparable and seemed to have a closer bond despite a five-year gap. I took on the protective older sibling role, though not the bullying aspect that Sophia had thrived on. At the time I did not realise just how instrumental Adela would be in helping me to come to terms with my sexuality.

There is no denying there was something different about me, but I was not moulded into this; I feel I was programmed that way. When the puberty switch was flicked, those differences were amplified. The interest in sport switched off, the gender of my friends became female-biased and my level of sensitivity soared. I enjoyed spending more time with my grandparents, rather than hanging out with friends who were causing havoc in my neighbourhood. I spent my free time writing plays to perform to my family and I developed a fascination with animals. I spent my fifteenth birthday with my grandmother and Aunt Jess watching *Miss Saigon* at the local theatre.

I really loved my time with my grandparents and consider myself to be very privileged in the amount of time I got to spend with them. I would visit frequently and go shopping with them or bake cakes with my grandmother – much to my grandfather's despair. Even back then he would call me 'Mary', but strangely enough I saw it as a sign of affection. My grandfather was a former Italian stallion and in his mind he still is today, despite being in his early eighties. Exceptionally good-looking and with the charm of Casanova, he bathed in the attention of women. Without question he was, and to some extent still is, a chauvinist! He has never hidden his feelings about homosexuals and it was these that would lock up my own feelings for many more years to come.

And so it started – the onset of bullying. Like most people, I had encountered the odd bit of name-calling, but it was not until I was fifteen that the references to my apparent homosexuality kicked in. I say apparent, because at the time I did not know I was gay, so how did my bullies? We often talk about the 'gaydar' – a secret tool enabling one gay guy to pick out another gay guy in a crowded room; but were high school bullies armed with this same invaluable weapon? Personally I seem to have missed out on the luxury of this resource and as an adult I frequently found myself pursuing the 'wrong' type of guy whilst being naïve in the pursuits of my fellow homosexuals. Or maybe my bullies were themselves frustrated wannabe gays too and so they took their misery out on me? You hear horror stories of the bullying some people face during those wonderful years in secondary school. In comparison, my experiences were mild, but nevertheless significant in their contribution to the confusion shaping the young man I was growing up to be. The height of the bullying was when I noticed a picture of myself drawn on the toilet cubicle door, being entered from behind by the maths teacher! I mean come on, if you have to draw such graphic pictures of me then choose the hot PE teacher, not the mid-fifties pervert who still referred to the Year 11 pupils as, 'my boys'. And then came the walk of shame when I left the toilet to return to class only to be greeted by a corridor of hysterically laughing twats, all shouting homophobic comments.

If that was not gruelling enough I was then rescued by my child development teacher who was breaking up the riot shouting, 'He is not gay, he is just sensitive!' Not sure at what point she thought that was going to be useful. So there it was, the explanation I needed. I was not gay, I was sensitive!

I'm not sure where it came from. One minute I was the popular kid in primary school, playing football with the popular boys and the next I was being labelled. At first I was part of the 'inner circle'. This was the group of boys who were the better-looking, more popular ones in the year group. I always seemed to have a girlfriend and often received many compliments about my cute face or sexy smile. That was until acne invaded and my mum thought it would be a great idea for me to have braces! I was part of the crew who shared porn tapes with each other. You would get the video for one night before having to discretely pass it on to the next horny teenager. Maybe when I was unable to join in the discussions the next day about the hot blonde babe who did it with four guys, the boys knew something was different about me. Maybe they saw me getting a semi when they used words like 'big cock' or 'shooting his load'. I could not make reference to a single girl from the film, because I clearly had been occupied by a certain anatomy part of her co-star! Yet still I didn't know this meant I was gay, because I had a *girlfriend* and I liked kissing her, so how could I be – right?

Well this horny teenager was now out of the loop. No more videos came my way and I had to improvise on how I achieved gratification. Of course coming from a working class family I was not fortunate enough to have access to satellite TV and, as we were just entering the nineties, the proliferation of widespread multimedia like the Internet was still in its infancy. Thank God for this blessing because

I would have been a porn whore for sure and certainly not achieved the academic success that I did. Instead I surfed the four channels of TV late at night desperate to see some naked male flesh. If you were lucky Channel 4 would have some weird programme showing in the early hours where a flaccid penis might provide a much-needed reward after hours of endless channel hopping. When Channel 5 was launched it was like a sexual revolution – if you were straight! Naked weather reports, naked volleyball and endless seedy programmes – but not a cock in sight!

At the age of fourteen I had taken a part-time job in the local newsagent. Every evening after school I would work for two or three hours. The two Indian owners were so much fun, though tight arses when it came to my hourly rate. But I didn't care about that. I was not working for the salary but for the view of the top magazine shelf, a pervert's delight. Here the sexy magazines from *Glamorous Grans* to *Busty Babes* sat patiently waiting for the dirty old men to come and take them home. And there, nestled right in the corner, was a row of five or so pieces of gay treasure. These gay magazines captured my attention throughout my shift. I could not see the full covers but I did not need to. I had an amazing imagination. *Vulcan*, *Zipper*, *Falcon* – I still remember their names now, like old friends. I particularly loved Tuesdays when the magazine guy came with the latest copies and I got a whole new set of 'boys' to entice me. During the quieter parts of my shift, when the owner was out the back stocktaking, I would dream about the contents of these magazines. I was longing to see inside and this craving was like an infectious disease taking a hold of all sensibility.

Two months later and I found myself a part of the criminal underworld. I had snatched a copy of *Fresh* and was flapping around nervously trying to stuff it down the sleeve of my jacket. My heart was pounding and I was breathless – was it the thrill of the cocks on my arm or the rush from entering the world of crooks and thieves? My legs were shaking like jelly yet my dick was starting to stir. I created a sudden illness, made my excuses and ran home at lightning speed. The speed at which men move when sexual pleasure is involved is quite amazing, in comparison to the speed at which we move on an everyday basis. It's comparable to the speed at which many women or gay men move when the shopping sales begin!

Of course, I don't think I need to explain what happened next. But that was a moment of sheer indulgence. It was New Year's Eve and my entire family were at a friend's party. I could not have planned the moment any better. An empty house with just me, Rick and his other well-endowed friends. The usual guilty feelings raged through my body afterwards, including a sense of panic. What the hell would I do with this magazine now? It was not like the videos where I got to pass them on and wash the smut from my hands. In a panic, I stuffed it into a plastic bag and rammed it under my mattress, before joining the festive celebrations, sexually satisfied but deeper in confusion.

Of course even writing this now it seems crazy to me. I was stealing gay porn magazines and jacking off over the contents – of course I was gay! But I see that now as a level-headed, rational adult and not a hormone-imbalanced teenager. All the time I kept convincing myself that everyone must be doing the same. I enjoyed that magazine or what was left of it for many nights to come. I would rush home from school and pleasure myself with this tatty scrap of manliness. Until one day, that magazine was not sitting patiently under my mattress waiting for me to come and retrieve it but was being grasped tightly in my mother's hands. So this was the moment when I would be 'outted' by my parents? Sadly not! With a nervous smirk, my parents asked me not to keep such things in the house where my little sister could easily find them. What? Where is the part where they ask me if I am gay, or they throw me out of the house in disgust for the shame I have brought to their home? Were they blind or naïve? Could they not notice the endless pieces of cock and yet no sign of a tit? I mean surely they looked – just a little? I counted at least ten tattered pieces of male form as my mother waved the clear plastic bag in front of me. More seriously, was this denial? Not my own but theirs. Did they know I was gay and chose to think of it as a phase or think that by ignoring it, it would go away? Why didn't they ask me the question? Would this have been the turning point in my life? Would this have stopped the misery that was to come?

CHAPTER THREE   (Part one)

With high school behind me, I moved forward into sixth-form college where I developed yet another crush on a male teacher. However, I was simultaneously having crushes on various girls. Mr Griffiths, or Chris as I preferred to think of him, was young, athletic and had a butt to die for: a firm peachy arse that he flaunted in his tight, navy trousers. He knew he was hot and savoured the attention from everyone. The group I was hanging out with included a sample of his female fan base. I am not sure how flattered he would be by the attention of these less fortunate looking females but, if he was anything like me, then any attention was rewarding. I was unable to cover up by own fascination with him whenever he walked by, even changing my route to classes just to ensure I would pass him in the corridor. The highlight of my day was receiving a smile from him. On reflection he was no hottie. With a drastically receding hairline, a growing gut and a gap between his front teeth, he was no Justin Timberlake. But there was a certain confidence or arrogance about him that made him so sexy – and clearly my female friends saw this too. As chief stalker of Chris, I took it to another level. I searched the phone directory late one evening to find his telephone number and frequently called just to hear him say hello. I am so embarrassed to admit that now but luckily one night his girlfriend answered and swore down the phone at me, putting an end to that ridiculous behaviour.

It was at this time that I met my first real-life gay. Joel was actually bisexual and proud of it. What fascinated me the most was that he received no negative attention at all, not even from the same idiots who had intimidated me for years. What I have come to realise is that people seem to have more of a problem dealing with homosexuals who don't admit they are gay. They get a lot of pleasure from trying to 'out' them. But once a guy admits he is indeed a cock-sucker, no-one seems to give a damn. Joel was a cute blond guy with a mop of curly hair. He was the drummer in an indie band at college and was dating a girl at the time who used to constantly send *me* love notes and poems in class. Stacey was freakishly over weight and displayed classic signs of being unstable. I did not quite understand her interest in me when she was already dating another guy. Maybe closet gay guys turned her on more than bisexuals! I am not sure how much I buy into this 'bisexual' label. I'm not saying it does not exist as I do believe there is a spectrum of sexuality and that, as adults, we can be anywhere along that spectrum. But I do feel that many gay guys hide behind bisexuality, often feeling it makes them seem more masculine if they say they still like women, when in reality their experiences with women are limited or non-existent. I think Joel was one of these guys. I also remember my parents sharing their thoughts when a bisexual character was written into a popular TV soap. The words 'disgusting' and 'greedy' were thrown around as well as stereotypical comments such as, *'It's because of men like that that bloody HIV is so widespread!'* Clearly biased and unjustified, but born out of ignorance not malice.

My fascination with Joel intensified. Not that I found him attractive. Skinny, hairless pink guys do nothing for me, but I just felt a connection to him. I often sat staring at him, wondering what it felt like to be him, imagining what his parents and close friends thought. I felt a need to be friends with him, but could never find a reason to talk with him and since he knew his girlfriend had a crush on me he was already displaying an overgrown male ego towards me. In fact, we never exchanged a single word in the two years that we studied at college. Maybe he didn't think the school was big enough for two gays or he didn't want to share the gay limelight with me, or maybe he just never used his gaydar on me and so failed to see the commonality between us. Whatever the reason, Joel made a significant impact on me because he made me start to question my feelings and for the first time provided somewhat of a positive role model. He gave me some confidence, without ever knowing it, a confidence that helped me to meet Pete.

Pete was a male masseur, aka male escort or prostitute – depending on your outlook! I found him when searching through the advertisements in the local newspaper. I was a naïve seventeen-year-old and I didn't know what it meant but the advert fascinated me: **'Male Escort – available for massage and more!'** It was the 'and more' that captured my attention. I looked at that same advert every night for a fortnight until my curiosity could take it no longer. I waited until the house was empty and plucked up enough courage to dial his number. My heart was thumping and I was breathless as he answered the phone with a dirty, suggestive tone in his voice. I slammed the phone down and almost passed out. It took another two weeks before I finally had the nerve to go for it again. This time I went into imitation mode and replied to him in the same seductive manner in which he talked to me. He must have thought I was crazy with a forced deeper, sexy voice. He told me it was twenty-five pounds for 'extras' and gave me the address, which was only doors away from my sister's place and a short walk from my college. I hung up with no commitment as to when I would visit and it took me another month before I finally turned up at his door. I was so naïve and so unaware of what he was offering and what my intentions were.

I walked past his door repeatedly as internally I refereed a match between the devil and the angel personas that sat on either shoulder. I knew it was wrong and I knew I should not go to his place, but I just kept thinking about touching his penis. I felt possessed and the power of these thoughts was uncontrollable. I finally knocked on the door praying he had not seen my zoochotic behaviour outside. What opened the door was a less than sexy middle-aged guy. Not the Adonis I had built up inside my head. Wearing shorts and grey socks, he ushered me into his apartment with a look of surprise or delight at how young I was. I never felt threatened, but I did feel incredibly uncomfortable. There was no need. Pete was so kind and so understanding. He talked to me about my feelings though never referred to me as being gay. He just reassured me that it was okay to explore and wonder. He put on some gay porn and this was the first time I had ever seen two men making out. I was horrified and shocked. I could not believe where the guy was inserting his manhood and I ran to the toilet to throw up. Pete was laughing, saying I would come to love such things. I tried to watch some more and although I was hard, I still felt disgust, especially when the guys were kissing. When Pete leant over and touched my chest, my threshold was reached and I made my excuses to leave. I had no money to pay Pete. Maybe I never had intended to receive those extras or maybe I thought my cute looks would get me a freebie, but Pete never expected anything. I think he felt sorry for me or saw something of himself in me from his younger days. As I was leaving, he grabbed my hand, kissed my lips gently and placed a gay DVD in my hand. This was my first gay kiss and it disgusted me! The taste of tobacco was overwhelming. I appreciated his kind gesture all the same and was certainly grateful for the gay gem he had given me. That would be the last time I would kiss a guy for almost a decade! However, it would not be the last time I would hear from Pete, unfortunately.

I turned my attention to actively searching for a girlfriend. I pursued a number of girls, all with little success. I was the cute guy with a lovely personality, but the college girls suddenly felt that they should be dating more mature guys and us teenagers were not good enough for them. I even tried my luck with the less attractive girls and still had no joy for the entire first year of college! However, one girl in particular fascinated me. She was beautiful like an English rose yet alternative, in a good way. She did not appear trendy but had the confidence to carry her own style. Maria occupied my mind on a fulltime basis, to the extent that I changed one of my A-level courses just to be in the same class as her! I realise now that my fascination was sexually very immature. Despite being constantly horny I never once imagined her naked. I never once thought about touching her pert breasts or running my hands up her tense thighs. Instead I thought only about kissing her and walking through the park holding hands. I thought about taking her home to meet my mother or marrying her. But never anything sexual – why was that? I thought it was because I was quite under-confident at the time, especially after the years of teasing at school. As a regular churchgoer I thought it was possibly Catholic naïvety. I now know it was because I was gay. I just wished I had realised it at the time, because after months of pursuing that girl she went on to become my wife many years later and the woman whose heart I would eventually break.

I still remember the time now. It was 5.15 p.m. exactly. The reason I still remember after all these years is because my parents were very into routines, especially around meal times. Dinner was 5.00 p.m. every day without fail, regardless of how hungry you were; except on a Thursday which was fish 'n' chip night when Aunt Jess and Uncle Sam would join us for dinner and we had to wait until 5.30 p.m. for the local Chinese take-away to open. Should anyone dare to knock on the door or ring the telephone – look out! My mother would have just served me my gourmet delight. We used to mock my mother for her lack of culinary skills, but in fairness we were such fussy eaters and she could never provide just one choice.

The telephone rang and my father went off on one of his usual rants about why people call during meal times. I tried to explain to him that most people lacked the power of telepathy and that maybe not everyone was as sad as us eating at the same time each day. Needless to say those backhanded comments did not go down too well. That, coupled with the phone call my mother just received, were set to make my evening less than pleasurable!

I was such a nosey teenager, always listening in to other people's conversations, especially when my family were bitching about particular relatives. So I was well-trained in this art form and put my skills into action to home in on my mother's telephone conversation. I'm not sure what happened next. Did I pass out or have a small episode?

Because what I was hearing was broken words only and these seemed to be repeating at a heightened volume.

'Massage!'

'Escort!'

'Masseur!'

Jesus Christ it was Pete! I was frozen to my chair as the life and colour drained slowly away from me. I tried to think of one hundred and one excuses to explain myself when my mother returned, screaming at me, but I could not even master one as the handle of the door lowered and my mothered reappeared, looking paler than when she had left. Luckily the rest of the family was fixated on Ricky Lake and the story of the transsexual who had been fired from his/her job for using the female toilets! My mother looked at me and desperately tried to hide her emotion, though her eyes told me enough. She returned to the kitchen and continued with her motherly duties. Not talking about it now felt worse than the thought of having to explain myself, because now I was dealing with uncertainty. What exactly had Pete said to her? Did she know this involved me? My God, did she even know what a male masseur was?

For three long days and nights I was left wondering the answers to these questions, until she casually, though awkwardly, brought the topic up whilst my father was at a football match. She asked me if something was troubling me and that if I needed to talk she was there for me. This was finally the moment when I could lift the huge weight of confusion, misery and guilt from my shoulders and share the burden. Already I could feel a defensive wall building up. Was I really ready to discuss my deepest darkest thoughts about men?

'Son, if you have a medical problem, then you should talk to me about it.' Did I just hear my mother correctly?

Was she now referring to these feelings as a 'medical problem'? Oh God you hear of these crazy Americans who believe that gay people are mutations and that with 'therapy' they can be saved or cured. Had my mother watched the same TV programme and was now assuming I was gay and needed the same method of treatment?

'Mum, I'm not sure I understand you,' I replied, with a clear nervous lilt to my voice.

'Dr Pete, the doctor you visited, he called to say he had missed your call and that if you needed to discuss anything from your last session you could drop by again.' What the hell was going on? Had Pete used some common sense and, on realising this was *my* number and *my* mother, suddenly taken on the role of GP? Or was my mother really so naïve as to the exact nature of the 'service' that Dr Pete was providing to his 'patients'? Yet again, was this another example of denial from my parents as to what or who I really was? I guess I will never know the exact words spoken during that telephone conversation or what my mother was truly aware of. I never spoke with Pete again and thankfully he never again called the house. The incident instilled a great fear about the meaning of my behaviour and I chose to bury my head and focus on trying to live in a way others expected. It was yet another missed opportunity for me to be shaken out of this period of denial, a denial that now took me so much deeper than ever before.

CHAPTER FOUR

Perseverance does pay off sometimes and my efforts to get a girlfriend came to fruition. I had always been and continue to be a natural flirt with a glint of cheekiness. But I always felt more confident with older women like my friends' mothers or the old lady next door! Clearly there was no sexual motive here for my flirtatious behaviour and therefore when it came to a real girlfriend I was pretty clumsy. With Maria it was different, easier, even natural. She captured my attention, probably because of the element of chase that was woven into the beginning of the relationship. We had both finished sixth-form college and were set for the big move to university. Admittedly I was not going very far away. In fact I was staying at home and attending my local university.

The summer before the start of university was amazing and it seemed to last forever. No pressure, no stress, no worries. Just endless days hanging out with great friends and wonderful memories. And it was during this time that Maria and I started dating. We were at Michael's birthday party and, after a lot of persuading, I convinced Maria to sit outside with me. I was terrified and shaking from head to toe, which I explained as being cold in the night air. But it was fear. Fear of being turned down, fear of having to kiss her, fear that she would try to take things further. I was eighteen but still a virgin and clueless about how to pleasure a girl. Maria was probably equally nervous and inexperienced. I remember her being so animated when she was talking to me, but I wasn't listening to a word she was saying. Instead I was looking intensely at her lips, imagining how soft they would feel pressed against mine. Her fiery red hair mesmerised me and so many times I reached out to run my fingers through the long silky strands whilst she was nervously looking elsewhere. We were both so immature and three hours passed before I finally sealed that first kiss. It most definitely was not my finest moment. The small knocking of heads in the first move, the accidental biting of the lip and the friction burn from my stubble that I left around her mouth probably failed to make the earth move! Needless to say there was something, because the sun would rise before we returned to join the group, who were keen to know of any developments. During the entire magical moment, I kept my hands to myself. I wondered if she considered me a gentleman or a little weird. It never even entered my mind to touch her intimately. I certainly loved the kisses and could not wait for a repeat session.

Maria dropped out of university within the first few months, closely following by Michael who followed suit. Maria's reason – boredom! Michael was able to top that and revealed that he was going to move to Ireland to train to be a missionary priest. I think the shock was apparent on my face when he told us both. It was no real surprise as Michael was incredibly angelic and reverent but I had no idea he was even contemplating this change. I thought we were closer. I assumed he would have confided in me but then I never confided in him so why should he be any different? During the year that Maria lived at home before enrolling again, and with all our old friends living all over the country, we became extremely close: best friends. It didn't help me to settle at university though as I would often rush home to see her whenever I could.

I made friends with a small group who were also studying zoology but I never really clicked with any of them except for Tom and Eleanor who were rather well spoken but great fun. I sensed some chemistry between them despite Tom already being in a relationship with Nifah who was also in some of my classes. Tom and I would go out once a week drinking at the student union bar and over time he introduced me to some of the other friends from his dorm. Living at home made it more difficult for me to make friends and I still remained painfully shy. Nifah seemed to find this particularly endearing and would often tease me by flirting. Tom didn't seem bothered by this and Maria just laughed when I retold the stories. Maria had met my university friends only once and wasn't really interested in repeating the awkward event. Nifah had spent the whole night staring at me despite my girlfriend being sat next to me. Maria was not at all threatened by this and found it only humorous. I sensed that Tom was becoming a little frustrated with the wandering eyes of his girlfriend and my initial instincts about his attraction to Eleanor were confirmed when he ended things with Nifah.

Over the next few months Nifah clearly took the position of my second official female stalker. This one was different from Stacey, the sweet college girl, because this one was crazy! Imagine Glenn Close in *Fatal Attraction* and you are thinking along the right lines. She frequently 'forced' herself on me, despite knowing I was happy with Maria. She once pushed me up against the wall outside one of the science labs and grabbed my crotch. I only told my grandfather about this, who explained that for most guys that was a fantasy come true! Maybe if she hadn't squashed my left testicle and winded me in the process, it might have been. But there was something about her that freaked me out. Was it the fact she was so forward? Possibly. Or was it that she was once the girlfriend of my friend? Or, was it the thick line of hair growing above her top lip? Most definitely! And the behaviour continued to become more worrying. Nifah stole items of my clothing when I stayed over at Tom's house which unfortunately she still had to share with him on account of the year-long lease agreement they had signed when living a life of bliss together. Now that she was single she would text me totally inappropriate messages and at the end of year Summer Ball she even created a whole story around our first time and her losing her virginity to me! It was common knowledge that her and Tom had once enjoyed a very expressive love affair as we would often hear them in the next room. I was also not impressed that Maria had left me to attend the ball alone on account of being unable to find a suitable gown she felt comfortable wearing! Thankfully Nifah's strict Muslim parents were unhappy with her new university lifestyle and after the first year she dropped out and was sent packing to Pakistan where I was told she married a family friend. I have never heard from her since, but still live in fear of receiving that friend request on Facebook! We all know the psychos never disappear that easily!

Maria and I spent most weekends and evenings together as her gap year came to a close. Even if there was a party or a gathering at university, I preferred to spend my time with Maria. I still tried to see my friends once or twice a week but most of the time I was thinking of Maria. We were very different in so many respects and so similar in other ways. We hated and even mocked each other's music collection and dressed in completely different styles. Every night we would meet up at either my house or her house. My parents seemed pleased, or relieved, that I was dating, although

Maria was painfully shy and took a long time to form any kind of relationship with them. I on the other hand used my charm and good looks to win over Maria's mother with ease. Maria and I both lacked physical experiences with a significant other and therefore we took a long time to become more intimate with each other. We followed the same pattern each night. We would watch a movie and feel sleepy and lie next to each other on the sofa before starting to kiss. The kissing progressed into fondling and always stopped at this point. It felt amazing and I was so turned on and could not wait for the next evening to repeat the whole experience again. I never tried to take it further. It was not out of Catholic guilt as neither of us were practising the religion at the time. Typical teenagers, we had turned away from God. It was fear. Fear of getting her pregnant, fear of catching a sexually transmitted disease and fear of doing something wrong. I also remained incredibly self-conscious of my body. Sometimes I just wondered if I was just one of the very few gentleman left or just not interested. Each night I left with a smile and a set of 'blue balls', a term I use to describe the pain that men experience when arousal doesn't lead to completion. Try explaining to your parents why you can't stand up and when you do you have to cup your balls to ease the pain!

Maria's gap year was now over and I was relieved that she had enrolled at a neighbouring university. Although she was moving into student accommodation it was only a 30-minute drive away. The evening before Maria left for university we finally took things further. I wish I could write that it was magical and special in every way. The love and intimacy certainly was but it was awkward to say the least. I always wondered how people seem to know instinctively how to have sex. Well they don't if they are unknowingly gay trying to have sex with a girl. I was clueless and misguided. I fumbled and struggled and failed to stay erect throughout. Of course she kindly hugged me and put it down to first time nerves. More difficult to explain after the second and third. And so I began to think of guys during the next few sessions and things really improved. I felt aroused and so horny at times, but something did not seem right and I did not understand. I never thought it was because I wanted to have sex with a guy – I just thought I was a crap lover. It was not a conscious move to start thinking of guys during these moments, it just happened and then became a habit. During foreplay it was all about Maria; her curves, her cupcake breasts, her luscious red hair all drove me crazy, but the moment we became one I was overwhelmed with images of naked men racing through my mind. Every fantasy was replayed and seemed to make me hornier and harder. Then with climax came waves of guilt and confusion, with no way of explaining to myself why this was happening. The arousal came from Maria's touch but the mechanics seemed to be wrong and no matter how much I wanted it to be right I was increasingly becoming aware that something was not right. But how could I discuss this with the person whom I had fallen in love with? And what exactly would I say? I did not even understand it myself or I chose not to. Like most things we dislike, I chose to ignore it; to bury it deeper and cover it with other distractions and instead turn my attention to my career, my body and all the other things that gay men strive to perfect because we cannot perfect the most meaningful thing of all – an intimate relationship.

CHAPTER FIVE

The denial of my sexuality led me to try to achieve validation and satisfaction in other areas of my life. I immersed myself in trying to achieve the hottest body I could, striving for the best education, driving the best cars and wearing the latest clothes. Not always easy when managing on a government student grant and a part-time job only! But during the denial period I was not aware that achieving all of this would still bring little happiness, or happiness that would not last.

Surrounded by a more diverse and a much more attractive selection of young guys at university, I became obsessed with trying to improve my appearance – particularly my body. Puberty may have come early but the growth spurts I had enjoyed at the end of primary school ended prematurely. I was now a relatively short adult with a slim physique. My face also refused to age and I still resembled a cute high school pupil despite turning twenty. My fascination with men was now more about trying to be like them rather than being sexually attracted to them. I was now in a successful two-year relationship and having regular, sometimes crazy sex with a girl. Of course I was not gay. I believed I just liked looking at guys because I wanted to look like them, in the same way that girls love to look through glossy magazines at sexy, scantily clad models. This was not the truth of course but at the time I truly believed it to be. I was quite self-conscious about portraying a feminine side and the gym helped to make me feel more masculine. I had the perception of gay men being skinny, effeminate and flamboyant. This was probably due to the gay characters portrayed on TV. So sub-consciously I seemed to try to make myself the opposite.

Although my body significantly improved, the protein shakes, excessive tins of tuna, chicken breasts and nuts did not make the impact I had hoped and so the obsession grew. The gym also provided an outlet for admiring sexy guys, particularly in the changing rooms. It was such a thrill seeing young athletic guys walking around with everything on show. This also contributed to the onset of a mild depression that I was experiencing because I hated my body and I hated myself for some of the thoughts that I had about these men. Of course people who are depressed do not know they are depressed at the time and I just believed myself to be a very moody, serious guy. I now recognise that I was mildly depressed yet I did a great job at hiding it from my loved ones and even myself. I think my Aunt Jess and to some extent my grandfather, sometimes picked up on my unhappiness. Maybe being one step removed in comparison to my mother they could sense something was not right, though neither of them ever questioned me.

I was now aware that gay guys were all around me – at university, in the gym and whilst out and about. This was quite a moment of enlightenment for me as I had come to believe that I was unique as no one else was talking about what I was experiencing. So now I became overly paranoid that these gay guys would 'sense' something different about me and try to make a move or tell others about me. So I distanced myself from anyone who was remotely gay or any activities that could be perceived as gay. Well, all things except for the M People and Eternal concerts that I attended – a slight oversight on my part for sure!

However, on a university research trip to Kenya in my final year, I spent the night with my first gay guy. Unfortunately Tom's finances had not allowed him to attend the trip but his girlfriend Eleanor was there to keep me company. We had been put into groups of four and this sissy gay guy called Chris had insisted on sharing with me. I had been well aware that this guy was gay. From the flamboyant scarves to the purple corduroy jeans, he fulfilled every stereotype I held on to. He had never shown any attraction towards me previously though we were not really socialising in the same circle. Our only interaction was during our lectures on evolution! I had never really spoken with Chris, maybe because I intentionally avoided him for fear of being 'outted' by him. And now here he was excitedly trying to be my roommate. I felt everyone would be talking and whispering about us, even though no one even noticed or cared for that matter. I accepted my fate though it became increasingly uncomfortable.

There were two double beds in the room and four guys. Would it seem too obvious if I suggested three of us share one bed and let Chris ride solo? The horny glint in his eye was also unnerving. Maybe if he had been hot this would have been a dream come true, but he made my skin crawl. He was mixed race but a mixture that was not working in his favour. He could not have weighed more than 50 kg and was incredibly camp. I guessed I would not be getting much sleep for fear of being touched by him. Whilst drinking around the campfire he asked me in front of an audience if I worked out because he said I had a great body. I was incredibly shy and such attention was toe curling, especially coming from a gay guy.

My close friend Eleanor whispered in my ear, 'You're gonna get some tonight!' and started laughing uncontrollably, thinking this was just harmless fun and not knowing of the struggle I was experiencing around my sexuality. It makes me smile so much now when I remember that on that very night one of the girls, Isabella, who was a lesbian apparently, made a move on Eleanor in the communal showers! Guess that could be called Karma!

Chris stared intensely at me the whole evening and whilst I was silently pleased that someone was noticing the improvement in my physique, he was not the admirer I would have wished for. After forcing Eleanor to stay awake drinking until 2 a.m., I finally took to my bed along with Chris who moved at lightning speed when he saw me returning to my room. After showering, I crashed into bed wearing loose boxers and a white T-shirt.

'You have a great chest!' Chris whispered, as I slipped nervously into bed next to him.

'And no fucking moaning from you two homos tonight!' shouted Paul, one of the other lads in the room. Was this just laddish banter or did they really think I was gay like Chris? After finally falling asleep, I woke up to feel the hot breath of Chris on the back of my neck. I seized and felt paralysed. I kept thinking of the most polite way to ask him to stop. I died at the thought of his crotch pressing up against me. I felt something wet running down the back of my neck and was convinced he was running his tongue along that sensitive spot. Reaching my limit I turned over quickly, ready to tell him that I found his behaviour anything but pleasurable, but he was in a drink-induced coma with small amounts of dribble exuding from his mouth. The relief was immense. The following day saw the sudden onset of salmonella and I was then quarantined from the group. Never have I been so happy to be poisoned!

The trouble with receiving compliments about the improvements in your body is that it fuels the desire for further improvement. With my final exams now complete, and with a long summer before the start of my teacher training course, I used all my free time to frequent the gym. I was not productive and used my energies to compare myself to the other guys, rather than pushing myself. I was so self-critical and to a large extent this has remained even today. I never felt attractive. I knew I had a handsome face, but girls my own age never gave me much attention – and because I had not accepted I was gay, I guess I overlooked any attention from guys – except Chris of course!

During the week before my graduation this changed. I had wandered off to the changing rooms midway through my workout, probably hoping to see a cute guy showering, though under the pretence that I needed the toilet. I glanced into the shower area and noticed the Adonis splashing about. I write this tongue-in-cheek now as at the time it was as if time had slowed down and all his movements were exaggerated. He was young, probably thirty, tall and with a tanned, toned body. He looked over at me and I froze. Had he noticed me staring and was about to give me a piece of his mind? He gave me the biggest smile with the whitest teeth and instead of clenching his fist he clenched his cock and for sure was displaying it just for me. I asked him what time it was. Yes, that's right. I asked the naked guy in the shower, wearing no watch, what time it was. Of all the things you can ask a hot guy who is waving his cock at you, I asked what frigging time it was! He just laughed and splashed about some more, clearly aware of my lack of experience and nervousness.

'Are you showering now, or still working out?' he asked. I had only been at the gym for twenty minutes but now the plan had changed. I rarely showered at the gym because I was quite shy and communal showers were a little intimidating. But there was something about this guy that took that shyness away because suddenly I too was splashing about opposite him. I have no idea what I thought I was going to do, where this was going or what this meant. I knew I needed to meet Maria in about an hour and I still had the thirty-minute drive ahead of me. I did not even feel guilty about my impending adventure. I just thought of it as making friends. He chatted away to me the entire time, the hot suds racing down the entire length of his toned body. His legs were incredibly masculine and hairy. The thick wet hair was so enticing and I longed to reach out and run my hands along their length. As he turned to rinse his chest I caught sight of his tight butt that was shapely and pert. I paid no attention to cleaning my own body but just stood frozen in admiration. Never did he refer to being gay or act suggestively, just small talk about the gym, what I was doing at university and his job. I have no recollection of his job or his name or any other information he gave because I was just in awe of his wonderful physique and handsome face. God he was so handsome and here he was talking to *me*. I just remember him being very thorough when cleaning his dick. He was uncut and this was a fascination in itself for me as I was cut myself. He was slowly retracting his foreskin and cupping his balls as he cleaned. It was either my stimulating conversation or the attention he was giving himself, but something was making that boy grow! He never got hard but for sure there was some sign of excitement. I felt like we had showered for hours but in reality it was no more than ten minutes. So engrossed was I in admiring his body, I failed to notice that I was standing proud! I was in a communal shower with a stiff cock. Thankfully, it being the early afternoon, there were very few people working out in the gym and so my steamy viewing pleasure was undisturbed.

Hot guy then walked over to me and gently whispered, 'You are way hotter than you realise Jack – remember that!' And he left. He never made a move, asked for my number or mocked me. He had rocked my world without even knowing it. He had changed my ignorance into enlightenment. He had made me realise I was attractive to men and good-looking men at that. At the time I had not stopped for a moment to relate this to me being gay. I had not touched him, or cheated or exchanged numbers. I had just made friends. I did not feel guilt or think about Maria. I just seemed to separate the two: my feelings for Maria and my thoughts about this guy. It was this ability to put my straight and gay thoughts into separate boxes that would lead to my ability to 'control' my homosexuality for many years to come.

CHAPTER SIX

We all know that most gay guys love to shop. Is it genetic or a learned behaviour? I was the 'straight' guy proving that it was not only gay guys who love to spend! Well that's what Maria and I would say to others who questioned me. We used the same theory when some of our friends laughed at my CD collection. The trouble was I really believed it.

Unable to be honest with others or myself and therefore receive approval, I turned my attention to mindless activities like shopping. Shopping filled that gap, the gap that I believe the majority of straight people do not live with. The gap is the failure to achieve acceptance. Those in heterosexual relationships are approved by society and their families. They live an honest life accepted by others. Like many gay guys I felt my true self would never be approved of or accepted so I tried to gain the same attention through other means. I have come to realise that gay guys are attention seekers and thrive on it, even if most of us deny it. It was not until I separated from my first boyfriend that I accepted this. In one of his emotionally charged emails where he was criticising me, he kindly referred to me as an attention seeker. I was furious. I cursed him and felt great pain at those words. It was the result of his bad behaviour that had led to the breakdown of our relationship, so who was he to attack my character? But he was so right. I am indeed an attention seeker and this has been evident for a long time. I play the innocent, naïve card so well at times but I now recognise it is my method of gaining the attention of others – hence the disproportionately high number of stalkers I have entertained over the years!

I have the eyes of a security camera, forever scanning the crowds of people in search of someone taking a second glance at me. And I do not care who it is who is looking; men, women, old or young – I'll take it all. Always pushing for compliments, forever seeking approval. Then when I get the attention it always fails to satisfy me and my craving grows stronger. Over the years I have even become immune to the high we get from the kind words of others. Like an addict I have a yearning for an even greater high. The compliments from those who care most about me have little effect; in fact I am not even sure I hear the words. Instead I desire the quick glance of the cute girl on the bus or the look of approval from a straight guy admiring my body or the smile of the cougar at work who senses I am gay and thinks, what a waste! I recognise how utterly shallow and empty this is, but it is there inside me and it is real and it is present in the vast majority of gay guys, especially those who are unhappy. But what I now realise is that it is curable or at best manageable. And what is it that takes away this need? True love that is based on acceptance. Now that I am officially gay and in a loving relationship, this void has been filled. I had not achieved this status with the first boyfriend because I was not ready to accept my own sexuality.

I lived at home throughout university and was one of the fortunate students who received the last of the government student grants up until 1997. I spent the lot. I spent hundreds of pounds on the latest clothes and gadgets each year. I repeatedly changed my car, always striving for better. It was an unconscious release. It would impress my family and give me status with my friends, I thought. My clothes always impressed others. People always commented on how well I dressed and the effort I always made. It was because of this that I attracted the attention of another guy, Gavin, on my post-graduate teaching course in 1998. I was going out more and not so needy of Maria's attention. In fact, we were going through a difficult patch, although I did not realise the true extent of this at the time. She was distant and would often convince me to spend more time with my friends rather than rushing to see her at her university each weekend. She was enjoying a great social life and didn't want to be held back by having to spend her free time with me only. We were quite a big group of friends and often hung out together, despite being on a really intense post-graduate teaching course.

One drunken night we all ended up lying on Gavin's bed and one by one we fell asleep. Gavin was resting his head on the pillow and smiling back at me. I had not considered Gavin to be gay at the time. He certainly did not fit the typical stereotype. He was older than me; maybe early thirties. He was tall, with a well-built physique, slicked back hair and a good eye for fashion. He had a gorgeous smile but his scarred face from his pubescent acne made him a little less attractive. Josh and Katie had nodded off due to the effect of Gavin's moving monologue on world poverty! I have to admit, another one of those and I too would have been out of it, but the gentle, slightly suggestive brush over my chest was now keeping me wide-awake. I tried to ignore what had happened but with the commencement of each new topic, Gavin was edging forward. I remember glancing over at Josh who was now in a more compromising position with Katie and her left breast. I think I knew what was coming and for the first time I was going to let it happen with full control and with total consent. Looking over at the young lovers, I was concerned they would wake up and catch my thoughtless embrace with Gavin. Katie was such a beautiful girl. Her red-infused spirals were so eye catching and it was clear to see why Josh would be so in love with her. Admittedly he was no stud but he had the wit and the charm for sure.

I was furiously biting on my lower lip to control my nerves, but my state of arousal was apparent. I wanted this to happen and so I took the lead. I leaned in and gently placed a hand on Gavin's left cheek, which was softer than I would have imagined. I pulled myself towards him and felt his breath roll across my drying lips. He took the leading role now and grabbed my crotch with assertiveness bordering on aggression. I rested my hand gently upon his groin whilst he ran his hands down into my Calvin's. There was anger and haste in his movements which I had not witnessed before. The intensity was unreal and my climax inevitable. I have no idea how Katie did not wake up as my spasms of delight must have nudged her on several occasions. I lifted her slender legs onto the bed to stop her from falling off and missed Gavin's hasty exit. I crept up to the bathroom where I guessed he had gone to find him vigorously washing himself.

'Gav? What's up?' His silence was unnerving.

'Get the fuck out of my house you fucking bender!' His chest was covered in post-coital red patches and his eyes were possessed.

I ran from the house without a single backward glance wondering what the hell was really going on, but was halted in my stride by the sound of Gavin calling me from behind. He had chased after me to apologise I assumed. How wrong I was. There was no apology only a threat. A threat to expose me for the homo I was to all my fellow students and Maria. For the first time in my complicated little life I felt a sense of guilt and a sense of panic about the events that were about to unfold. Returning to my house I could not comprehend Gavin's behaviour? Was he gay? Was he in a similar state of denial to me? I realised that he had never been seen out dating a girl but his sexuality was not a topic that had been discussed. I felt such confusion and considered talking with Michael who remained my oldest and closest friend from High School. But I didn't know how to start or what to say. I didn't understand the events in my life so how could I express this to another person. The fact he was on the road to becoming a priest added to my difficulty. As much as I knew Michael loved me, could he separate his religious beliefs from the need to help his friend?

My thoughts were broken by the sound of the house phone ringing. It was Maria and I assumed she had spoken with Gavin. I was still wondering what exactly I was going to say to explain the night's events. She had only met Gavin the once but they seemed to have much in common and had been very chatty all night, even exchanging numbers. So understandably I assumed he had made the call. Maria was certainly distant on the phone, but she did not seem angry. She asked if we could meet some place within an hour but I was confused as to why we could not just meet at one of our houses. Maria did not even let me finish my sentence before stating the place and time and hanging up.

I arrived at the pier a little late and found Maria in her car crying. My thoughts were not about myself and how I would explain last night, but for Maria's apparent unhappiness and despair. I was very protective of her and had taken on an older brother role over the past few years.

I never wanted anyone or anything to hurt her, least of all me and my stupid behaviour.

'I'm sorry Jack, I can't do this anymore.' The words from Maria's lips rang repeatedly in my ears, as tears of guilt began to run down my cheeks. It was bitterly cold outside and already a thin layer of ice was forming on the windscreen. At least the cold had prevented a larger audience from gathering outside.

'But why? You know you mean the world to me.' My voice was cracking with each word until I finally broke into a hysterical outburst, quickly followed by one from Maria. The need to talk about what had happened with Gavin and the on-going confusion with my sexuality was not there. I just felt total despair. I loved this girl so much and this confused me even more. Surely if I was gay I would have welcomed this break-up. After all I was now in university surrounded by hot young males and the freedom to do whatever I wanted. So from this event was born the belief that I could not be gay, I was just exploring.

'I slept with Mike. I'm sorry. It was wrong, it shouldn't have happened and I can't explain why but I am so...' Maria broke down at this point as the words were on playback in my head space. I took a moment of self-indulgence to take some sense of relief that Gavin had not indeed exposed me and that I was not responsible for what was unfolding. The moment was brief before my instincts to protect Maria kicked in.

'Maria, I love you and I can forgive you. We can forget it and start again.' Truly one of my most naïve moments born out of my own guilt from my encounter with Gavin. Inside I was broken. I never would have foreseen this. Maria was such a sweet girl, always so innocent. I was her first and only boyfriend and this was not her style. I could not hate her for this even if I had wanted to. But I certainly fucking hated Mike. I had met him a few times when I had stayed with Maria at her university. He was everything I was not and not necessarily in a good way. He had confidence and probably charm no doubt, but this was accompanied by a gut, courtesy of the beer. After all my efforts in the gym, how the hell could she have cheated on me with a fat guy, for Christ sake? Looking back I think I was more concerned with that than her adultery!

'I need space Jack. We should be making the most of our time in university. I mean I'm confused, I don't know...' I interrupted Maria to save her from the babble.

'It's fine. I understand.' With that I stepped out of the car and out into the biting cold air. The weather was so apt: grey, miserable and cold. I walked along the pier, thoughts racing through my head until I could take no more. I cried with an intensity I had not known previously. My heart was so heavy, my body could barely accommodate it. I had no awareness of who or what was around me and I did not care. This was about me; this was my moment. Images of Maria and Mike ran through my mind, tormenting me until my stomach wrenched. I pictured him naked and imagined the positions he had explored with her. It was sick yet seemed an incredibly natural thing to do. I wondered if she felt more satisfied by this apparent alpha male and was herself questioning my sexuality now that she could make a comparison. Was she in love with him? What would I do now? Why the hell had I walked away so easily? Had I been subconsciously looking for this way out?

I arrived home late evening and tried to put on a mask to hide my feelings from my parents. As with all mothers, mine was equipped with a sixth sense, the one given to them to know what is going on with their children, aiding them in making pre-emptive strikes. Admittedly they get it wrong sometimes but it certainly gives them a skill unknown to fathers.

'Son, I can read you like a book, what's wrong?' My mother never failed to use a certain tone of voice with perfection every time. It was soft enough to make the hardest of men crumble.

Dropping my fork to the plate I once again fell apart. The tears streamed down my cheeks which had now nicely defrosted by the fire. Unable to string the words together, my mother gave a much-needed hug, whilst my father shifted awkwardly in his chair, trying to continue eating, unable to find something appropriate to say. I never did tell my parents what Maria had done. She had broken my heart but I would still give my own life to protect her and I certainly would never have let my parents talk badly of her.

'I never thought you had chemistry anyway, son.' The words hurt but the intention from my mother was not malicious. After all, she was right. We clearly did not have the right chemistry and it is a shame my mother could not or chose not to elaborate more. I did not even need to tell my parents we had split up. They had already sensed it and they spent the entire night protecting me in a wall of unconditional love that only parents know how.

Six months passed with little word from Maria and yet I could not let go. Gavin and I never spoke to each other after that night which was difficult to explain to our other friends as it made no sense. My teaching course was now complete and Gavin had moved back to Chester so there was no reason to speak with him but it still upset me somewhat. He never did speak with Maria and his reaction indicated he was struggling with his own sexuality and his anger was indicative of his own fear.

I was now in my first year of teaching in a small village just outside my hometown and Maria had a part-time job cleaning offices in the evening whilst finishing her final year. She had taken over my part-time job when I completed university so I knew where to find her. Following one of my lengthy conversations with my grandfather, he encouraged me to be more assertive and so I drove to see her at work, which was conveniently on the way home from my grandfather's home. Luckily the offices were empty and Maria worked alone, so there was no risk of creating drama to a crowd. It was awkward to begin with and Maria certainly did not appreciate me turning up unannounced. For me it felt right. I followed her around like a puppy, chatting away and trying to explain why we should be together. She was not very forthcoming as we stepped into the office toilets but I continued anyway. Now I do not know how we got to this point, but suddenly we were in the height of an aggressive yet passionate embrace. I had never seen Maria so wild, so controlling. She unzipped my trousers, pushed them to my ankles and within moments I was inside her. For the first time ever we were having unprotected sex, in a toilet, in a public place and it was electric. I had always hated condoms, and being circumcised I felt they further desensitised my cock. So for me this was heaven. Each thrust was magical as I could feel her pleasure intensifying. She was a different girl, more confident – slimmer I noticed. Her face reddened as her orgasm was achieved and mine was quick to follow. I threw my arms around her and kissed the small of her neck but a sudden coldness oozed from her. She dressed and ordered me to do the same.

'I told you not to come. I told you I needed space. God damn it, Jack, why do you always push?' I did not understand. We had just had crazy sex and now she was pushing me away once again and this time without a single tear. My efforts to reason with her were pointless. She was in a zone and a zone in which I was not permitted.

Surprisingly I left relatively calm, secretly thinking that my killer performance in the toilets was going to get her running back to me. Reality soon set in as I now accepted that it had been a mistake, a misjudgement on her part and we were still not back together. My somberness turned to despair and in turn anger as my mind momentarily drifted from my driving as I entered the motorway from the slip road. I fought back my tears and focused on the drive home.

Up ahead I noticed that a small white van appeared not to be moving and so I cautiously slowed down. The most incredible bang rang in my ears followed by the multiple somersaults of my car. With every turn and tumble my head was thrashed against the side window, which was now shattered. No luxury of airbags, I was thrown into the steering wheel, as blood trickled down the side of my head. The car was now travelling at high speed on its side, receiving multiple hits from other vehicles as I crossed the congested lanes of traffic. I truly believed my life would end in one final explosion and the fear was intense. With one final push from a passing car, my shattered vehicle was thrust into the barrier and with it came the greatest pain I have ever known.

Having watched too many episodes of hospital dramas on TV, I was convinced the sound of water trickling from my car was in fact petrol and that my life would end in flames. I scrambled out of my car despite the agony and stumbled along the hard shoulder. I looked back at the wreck that was once my pride and joy and was astonished by how the wheels of my car had been torn away and were lying in the road with the axel and a set of ladders. These had fallen from the van I had seen in the outer lane and which had caused this horrific accident. There must have been a dozen vehicles involved and for a split second I worried that my troubles with Maria had affected my judgement. I fell to the ground as the reality of the pain kicked in. The traffic was now at a standstill and I could not understand why no one was running to help me. This was my last memory before I passed out.

A & E is not a pretty sight at the best of times, but when you are in agony and experiencing a sense of fear like no other, it is even worse. There were so many people fussing over me and yet I felt so alone, so scared. Lying in just my little white boxers, I felt waves of sickness. My neck was supported by a brace and my arms were lined with needles and drips galore. The haunting sound of the monitors filled the room and I struggled to comprehend the extent of my injuries. Moments of sheer panic rose up as I recalled the sound of the metal scraping on the ground, the glass shattering and then relived that final blow that had caused such pain throughout my body.

I looked down to see the doctor messing with my feet and looking concerned as he spoke to the student who was busily taking notes. It was then that it hit me and it hit me like nothing had ever done so before or since. I could not feel the doctor pressing my feet. I could not feel my legs. I could not move. I sobbed uncontrollably as my heart monitor began to race. One final wave of sickness came that was enough to make me vomit, causing panic in my cubicle, for fear of me choking. The staff nurse rushed to turn my head just in time. I opened my eyes and wiped away the tears and there were my parents, my grandfather and Aunt Jess. My mother was beside herself and my father was desperately trying to look brave. My mother's tears made me more fearful of my future.

'Mum, I can't feel my...'

'Shhhh it's okay. The doctor says your body is just in shock – give it a day or two. You have been extremely lucky; someone is clearly watching over you.' The morphine was setting in now and I settled off to sleep in a brief moment of calmness.

Writing this now, it still upsets me terribly. For years those sounds and images haunted me and the accident has left me with a dull pain in my lower back that helps to remind me of just how lucky I was. But it was my mother's words that moved me most, 'Someone is watching over you!' She was right. No one should have survived that accident. The photos serve to prove that, but I did indeed survive. For many years I struggled with the question as to why I would have survived whilst so many other people die in similar accidents. I had convinced myself I was a bad person because of my homosexual thoughts, so why would God save a homo when religion tells me it is a sin that will lead to an afterlife spent in hell? Was I having a second chance to live a good life or had I just cheated death? Now I am in a better emotional place it is the same words that comfort me today. I was given a second chance, but not to be a good, aka straight, guy. God loves me for who I am, gay and all. It was this belief that finally helped me to admit to myself and others that I was gay years later and during the low times when I first came out.

I would have to wait until the next day before my greatest fear would be quashed. I had indeed broken my back but there was no nerve damage and therefore I could walk after a few weeks of bed rest. But the psychological trauma was going to prove my biggest challenge. This was greatly eased by my wonderfully supportive family and Maria. She had been the first to receive the call from the traffic police as her number was listed as an emergency contact in my wallet. The call I am sure was horrendous to take. Maria had stayed by my side every day for two weeks, despite facing her final exams in the coming weeks, alongside my dearest friend Michael, who had flown in from Ireland.

'I'm never letting you out of my sight again!' she gently whispered on that first night at the hospital and I could see from her eyes that she meant it. But maybe she should not have. Maybe she should never have come back to save me, because what would be her repayment for supporting me? For being the person who calmed me down in the night when woken by the nightmares or reassuring me in the months I was faced with impotence, despair and frustration? Abandonment!

CHAPTER SEVEN

After three years of physiotherapy, numerous assessments, physical and psychological, I received an out-of-court settlement just before my twenty-fifth birthday. This provided Maria and I with the means to put down a small deposit on our first house and make plans to get married. We had been living together for two years since I had proposed after the accident, and despite the post-traumatic stress, it had been a great couple of years. I was really happy and loving the experience of setting up home together. I felt secure, loved and, most significantly, I felt straight! This had always been the pattern and continued for some years to come. My level of 'straightness' was directly correlated with my level of overall happiness.

We enjoyed a good sex life and I rarely found myself thinking about guys or having the need to pursue my desires through Internet porn. However, during sex I would still sometimes close my eyes and imagine the touch of a muscular man or the feelings of pleasuring a hot college guy. Physically I knew I preferred the look of a naked man to a naked woman but when touching Maria I unquestionably felt aroused. Caressing her soft breasts and watching her nipples infuse with blood would always make me hard. When I ran my hands along her thighs and touched how moist she felt, I immediately wanted to enter her. Once inside, something didn't seem right. I became bored or distracted and in order to maintain my erection and to eventually achieve an orgasm, I found a need to arouse myself further by thinking about men. I imagined I was fucking a hot arse and that would enable me to cum a little quicker. It was not about Maria, it was about the battle that was taking place in my head.

I was already enjoying success in my job and life was pretty damn good. However, something had changed inside me on the day of the accident, something more profound than I had realised, and it would take some time before the true extent would become apparent. This feeling of having been 'saved' troubled me significantly and started to act as an inner voice, encouraging me to accept that you only have one life and you should make the most of it. In the later years of my marriage it would give me an excuse to justify decisions or choices, albeit sub-consciously.

I had spent many nights trying to discuss my feelings and struggles around the accident with Michael. He was home for three months before relocating to Rome for the final stage of his training. He was so articulate but I couldn't help but feel I was being psychologically assessed rather than supported by a close friend. I was sure he was using me as an experiment for his module on counselling! Just being able to talk with him was comforting. Maria was always too emotional when I tried to explain the complexities of my feelings – I think it unnerved her somewhat or maybe she felt helpless; unable to find the words in the same way as Michael could. The three of us were incredibly close. We had all known each other for such a long time and Maria and I always felt a sense of responsibility for Michael's welfare. We always worried about the life he would face as a missionary in some war-torn country.

After a few hours of arguing with my parents and then Maria about some of the wedding choices, I decided to hit the gym to release my stress. I always cared more about pleasing others despite the effect it had on me and this led to my own unhappiness at times. The wedding was on a tiny scale and not exactly traditional. This had been Maria's choice, as she did not have a large family and did not like being the centre of attention. For me, I had no real preference either way, I just wanted her to be happy. But it did result in some of the people I cared most about not being on the invite list, including Adela, Aunt Jess and my grandfather. I don't know why I didn't fight for those that I cared about so much. Protecting Maria and pleasing her was always my number one priority and maybe this was born out of guilt for my inability to be the man she thought I was. Did I know deep down that the wedding was a mistake and therefore the fewer people there were to witness it the better?

The post workout swim and relax time in the sauna provided a moment of tranquillity that quickly evolved into one of the most significant moments of my life.

After a second swim I took a much-needed pee and could not help but notice the particularly tall guy at the urinal next to me in the tight blue speedos. Dark-skinned and slightly hairy, he was pleasing to the eye but clearly his body was 'work in progress'. Normally speedos are a definite no for me! What was eye catching was the size of his penis. I am not one for toilet voyeurism, but you could have seen this animal from the opposite side of the changing room! I have never quite understood why some guys feel the need to swing and shake their dicks like it is some kind of aerobic workout. It is asking for attention, if you ask me. I am pretty sure a gentle flick and a discreet left-right shuffle achieves the same result. I found myself staring and becoming pretty aroused. It was fairly late and so very few people were around and my mind was experiencing a traffic jam of horny thoughts. He was clearly looking at me, but I did not have the confidence to make eye contact and so forced my now erect cock back into my board shorts and headed back to the pool like a giggly school girl exiting her first biology lesson on reproduction.

Back in the pool my excitement levels rose as he walked into the pool area, stood at the side like a proud peacock, before diving into the pool and impressing me with his multiple lengths that he completed with ease. Clearly he was a natural swimmer, which explained the broad shoulders. I decided my rather clumsy breast-stroke technique would cause great embarrassment, so I decided to take to the steam room where I would indulge myself in thoughts of the contents of his speedos.

The concept of time had lost all significance. I was in a world of fantasy where time had no place, only erotic thoughts. The door opened and startled me slightly as the colder air rushed in and a tall figure appeared within the hot aromatic steam. I had hoped for this moment and here it was, right in front of me. Whether this guy was gay or not had not even been a consideration and so maybe this was the first time my natural gay instincts, aka 'gaydar', were in operation.

'Hey, how's it going?' he asked, with a deep, distinctively Welsh accent.

I managed a pathetic one-syllable response before pushing back my shoulders to enlarge my chest, trying to make my pathetic frame look more impressive than it was.

'You're so cute!' he sniggered as he moved over to my side of the room. 'So how long have you been working out here? I have noticed you a few times before.' In just those five seconds of talk I had done an all over body assessment of him. His hair was thinning, but his face cute. He was battling the thirty-something spread, but was still athletic. And that bloody package was still right there looking back at me!

'Just touch it mate. You've been staring at it all night so you might as well have a feel., Life's too short not to.' Life's too short not to... My God, he had just spoken the words I had been repeating over and over in my mind ever since the accident. Was this a sign from God? A day pass into 'Gay Land'?

'I'm getting married!' I blurted out, my heart once more pumping with an intensity similar to when I had visited Pete back in my early teens.

'Well, congratulations, but you can still touch it if you like!' He clearly loved the chase as there was now some movement in those speedos that left little room for manoeuvring. Breathless and now pretty hot from the extended stay in the steam room, I shuffled sideways and placed my hand onto his hairy, muscular thigh. I ran my hand slowly to his crotch, enjoying the journey along his thick, black hair. I cupped his balls and then felt the full length of penis which was pretty impressive, although intimidating. I had never imagined a 'real-life' cock could be of this size. Without warning his lips were pressing intensely on mine and his hands were dancing all over my chest. He slipped his tongue inside my mouth and kissed me with a passion I had not experienced before. I savoured every moment, not stopping to think about who might walk in on us. He pulled away and praised me for my kisses before exiting the room, leaving me floundering in a pool of pleasure. Assuming the end of this delightful encounter and my swift return to reality, I showered and headed for my locker. Steam room guy was standing there in all his glory, towelling his back. I mean come on – this was ridiculous, temptation quite literally in your face. Was this God giving me a sign that my thoughts were acceptable and this was permission? Or was this the devil tempting me with lurid wonders? Or was this just the Catholic in me talking? His cock was swinging back and forth and once again hypnotising me like a pendulum.

'You like it don't you. You can't take your eyes off it!' he chuckled, so proud of what God had blessed him with. I tried to focus on dressing as I battled in my head with what was going on and why I had actively engaged in a steam room snog. The battle was not one of guilt but of confusion, confusion as to why this was happening now. I was happy. I was getting frigging married and I had not had these thoughts for such a long time and certainly not at this intensity.

'I'll meet you in my car outside when you're done.' He laughed and walked off looking rather dashing in his fitted shirt and designer jeans. Did he just give me a return pass? I wandered through the gym's corridors in a daze, recalling the evening's events and smiling. Then I packaged it all into a nice neat box and filed it right at the back of my mind under the 'It didn't really happen' category.

'Get in Mr Married Guy!' There he was, the handsome stranger sat in a slick black Audi TT with personalised plate and leather interior and there I was getting in! No thoughts, no hesitations, no guilt. He spun the car around to a quieter part of the car park and before the wheels had even stopped turning he was back on my lips, with a greater intensity, breathing heavy and touching me more vigorously.

'Can I see it?' I whispered with a greater confidence, now that I knew he clearly found me attractive.

'I think you have seen enough of him already,' he joked, but he did not put up a fight as I unzipped his jeans and grabbed the thick shaft whilst basking in amazement at its size. I noticed the foreskin was particularly tight and did not retract over the head but this did not stop me going down on him. For the first time in my life I was having oral sex with a guy, something I had dreamt of and longed for at times. I was lost in pleasure until from nowhere came a bolt of guilt. A sense of time had returned and I knew that I would now need an excuse to explain my whereabouts to Maria. After all, I was not exactly in possession of the body of a guy who went to the gym for three hours per session. I was riddled with guilt and clearly it was all over my face.

'Hey, it's okay, it doesn't mean anything. You can still get married and play the straight life!'

'No, I am straight!' I retorted. 'I'm not playing anything!' and I exited the car with haste, failing to satisfy either of our primal needs.

'Hey, don't I even get to know the name of the cute stranger who sucked my cock?' I walked away but then stopped. I turned back and returned to the car, leant in and kissed him and told him my name. He handed me his name card and asked me to call him.

'You're a great kisser Jack! We can be friends. Friends with benefits.' My God, he had just given me the perfect justification and the perfect way for me to deal with all of this. I did not want to be gay and live with a guy. That thought horrified me. I wanted to get married and have a family. But I knew I liked men and now this was a way to have both – a friend with benefits. I mean friends do most things together. They talk, share thoughts and secrets, hug, kiss, so why not indulge in some more intimate fun? It did not have anything to do with love or being deceitful, it was just a different type of fun. Amazing how powerful and persuasive the mind can be and how our bad choices can always be justified to ourselves, if we really want them to be.

Looking back I realise just how much Maria trusted me and how she never doubted my sexuality. Even though I returned at nearly midnight from the gym after almost three hours, she never really questioned me. She referred to me as obsessive and went off to bed laughing playfully. I often heard stories of guys who had affairs or one night stands and could not bear to look at their girlfriends or wives because they were so full of guilt and so they blurted out their crimes on the spot. Well I felt nothing inside. I did not feel guilt. I did not feel remorse or regret. For me nothing had changed. I still really loved Maria and was still excited about getting married and now I had a new friend. I went on to tell Maria all about Gareth, my doctor friend. The fancy car he drove, the impressive swimming and a little bit of background information that I was improvising for some strange reason. Here I was creating my own little fantasy friend like a four year old. Except he was not fantasy; he was real. What was a fantasy was the story I was creating around him. I had convinced myself that Gareth was my friend and no more. The fact I had sucked him off in his car was irrelevant in my head. Maria accepted it because she had no reason not to, which only made my new behaviour more acceptable.

CHAPTER EIGHT

The secretive texting began within hours and thus began the deceit. I did not recognise or accept I was being deceitful at the time. I still truly felt that I *was* straight, but just liked guys for sexual pleasure. Gareth began texting me about all the things he wanted to do to me and teasing me about how great my kissing was. I felt so alive with this new attention. As great as Maria was, she was never really one for praise. She never told me how handsome I was or complimented me on my technique in the bedroom, so this style of praise was addictive and I lapped it up. I found myself returning equally erotic texts though it did not come naturally to me. I was still struggling with the fact that I had kissed a guy. It was hard to forget because the skin above my top lip was so red and sore from his late night stubble.

My phone became an extension of my body for fear of Maria discovering my deceitful behaviour. It went everywhere with me and at every opportunity I would check for new messages from Gareth. I was certainly very keen and within days we were arranging to meet. He seemed a little reluctant to give me his address and instead we agreed that I would call him when on my way home from work at six. All day I thought about nothing else but Gareth. I was able to put Maria into another neat box at the back of my mind where she would sit until I returned home later that evening. The build up to the evening meeting with Gareth was intense and I knew that this was going to be the night I had intercourse with a guy for the first time. I never stopped to consider the consequences, the risks, the meanings. I just got absorbed in the moment. I had even told Maria I was meeting Gareth for a drink so there was no need for a sense of guilt.

The drive home seemed so much longer on that day and I repeatedly tried to call Gareth on the way. He was not answering his phone. I knew he lived near the gym and so I stopped just outside the entrance and tried calling again. Still no answer. Disappointment punched me hard and I began to feel anger and frustration. I wanted this so badly and had waited all day for this moment. I accepted defeat and drove home. Angrily snapping at Maria on the way to the bathroom, I slammed the door and sat on the toilet crying. What the fuck was going on in that messed up head of mine? What the hell did I think was going to happen tonight with Gareth? What was I playing at? I was getting married in a few months. I felt this concoction of emotion that quickly transpired into the need to vomit. I had never experienced confusion like this, but within minutes everything was boxed away and my composure gathered. Maria was outside the bathroom looking concerned and again I snapped at her and told her that it was just a migraine. I remember the way she looked at me. Disappointment. I was Mr Nice Guy and had never spoken badly to her and now I was speaking to her with no respect on more than one occasion. This added to my heartache and frustration and so I took to my bed where I cried whilst Maria lovingly drove to the pharmacy for some medication for my fantasy migraine. Repeatedly I sent texts to Gareth, but no messages were returned. He was in his mid-thirties and I sense was more emotionally stable than myself. I was losing all sense of reality. I did not even know this guy so why did I care so much and why was this behaviour not making me question my sexuality? I was not hoping to have an affair with Gareth; the thought somewhat disgusted me. I just wanted his friendship, though admittedly with the perks.

I returned to the gym the same time each day for two weeks in the hope of seeing Gareth there and it was not until I changed my routine that I was successful. My first thought was that he was avoiding me. He looked pleased to see me as he stood butt naked, shaving in the mirror. He certainly was not shy! I tried to play it cool but my efforts failed and instead I sounded strangely possessive. Gareth explained he had been busy at work, planning his forthcoming move to Australia. He did not show any interest in meeting up and I was too caught up in my thoughts about him leaving to pursue it. I watched him dress whilst making hopeless small talk and wished him luck as he walked away for the last time. I had lost what would have been the perfect friend for me, but I was also somewhat relieved. I recognised my behaviour had been foolish and crazy and not what I really wanted. I wanted to be with Maria so now I could focus on making her happy again.

And so why do I consider this to be a significant moment in my life? Because this was the beginning of my deceit. Not intentional deceit but deceit all the same. I was a good guy, but was making bad choices. It was my failure to accept this that led to my continuing deceit. I believed I was a good person and therefore I prevented myself feeling any guilt. This was a clear message to myself that I was gay and that I should not have been getting married. All the other incidents previously could be put down to a 'phase' or hormonal imbalances during puberty or even harmless exploration like so many other straight guys. But this was different. I was an adult and I should have recognised what I was doing and what the implications were. However, I did not and I do not know why. I could blame confusion, fear, society or selfish desires. I honestly have no answer for you. And now it makes me consider the 'sliding doors scenario'. How would my life have turned out if this event had led me to admit to my sexuality at that time? Would I have been more or less successful in my career, had more fun, enjoyed happiness from a younger age, destroyed my family relationships or gone completely off the rails? I have always believed that everything happens for a reason but it is hard to hold on to that when you cause so much hurt to another person in the process.

CHAPTER NINE

A few more weeks of wedding-induced stress before the day finally arrived. August 16th 2001 was the day, and I embraced it with total awareness of what I was doing. Never once did I doubt this next move in my life. This was something I had been pre-programmed to work towards, albeit by society. It was the natural next step for me to take and I could not have felt more positive. I recognised my unusual interest in men and had now found a way to 'manage' it. And as for Gareth? Well, conveniently I had filed and stored that one deep in my sub-conscience so it was not a factor for consideration. Of course, nothing stays neatly stored and filed for long before something comes along and messes up your system!

The day of the wedding was incredible. I was feeling ecstatic and had no reservations, no concerns and no worries. Michael had been instrumental in helping with the arrangements and had taken on the role of unofficial best man. Life was exciting and dynamic and therefore my desires about men were at a low. Admittedly I had continued to indulge in periods of escapism through gay porn since my encounter with Gareth, though my emotions seemed under control. On many occasions I wondered if I watched my X-rated material out of habit or out of true need. Sometimes I would not be that interested and I hated the feelings that riddled my mind post-climax. So here was my attempt at living the straight life.

Although a Catholic wedding, this was far from traditional in any respect. You could see the sense of fear on the priest's face when Maria had run through the arrangements. Or was the fear not for the lack of tradition but rather a fear for Maria and what the future would hold? I always found it unusual that Maria and I were not expected to attend the marriage preparation course beforehand. It is normally a requirement. The priest had said that since we both worked in Catholic education there was no need. The preparations normally ask couples to question each other to iron out potential problems in the future, i.e. who will take out the rubbish each week? Do you want children? Who will care for the children? I guess these were not really the questions Maria needed to ask me; we had much bigger problems to come. However, there was one issue that caused friction at times and would become a significant factor for me and my ability to stay in this relationship: having children. I had always loved children so much, having grown up around younger nephews, nieces and cousins. I would often babysit for the children in my street when in my mid-teens. People would often comment what a wonderful father I would be when I was older and I never imagined that one day I would give up the basic human need of being a dad. I have so much unresolved emotion around this issue even today.

Maria had always stated that she never wanted children, from the first year when we started dating. Being a teacher, she too loved children and she had a great relationship with one of my young nephews, but she never wanted one of her own. The problem seemed to revolve more around her fear of putting on excessive weight and the lack of confidence in her body. The thought of a doctor examining her terrified her. I always felt this was something she would 'grow out of' and so it was never a reason for me to end the relationship in the early days. It did somewhat alarm me when she would refer to carrying a child as 'repulsive' and how it was similar to an alien 'sucking the life out of you from inside'. However, I was now in love and so I accepted her opinion, especially when she played the liberated female card, 'it's my body...' blah blah blah. Yet it did lead to many arguments at times, which were born out of my frustration and selfish desires to be a father. I do feel that women can be a little self-centred around this matter. As men, we cannot carry a child; this is a gift bestowed on women from God. To have your child growing inside you is a miracle and something that a man can never experience. It is definitely where women do have an advantage over us! To carry a child for a man is the greatest gift you can offer. An act of true selflessness. But many women choose not to embrace this for reasons of independence, freedom, career. I do respect this but I struggle with it too and maybe that is out of my own selfishness. After all, Maria had always been upfront with me about this matter from the very beginning. I guess I just fooled myself into believing she would change her mind. Sadly, she would when it was too late.

There were no wedding cars, no photographer, no choir or organist, no reception, no wedding cake and no first dance. You can imagine defending these choices to our parents. When I reflect back on that day I wonder if I should have read into this. Was it fate that the wedding was so low key because in years to come it would be something that never existed and something that only brought feelings of sadness? At the time I believed it was because we were stripping away all the pomp and circumstance that often overshadows this great sacrament. We wanted this to be just about us and we wanted only those we cared about most to witness this, although I will still never forgive myself for not inviting my little sister. This ridiculous situation had come from Maria's strained relationship with her own sister. They had never enjoyed a close relationship and when her sister refused to come without the boyfriend that Maria detested, it was concluded that only parents and joint friends would attend. Sometimes my desire to make Maria happy overshadowed my own needs and wishes. I had shared some of my most significant moments in life with my grandfather and Aunt Jess and now they were not here to witness this beautiful moment.

I collected Maria from her mother's house. No, we had not separated for the night in keeping with tradition, but rather she had been shopping near her mother's house first thing in the morning. Wearing my new navy suit and trademark shiny shoes, I stood anxiously waiting to see what the hell Maria would be wearing. I had half imagined one of her tie-dye numbers with a pair of Doctor Martin boots but was totally dazzled when she finally appeared. She looked truly amazing. I had never seen her look so beautiful before. So elegant. Her skin was like porcelain and her hair was so silky. She was wearing an incredible two-piece wedding gown. A fitted bodice enhanced her curvaceous body and the beautiful silk skirt swept gracefully over her hips. I was breathless, (and relieved)! A few of the neighbours had heard of the forthcoming event and assembled outside, which Maria did not appreciate. She often came across as hard and stuck up, but it was more out of embarrassment and a lack of self-confidence.

It was a short drive to the church and the butterflies in my stomach appeared somewhat hyperactive. You often see in movies the scene where the best man gives the groom his final talk; 'Are you sure you want to do this?' I wish Michael had given me that speech. Asked me, 'What the fuck are you doing?' If maybe he had made me talk about who I really was then maybe...

The seven guests, including Michael, had all been seated around the altar, creating a very intimate atmosphere. The church was incredibly large and I had feared our guest list would make the event look pitiful. But the focus was on the altar and not on the rows of pews left unfilled. The elderly women from Sunday's congregation had done a great job with the flowers and the music selection by my close friend and self-appointed best man had been perfect. Maria did not enter the church from the back and walk up the aisle with her father. She was not on speaking terms with her father following the break-up of her parents' relationship many years before. A rather selfish man full of regrets, he had never been considered in the list of invitations. So instead we entered the church together from the side. The poor priest was struggling with these alternative arrangements, but later he did say that it was the most moving ceremony he had ever blessed. I still remember his face when Maria arrived at the church. It was similar to my relief when I saw her and yet his face failed to hide his surprise and both Maria and I broke out into a state of giggles. He was an elderly gentleman with a curved spine. Incredibly lovely and genuine, he had been a part of both our lives for many years. He was the chaplain at the high school that Maria and I had attended together and he had also baptised Maria as a child.

He simply looked at Maria and said, 'Well, that will do nicely!' As we came around the corner to where the guests were seated, our friends and Maria's mother looked so happy for us. My parents were smiling too of course but I felt there was something missing. Was it because my sister and grandfather were missing from the guest list? Or was it because my mother generally was not that comfortable in these situations? I prayed to God it was not because they thought this was a mistake. They say your parents know you better than yourself. After all, your mother carried you inside her for nine months. You are genetically half of each parent; a carbon copy of them, so they should know you. Did they know more than I realised and yet never spoke out? Did they sit there anxiously praying that my alter ego would never rise up and lead to me breaking the very vows I stood making now in front of them? Maybe I just read into things too much now. It is a by-product of turning your life upside down when in your thirties. You read into every little event, every conversation that went on before, every look someone gave you. And I imagine the other people around you go through the same process, most of all your parents and ex-wife when you finally reveal who you really are.

I spoke my vows with such pride and emotion. I could barely speak and my voice was breaking with every word. It is an incredibly moving experience to tell the person you love that you will always protect and cherish them, till death do you part. As I write this chapter I feel shame and remorse that I could not fulfil these words. I know it was not my fault. I was trying to make a promise I was unable to keep. But all the same it does not hurt any less. I stood there before the girl who would have given her life for me and I promised to love her no matter what. I feel a fake and I feel this way because that is exactly what I was. I did not know it at the time but a fake I was all the same. People have been incredibly supportive to me through all of this and yet I feel they are too generous. Would I get the same sympathy if I had married Maria without her knowing I was a serial killer or a persistent adulterer? Yet I let her marry me without her knowing I was gay, so what is the difference? False pretences all the same.

Following the ceremony we took a few limited pictures before moving to the hotel for an intimate meal. The conversation was good and the smiles plentiful, although my parents continued to look uncomfortable. I put this down to the choice of restaurant. My parents were more your pub grub type of people rather than a place with endless amounts of cutlery and rules of engagement that no one ever shares with you. There were no speeches, no moving words, no embarrassing uncles doing the drunken jive and no friend sleeping with the fat bridesmaid left sitting in the corner of the room with her plate of nibbles. It was sophisticated and classy, but insignificant. It was as if it was set up to be understated so that when the dirty little secret would come out there would be fewer people to keep silenced.

My parents left quite swiftly after the food, just missing out on the champagne that was delivered from Eleanor, who had not made the guest list. I was getting a little tipsy now and just wanted to sleep. I remember feeling an incredible sense of pressure about the need to have sex on the wedding night. It was crazy considering we had lived together for a few years yet it still seemed to be an expectation I placed on myself. After finally freeing ourselves from the last few friends we took to our room. Michael and one of Maria's university friends at some point had escaped the table unnoticed and kindly decorated our room with balloons and confetti in our bed. It made us both smile though Maria was less than happy that someone had emptied her overnight bag and hung up her clothes and knickers! A little bit of sweet-talking brought her around and soon we were getting intimate.

What I find incredible is that I have not a single photo of that significant day. Any photos Maria had she destroyed in anger when we first separated. My parents probably have a few tied up in a bag, locked inside a box and stored in the back of some cupboard. No photos: only memories and regrets.

CHAPTER TEN

The honeymoon trip to Canada had been great, although short. Maria was not one for beach holidays so we opted for a city break to Toronto instead. A costly alternative, we could only manage a six-day romance.

Maria was not the easiest of people to go on holiday with. She had high expectations in terms of hotel accommodation, dining and modes of transport. All of this came at a price and only being a young teacher it was hard to satisfy her needs. But the price of not meeting these standards was far more costly. The avoidance of tears, tantrums and moods made every addition to the credit card justified. She would also create over ambitious itineraries that sucked any possible enjoyment out of the trip. Maria was one of those teachers who was always on duty and I was now one of her pupils following my daily timetable and look out if I was late for any activity! I mean most people go away to rest, sleep late, romance and generally recharge. These words were not in Maria's vocabulary. It was up at 7 a.m., breakfast and out by 8.30 a.m. and then every minute of that jam-packed day would be taken up with shopping, sight-seeing and photo opportunities. There was no time to let lunch settle. Despite my pleas for mercy, Maria insisted that this was a once in a lifetime opportunity and no time should be wasted. The first child of so many couples is conceived on the honeymoon. Well there was zero chance of our baby being named Toronto! What I did take great pleasure in was that on day four, when Maria could not walk due to a sore back from overdoing the shopping and walking, she pleaded with me for a slower pace! Lucky for her I am a laid back, gentle man and I just took silent pleasure instead. On day five we struggled for something to do because we had been so intense on days one to four! Of course it would not have been wise to sarcastically point out the errors in Maria's planning and once again I took a silent moment to gloat.

Our hotel was right in the centre of Toronto and the first evening walk back to the hotel revealed a row of gay cinemas with very enticing advertisements outside. I was shocked to think that they actually showed gay porn inside public cinemas and my mind raced with thoughts about what kind of things went on inside. I was totally preoccupied with these thoughts and incapable of paying attention to Maria who was busily trying to organise our day trip to Niagara the next day. I was desperately searching my mind for a reason why I needed to leave the hotel so that I could again walk past those provocative posters and maybe even muster up the courage to go inside. Maybe I could say I needed some fresh air or I was going to look for some snacks? I fought with myself and wrestled these thoughts to the ground. What the hell was I thinking? This was my honeymoon! Each night as we walked past the same cinema my mind would wonder but that was all. I controlled my desires and focused on my wife instead. Admittedly before drifting off to sleep I would indulge in a few minutes of daydreaming, imaging rows of fit young men with trousers around their ankles masturbating each other as some sex flick played in the background. Of course the reality was probably a few dirty old men breathing heavily in the back rows, rubbing vigorously on the old boy that saw little action these days!

Returning back home, Maria and I slipped into married life easily; after all we had been living together for some time now so nothing had really changed. Wearing the wedding ring took some getting used to but I always felt a sense of pride when looking at it. Within a few months the pressure to have children was building from family and this would add friction to our relationship in the years to follow. My mother was probably the least tactful in this respect, but it was born only out of her desire to see me as a proud father. However, she was insensitive to Maria's feelings. No-one understood Maria as well as I did and this pressure was never going to achieve the desired goal. Besides which, we were still young and still ambitious. There was plenty of time for starting a family. This was just a different way of thinking from my parents. My mother had conceived her first child at the age of eighteen and had all three children within her twenties. Family was central to everything that my mother did and the idea of travelling, careers and flash cars was alien. My own sisters even followed the same path, both being teenage mothers and just about finishing high school. But I was different and always had been.

There was ambition burning inside me and a determination never seen in any of my relatives. I was the only one from my family to ever study at university. I think this level of ambition came from my late grandmother. She was incredibly talented across so many disciplines. A poet, painter, aspiring author and amazing cake decorator, she never had the opportunity to be truly successful because she fell in love with a hot Italian guy who swept her off her feet. My grandfather had spotted my grandmother at the tender age of fifteen and set his sights on making her his wife just a year later. They secretly married in Bethnal Green and later revealed to their parents that they were expecting their first child! The women in my family are incredibly fertile and prone to teenage pregnancy!

Although my grandmother was never able to flourish fully, she enjoyed a wonderful family life and inspired me so much. I never realised the impact she had on my life whilst she was still alive. But I now recognise that I have the same desires, hopes and aspirations as she did. I share and owe my creativity to her. She was the most amazing woman – so selfless, so gentle. I had the most wonderful times with her and my grandfather and was incredibly close to them both. Her death when I was just sixteen had a tremendous impact on me and even today I still feel such pain around this. I feel blessed that I had the opportunity to know her as many of my friends had very elderly grandparents or never even knew them. But she was only fifty-seven when she died and, like others in my family, I felt robbed that she had been taken away from me too early in her life. She knew me so well and she understood me better than anyone else in my family. She saw so much of herself in me and encouraged me to aim high and achieve all that I wanted, without any pressure at any time. She always knew I would study at university and she always looked at me with such pride. I only wish she could have seen the success I have achieved in my career. I often wonder if the rest of my life would have unfolded differently if she had won her battle with cancer. Would she have been the one to ask the awkward question about my sexuality? Probably not. She was incredibly shy and avoided any talk of sex or sexuality. I think she probably knew I was different and I think she would have just sat quietly whilst I found my own way and then been ready to step in and tell me that everything was going to be okay just at the right time.

My ambition paid off during our first year of marriage and I was promoted to deputy head at a new school. I was just twenty-six and this was a tremendous achievement. My salary soared and at first my levels of happiness rose in parallel. Maria and I enjoyed countless weekends of lavish spending and I purchased my first sports car with retractable roof. Recognising the fault in endless spending sprees we decided to invest my additional salary in property and so we moved to our second house. A three-bedroom detached house with integrated garage, we were now truly living a middle-aged life albeit ten years too soon! The house was of a modern design on a fairly new estate just out of town. It was one of those estates I had aspired to live in when I was younger.

Now here we were along with the shiny new MR2 on the driveway and the cute fireman living in the house opposite. I lacked male friends and I often wonder if my fascination with men was born out of a desire to make friends rather than sexual interest. I admit, the fireman was hot and blessed with a great physique. However, he was shorter than me and must have been the one used to crawl through small spaces at the scene of an emergency. I made great attempts to befriend him, often taking the rubbish out at the same time he arrived home. We both worked out at the same gym – hence how I knew he was sporting a great body! Sadly, we never really moved past a wave and a simple hello in the three years that we lived opposite each other. Maybe I scared him with my intense staring or maybe he felt I was undressing him whenever we met – that would be about right if I was honest. I was growing bored and he was a flicker of excitement.

I was now shopping for paint and plants and spending weekends and holiday times decorating and walking the aisles of DIY stores. Following my usual pattern of behaviour, I had rushed into buying this house. I am incredibly impatient at times and I have the most amazing way of convincing myself that I am making the right choices or doing the right thing, (in the same way I convinced myself I was straight). This happens whenever I buy cars, houses or new IT products. I recognise the behaviour but I still have not learnt to change it. There were no major problems with the house but the level of renovation needed had not raised its head to me on the two visits I had made before signing. It was all fairly cosmetic but decorating was not something that interested me, though luckily Maria was very creative in terms of interior design and so took the lead. The garden was also incredibly high maintenance, being on three tiers, something that was very dangerous for young children, my mother had tactfully pointed out on her first visit, along with the lack of space for a nursery in the third bedroom! That caused quite an argument with Maria that evening when my parents left. I hated that garden so much and resented spending many a Sunday mowing the lawn after discovering the onset of Maria's apparent hayfever and inability to help.

Most people enjoy this moment in their life. They have found the perfect partner, closed the door on the party years and happily opened the door to middle age. But I was suffocating. I was never one for partying and family life was something I had always wanted, but something felt wrong. Senseless spending on designer clothes and expensive cars I could do, yet setting up home I was struggling with. My levels of happiness were dropping and therefore my desires surrounding men were rising. I was buying gay DVDs again and hiding them in the rafters of our garage. I had few friends and few interests and the pressure of my new job was not helping. I had failed to secure any long lasting friendships from university and since graduation I had only heard occasionally from Eleanor. Michael was now posted as a deacon in Rwanda and, with little access to modern methods of communication, I rarely heard from him. The worry I felt about the dangers he faced provided some distraction to my own struggles.

I felt a downward spiral into depression until unexpectedly at work I stumbled upon a new friend. I had signed up for a three-week professional development course in education where I had met a group of young teachers. We all got along so well and this was the first time in many years that I had made friends with other men who I seemed to have a lot in common with, even if this was mainly about work. By the third week we were meeting up for drinks after class and exchanging numbers. Nathan and I got along particularly well and seemed to have the same temperament. He had the most incredible eyes – intensely blue and overly large. He had attracted a lot of female attention on the course but I joked with him that this was only because they all knew I was married and off-bounds and unavailable!

Nathan would become one of my closest friends in the months to come. But he would also be the catalyst in helping me to finally reveal my true sexuality, though at the cost of our own friendship.

CHAPTER ELEVEN

$\mathbf{F}$riday night was cinema night for Maria and I. We were not that predictable by nature but because of the pressures at work, the long hours and the constant tiredness, movie escapism was the perfect way to end a stressful week. It was something Maria and I had a common interest in and something that gave us so much to talk about. She would often joke about how I was obsessed with wanting a life that replicated some rom-com movie. Every birthday, every Christmas, every key moment in my life resulted in disappointment because it was never as good as in the movies. I guess to some extent films also conditioned me into a straight life. Who knows how things would have unfolded had I watched *Brokeback Mountain* when I was younger. Instead I was influenced by films such as *Four Weddings and a Funeral*.

It was Julia Roberts' performance in *Notting Hill* that inspired me to propose to Maria just after my traumatic road traffic accident. However I would like to blame the post-traumatic stress I was going through at that time. After a terrible night's sleep caused by endless flashbacks and panic attacks, Michael had convinced me to go to the cinema. Reluctantly I had left the house. I was very self-conscious at the time owing to the fact that I was still wearing a metal jacket that made me look similar to a stormtrooper from *Star Wars* crossed with Robocop, minus the guns. There was no denying the additional attention I was receiving! The film was incredibly uplifting and when Julia's character pleaded with Hugh Grant's character, 'I'm just a girl, looking at a boy asking him to love me,' something happened inside me. Yes it was cheesy and uncool but I felt an overwhelming wave of love for Maria and a recognition of just how great she had been to me during the time of the accident.

My parents were sleeping when I returned home and I knew Michael would judge me if I shared my next idea with him. As he drove off down the street I found myself snatching the keys to my parents' car and speeding off in the opposite direction, despite my physical limitations. This was crazy and irrational, but *so* incredibly exciting. I hastily stopped at the local supermarket and bought the biggest, most lavish, bouquet of flowers, then continued on my reckless way. My over-sensitivity about my additional body armour had now evaporated and all I could focus on was Maria and my next move. I knew she had been attending her end of year graduation ball but I was hoping she would be back in the flat now that it was almost one in the morning. Pulling up outside her place I called her mobile.

'Maria, are you at home?' I spoke very quickly on account of the adrenaline.

'Jack, it's one a.m. What the hell...'

I quickly interrupted the forthcoming lecture about inappropriateness in favour of maintaining a more romantic direction.

'Look out of the window!' My heartbeat was like a drum as I knew I had not really thought this through, but it worked like this in the movies! Maria was not playing along and so I rang the bell and she came to answer the door still ranting to me on the phone about how late it was. She opened the door cautiously with her housemate nervously peering over her shoulder. They were both completely surprised to see *me* standing there, flowers in hand.

'Oh my god, you are so cute!' giggled her friend Kirsten before running up the stairs to spread the gossip to the third unseen housemate.

Without further thought I found myself declaring my undying love for Maria and asking her to be my wife, despite the fact that her flat was on a main road with many a drunken lout standing around the take-away next door. She struggled to take me seriously and of course took delight in pointing out the lack of engagement ring, though all the same she did agree. It was not the big romantic gesture I had imagined and I doubt it was the most moving experience of Maria's life, but it was spontaneous and genuine and I would not have changed it.

This particular week the cinema provided a much-needed sense of escapism. The new job was proving to be a real challenge and for one reason only – the crazy bitch of a boss. She had head-hunted me from my last school having heard great things about my teaching ability. Well that's what I had been led to believe when in fact what she really wanted was someone impressionable, someone to mould and manipulate. Sadly for her she would come to realise that I was not this guy. I may have given this impression on account of my gentle, unassuming nature, but I was my father's son and I had my limits.

On first meeting Ms Filsbury, Jean Filsbury, she seemed pretty awesome. In her late forties; very attractive and with a great eye for fashion, she appeared to be the perfect prospective boss. I was twenty-six and still a little naïve, so when she referred to me as handsome as well as bright at our first meeting, I melted. Her hair was desperately holding on to its blonder days and her eyes were particularly large and alluring. She also had the habit of standing particularly close to me whenever she talked, something I found uncomfortable on account of the personal bubble that shielded me. However, there is always a downside to working for a woman like this. I remember Eleanor once telling me that very few *nice* women get to top positions in companies. Within most there is a psychopath waiting to be unleashed! I think on this occasion Eleanor was right.

I think it had been about two months before I witnessed the transformation for myself. Summonsing me to her office she took on a new persona that I had only heard of from others. Accusing me of gossiping about her, she tore me down a few strips and left me helplessly trying to string together a few words in defence. What baffled me most was not where this unfounded accusation had come from in the first place, but how quickly she returned to her former self, whispering playfully, 'You naughty boy you!' as she flirtatiously played with my tie. Her white satin top cusped her breasts that seemed to be pressing ever so gently against my chest. She smelt so good too – a mixture of a fresh breeze and sweet apples – and so the need to defend myself passed. This was how she manipulated many a situation and my guess was that this was part of the reason she had made such progress in her career.

That particular week she was on top form. One of the teachers who had gone home sick the previous day was not well enough to return the next morning and apparently by some telepathic power I was supposed to have known this and organised for a supply teacher to cover. Ms Filsbury came shrieking down the corridor, her cream linen trousers flowing in the wind that her temper was generating, accusing me of being ineffective. Teachers from other schools often referred to Ms Filsbury as angelic on account of the way she moved – so graceful, so effortless. Well believe me she was anything but angel-like that day. She was out of her fucking mind. I could not help but giggle, maybe out of nervousness or maybe on account of the trail of tissue attached to her Jimmy Choo's.

The giggles did little to diffuse the situation. My punishment; she refused to drive with me to the meeting we were both attending that day. Instead I had to follow in my own car. She also refused to sit with me at the meeting and only spoke as I left saying cuttingly, 'I am so disappointed in you!' I felt like a naughty schoolboy, berated in front of my colleagues.

I returned to school at the end of the lunch break to find her already sitting amongst the staff, joking and laughing. She seemed delighted to see me and eagerly started chatting to me. Her opening question to me was, 'What do *you* wear – boxers or briefs?' I was not sure whether to be pleased I was no longer in her bad books or to be concerned at the new angle of conversation. When this question gained no real response from me she then asked, 'Do you have a hairy chest? I bet you do!' She was slightly blushing and inappropriately biting on her lower lip and playing the role of a virginal teenager. To be honest, although grounds for sexual harassment, I actually enjoyed this banter and I did not feel that this was her intention. I think she was capable of being very manipulative and this was one of her strategies.

Throughout the four years I worked for her we enjoyed a love-hate relationship. She could be incredibly compassionate at times and yet so cutting and insensitive at other times. Ms Filsbury also liked to surround herself with very young female teachers who were in awe of her beauty and lavish clothing. She was more than happy to spend hours talking fashion but when it came to school improvement, there was always something more pressing to divert her attention. She also enjoyed initiating new staff through her policy of 'sink or swim'. Many a times she left me ill-prepared for an important meeting with council officials I had known nothing about or she failed to turn up for an important event leaving me floundering.

Actually, I have a lot to thank her for. Ms Filsbury made me more flexible and adaptable. It is easy to manage easy people, but managing challenging personalities involved something new and this I gained from her. She taught me how *not* to be a head teacher.

Fridays always brought great joy for I knew it would be two more days before I endured her mood of the day. You never knew what you were going to get from her. Some would say it was unpredictable and therefore exciting. I would say it was nerve wracking and anything but enjoyable. But what we did know was that she would be displaying her latest purchases, parading her manicured nails or flicking back her freshly-dyed bob and matching tinted eyelashes.

Maria could sense that the week had been particularly challenging on account of my lack of narrative, post film. It was not the fault of the movie but my lack of interest and my distraction towards my phone that had been vibrating continuously. It was Nathan sounding pretty keen to meet for drinks the following week. I wasn't sure how Maria would feel about me missing movie night, but I knew how I felt – intrigued. Here was a straight guy, a rather cute straight guy, actively trying to get me to commit to a night of heavy drinking. He even offered for me to stay over at his place. Whatever was going to happen, it would take another seven days to unfold.

As Maria and I drove back home, grabbing a quick bite to eat on the way, I tried to talk to her about some of my feelings around work and life in general. I talked about the idea of working overseas or setting up a business. She laughed and sneered, 'What film did you get this idea from?' and the moment was lost. I felt this had been my first attempt at trying to tell Maria I was sinking. I was losing my sense of happiness and felt unsure of how to lift myself out of this. Her lack of compassion, albeit unintentional, only made me focus on Nathan and our forthcoming drink binge.

CHAPTER TWELVE

Eight bottles of beer, a couple of shots and a few girlie drinks and we were in the midst of our all night drinking session. Anyone who knows me will know that after one beer I am already tipsy. Throw in a few spirits and that is me finished. I am certainly a cheap date! Nathan was yet to discover my lack of alcohol tolerance but here I was with my first new male friend in a long time and I felt an unspoken pressure to keep up. Nathan owned his own house up on the side of the Welsh hills. This was a new experience for me. Being from the city I assumed everywhere outside of the capital was less developed and, to be honest, Nathan's quaint little terraced house with sheep in the driveway was doing everything to reinforce this stereotype. Nathan was in the middle of trying to renovate the house, though without the help of skilled experts. There were gigantic holes in the walls, ill-fitting doors and windows, an overly chatty boiler and leaks galore. It was incredibly cold too and the less-than-desirable neighbours' every movement could be clearly heard.

We talked for hours, him knocking back the beer, me sipping on my one vodka. We talked about family, work, relationships, university and, of course, sex. His piercing blue eyes were fascinating and were protected by the longest lashes I had seen on a man. His lips were incredibly full too and I noticed how he spoke so eloquently. He had some great stories to tell and I found myself fascinated by him. Here we were, two straight guys talking about girls and life in general and yet there was an unexplainable tension between us, a chemistry not yet explored. Was he just a particularly friendly, sensitive straight guy looking for new friends? Or did he feel different like me, and had found some of himself in me and was looking to reach out in search of an explanation?

We ordered in pizza and were provided with free entertainment as the neighbours began their weekly fight where she accused him of messing around and he retaliated with a string of abusive one-liners. It certainly gave us something to laugh about, although Nathan seemed embarrassed that I had witnessed such a thing on my first visit. He seemed to feel a sense of familiarity with me and began to open up about his troubled past. He did not divulge any real information, only hinted at his parents' failed marriage. Maybe this was the alcohol kicking in because I myself was now feeling less than steady. It felt so great to hang out with another guy, especially one as cool as Nathan. We both commented on how we felt like we had known each other for a long time.

'How about we go for a guys' weekend away somewhere, or what about a week abroad?' Nathan asked like an excited child. It seemed crazy since we had only just met, but why not. I needed some excitement in my life for Christ's sake. The conversation was endless, the jokes plentiful and as the levels of alcohol consumption rose the guards came down and the sexual tension rose. We were now both pretty drunk and lying top and tail on the sofa desperately trying to string a sentence or two together whilst mocking each other. Some film was playing in the background, one we had rented but paid little attention to as the conversation had been so good. I remember the sense of thrill I felt when his leg was slightly and innocently pressed against mine. A sense of warmth filled my body and my mind wandered. He was very comfortable complimenting me on my body and asked for tips on how to develop his slight frame. I joked he was built like a racehorse as his limbs were overly long and he retorted with insults about hobbits. I laughed so hard that I toppled off the edge of the sofa.

As 2 o'clock came and went I finally admitted defeat and asked to be excused, mocking the way Nathan spoke, which always sounded like we were in a board meeting – terribly formal and classy. As the lightweight drinker that I am, I needed some assistance in finding my way to my chamber and Nathan seemed only too happy to help. I slumped onto the bed, unable to undress as I heard Nathan brushing his teeth in the room next door. I think I passed out for a moment before awakening to the creaking sound of the guest bedroom door opening and the overly bright light from the hallway falling onto my face. Nathan was stood there in his bathrobe, his hairy chest peering out of the top and his hairy, thin legs dangling from the bottom. He must have been about 6 feet but looked much taller when looking up at him from the bed intoxicated by my overindulgences. He found my inability to handle alcohol most amusing and with my moans and groans as I tried to undress, he fell about in hysterics.

'Oh my God you had two drinks, Hobbit!'

'I'm dying Nath!' I replied as half my body slumped off the particularly small bed. Nathan grabbed me quickly and pushed me back on and then sat on the edge of the bed, my head close to his groin. I recognised the positive impact my behaviour was having and so over-played the drunken man card. I managed to pull my jeans and T-shirt off and rolled over slightly to give Nathan room to lie down next to me. My breathing became shallow and the blood made an attempt to rush to my groin. He was not even touching me but the anticipation of what might happen was incredible. I don't think Nathan had planned this or even desired for anything to happen, but he certainly had some kind of curiosity that he wanted to explore.

I made an over-dramatic groan as I turned my body towards him and let my hand rest upon his leg just above his knee. I was testing his reaction although pretending to be sleeping. He did not flinch or complain and neither did he encourage it. He seemed indifferent. Touching the hair on his legs was electrifying and I could feel my dick starting to pulsate. Another little groan and I moved my hand slowly further up his leg, again with no reaction. Was he sleeping? Was he aware of what I was doing but in denial? Had he planned this whole event? I began to snuggle in to him a little more and now my hand was a fraction away from his groin. His gown was now opening slightly and it was clear he was not wearing any bed wear. Would a straight guy seriously lie down next to another guy when wearing no underwear? I know how rugby guys mess around with each other and think nothing of playing with each other's dicks, but that is more for entertainment for the other team mates. This was potentially an intimate moment.

With one final groan and repositioning I brushed my hands across his balls and the tip of his penis. He made a slight groan and moved slightly to spread his legs, which in turn opened the robe a little more. I could now see his dick in all his glory and my own fella was now solid and pulsating rapidly. His cock was not overly big but impressive all the same. It was certainly a 'grower' and the thick mat of black hair surrounding it made me even more excited. I ran my hands slowly up the line of pubic hair that ran to his belly button and then up to his chest. His slender figure was not something that would ordinarily excite me but with his cock practically staring me in the face, I was certainly feeling incredibly horny. His dick was now standing upright and the foreskin was slowly retracting itself. Nathan's eyes were closed and his hands remained still. Was I taking advantage of a sleeping guy? Would he wake and punch me and kick me out of the house for being a homo? Or was he just playing dumb? Unable to provide answers for my endless questions I made the sudden move to grab his shaft and pull the foreskin right back. He was clearly excited as a trail of pre-cum oozed out and ran down the side of my fingers. I gently kissed his neck and then moved around to his lips but this was clearly not allowed as with every attempt he would turn his face to the side. Without a further thought I put his cock into my mouth and began to suck with haste, for fear of waking him up. It was exciting, yet it felt dangerous. His groans intensified and I felt he was now aware of what was going on. After all, can anyone really sleep through oral sex? His thick cock seemed to fit perfectly into my mouth and I could taste the pre-cum that continued to seep out. I picked up the pace, guided by his moans of pleasure until he unexpectedly climaxed in my mouth. This was the first time I had experienced this. The shock and bitter taste caused waves of nausea. Running to the bathroom I vomited profusely. Waves of embarrassment, guilt, confusion, rippled through my body. What would I say when I returned to the bedroom? Should we talk about it or pretend it was an alcohol-induced moment? I gingerly opened the bedroom door to find Nathan had gone and was now sleeping in his own bed in the room next door. No explanation, no conversation. We would have to wait until morning to see how things would unfold.

Courtesy of next door's entertainment we were both woken prematurely. I could hear Nathan in the kitchen and the smell of bacon drifting up the stairway. Despite the pounding headache I clearly remembered the events of last night and was trying to think of the best way to discuss what had happened. I assumed that Nathan was probably in fact gay and so I would need to explain to him that I was just curious, in fact straight and happily married.

'Morning Jack, good sleep? Sorry about crazy Sheila next door!' said Nathan with a chirpy morning tone.

'No worries Nath, I have to get back home soon anyway.' We both avoided any eye contact during this polite exchange and throughout breakfast it did not improve much. Nathan still managed to make me laugh with his stories, but there were times of silence and awkwardness. Should we discuss what happened? Who would speak first? So I made a hasty exit, citing the need to complete a pile of marking as my reason. As I drove down the winding streets to the bottom of the hill I recalled the events of the previous night. I enjoyed the flashback and entertained yet another erection. As I closed my eyes I could feel his cock in my hand and the taste of his cum. I could not ignore what had happened and I needed to know what it all meant. I pulled over and sent a text to him, *I know we both know something happened last night...* His reply was quick and to the point, *Yeah I know. But it will NEVER happen again!* I didn't know if I was relieved or offended. I was worried he was secretly gay and had hunted me down. Clearly this was not the case. But I was disappointed. I had felt a real connection to him and now he was dismissing the moment we had shared. I was confused. Was he the same as me – desperately seeking a straight life, but hounded by thoughts of intimacy with guys?

CHAPTER THIRTEEN

Nathan and I continued becoming very good friends over the next year, though we never addressed the meaning behind our drunken oral escapade. He was now in a serious relationship with a very pretty girl he had met through work and the four of us would hang out, when our schedules allowed for it. Nathan and Jess were now living together. Their relationship had quickly become very serious, with a marriage now planned in the autumn. I could not help but feel Nathan was not being entirely honest with himself. I think he was incredibly determined to live a life deemed 'normal' by society, whatever his true sexual preference was. On the other hand he may just have been curious and nothing more. After all, he didn't look or act in the slightest bit gay. He enjoyed sport, had a string of female sexual partners and had completely no dress sense! During the past year there had only been one further encounter between us although this time it involved little alcohol and no pretence of sleeping.

We had been watching a DVD, drinking beer and munching on some snacks. I was lying across the sofa and Nathan was lying in front on the rug. I loved chatting to Nathan so the silence induced by the film was difficult to uphold for me and I probably talked through the entire movie. Nathan was such a sweet guy that this didn't seem to piss him off.

'I bet you wouldn't talk so fucking much if this was a sex flick would you? Bloody hell!' he sniggered.

'I don't know actually, try me!' I joked back with excitement.

Nathan left the room, returning moments later with *Ghetto Gang Bangs* in hand and wearing his trademark dressing gown. I fell about laughing hysterically at his choice of film. 'Why the fuck have you got this film, Nath?' I was still laughing uncontrollably, though I think this was induced by a sense of excitement. Nathan went on to explain how the move to the new place had meant he needed to have a big porn clean up.

'And this is the one you chose to hold onto!' I sniggered. I was enjoying giving *him* a hard time for a change. When Nathan finally put the movie on it became clear why he had chosen this one considering his curiosity for men. It was full of cocks! The poor girl in the movie had a string of guys eagerly waiting in line to show her a good time. Clearly the producers of the film did not have strict casting requirements judging from the poor quality of men on display. What did intrigue me was how each time Nathan would fast forward to the moment when the guy climaxed and this seemed to really excite him. Without warning Nathan was now slowly masturbating. I felt excited, yet awkward. Should I do the same and pull out my cock or ignore him and focus on the movie? I chose neither and instead proceeded to grab his dick and masturbate it for him.

'Should we really be doing this?' he bashfully asked like a young schoolgirl.

'I can stop if you want,' I replied, intentionally using a teasing tone of voice.

'No, I like it.'

I continued to pleasure Nathan as the film played pointlessly in the background. It was not doing anything for me. As things proceeded to oral sex, Nathan grabbed at my crotch this time. He never undid my belt or encouraged me to remove my jeans. He just explored with haste and awkwardness at the outer layers, although this was quite a step, resulting in a quicker climax for him than I had anticipated.

Post shower Nathan returned to the room and just laughed about what had happened, joking that these days would be over once Jess moved in the following month. Sadly we never talked about what all of this meant. Admittedly we were not denying its occurrence anymore, but we never questioned ourselves about any deeper meaning. We never asked each other, 'Are *we* gay?' We just both assumed not as we were both now in loving, long-term relationships with girls. He seemed genuinely so excited about Jess moving in. The house was perfect for them and for the little family that they both desired once the wedding was over in six months. You could also completely understand why Nathan had fallen so quickly for Jessica. She was stunning both inside and out. Mixed Vietnamese and Welsh, she was full of Asian delight. Her coal-black hair framed her pale chiselled face like a portrait. She was sweet and funny and easy to get along with. She and Maria had become quite close, although they never socialised unless as a group of four with Nath and myself.

After Jess moved in I rarely saw Nathan and if I did it was always with the girls. We sent many texts, normally banter where Nath insulted my musical taste or laughed at one of my crazy stories from work involving the infamous Ms Filsbury. He seemed so content and so happy and this was only amplified when Jess and him were married. It was not until his wedding day that I actually realised the crush I had on him. I did not feel like I was in love with him; I knew the difference because of my feelings towards Maria, but there was definitely something there. Seeing him look so happy on his wedding day gave me enough satisfaction and I would be happy accepting his friendship only. There was a sense of relief knowing that our days of fooling around had ended, as I was not comfortable with the situation now that Maria and Jess were also friends. There would, however, be one final physical encounter that would be needed in order to make me finally realise that our physical encounters were wrong.

Six months of marriage had passed and Jessica and Nathan were expecting their first baby at the end of the year. Sadly this great news had caused tremendous friction between Maria and myself. Seeing how happy Nathan was with his great news, I could not help but once again bring up this topic with Maria. The subject had been off the table for some time now, but my overwhelming desire for children had remained. As most of our friends had remained single, it was easier for Maria to ignore, but now our closest friends were having children she knew it was going to be unavoidable and something she needed to face. In fact, when we drove off from Nathan and Jessica's house the evening when they had shared the news with us, Maria just broke down crying. I secretly hoped she had just gone through a life changing moment and that the tears were tears of realisation that she wanted to be a mother. This was not the case.

'Why are you crying Maria? This is great news for them.' I pretended I was shocked by her reaction.

'Now I know how much pressure you will put me under, because I know you want this so badly.'

I was furious inside. It was not a moment of revelation for her as I had hoped, but instead another moment of

Maria's selfishness. It was all about her again and I was the bad guy for putting the pressure on. I managed to control my fiery emotion and instead offered a gentle squeeze of her hand as I pulled to a stop at the traffic lights.

'There will not be any pressure from me Maria.' I'm not sure how I was able to say these words because inside I felt a sense of bitter disappointment. I desperately longed to be a father and it seemed Maria was no closer to making this a reality for me.

Just before Jess had the baby, she went to stay for the weekend at her parents and so Nathan had invited me over to stay for a well-overdue boys' night in. Maria was not happy I was planning on staying out all night as she felt we needed to spend some quality time together as we had both been working so hard recently. I was not going to give up a night with my best friend, so Maria would have to wait. She and I had been together for such a long time and therefore we knew each other so well. She knew that really I was still angry with her about her feelings about starting a family and choosing to spend my free evening with someone else. How well she knew me. It is practically impossible to hide your emotions from each other after such a long time, but I was an expert and so still able to keep some feelings exclusively to myself.

There was a different mood to my evening with Nathan this time around. We went out for a drink and grabbed a quick bite to eat before returning to his place, minus any alcohol. There was not really any need for me to stay the night since we were not drinking but I welcomed the retreat away from home. Nathan talked continuously about the impending birth of his little boy and I barely listened. I was delighted for him, I truly was, but I was both envious and jealous. I was envious for this was a moment I longed for. After all, I had been married for almost four years and he had only just met this girl! I was also jealous because I was losing my best friend to family life. We were not talking about porn or past conquests or even work. The topic of conversation was parenthood and I was literally quite sick of hearing about it. I wondered if Nathan was over emphasising his happiness to mask his unhappiness about his life in general, but maybe it was wishful thinking on my part. I wanted to believe he was the same as me and realised he had this overwhelming need to be intimate with guys whilst still desiring a straight life.

I was relieved to go to bed relatively early that evening. The guest room was adjacent to the master bedroom and so we were able to chat still as we were drifting off to sleep. As Nathan started the conversation I gently placed the pillow onto my face and gritted my teeth in preparation for the impending talk about babies. However, I was pleasantly pleased when Nathan came from a different angle.

'Christ I'm so frigging horny right now Jack! You can kiss sex goodbye when Maria gets pregnant!' I broke out into a chuckle that felt slightly forced. Maybe it was his reference to Maria getting pregnant that hit a sensitive zone.

'Well, God gave you hands to sort yourself out in times like these, Nath!' My answer was almost dismissive as I think Nathan had truly bored the life out of me that evening.

'Yeah, but much better when it is someone else's hand, hey Jack! Though I have this amazing new lube called *Pleasure 1000*. Wanna try some?'

Only really feeling half interested I wandered into his room wearing only a pair of black boxers. 'Hey Jack, the gym is really paying off. You look really good, especially those arms!' Was he actually flirting with me or speaking guy to guy? He was already trying his new lube and looking at me with an intense and clearly horny look. I drifted slowly over to his bed and sat down beside him. He poured some of the lube into my sweaty palm. It felt warm and silky as I rubbed it into my cock and then into his. Nathan lent across and grabbed my dick and began to massage it for me. This was the first time he had ever touched my cock and the moment was intense. But it was wrong and for the first time I *knew* it was wrong. He was married and about to become a dad. I was not going to be part of screwing up someone else's life. We clearly were never going to be entirely honest with each other and search for the meaning in our actions. We had made our choices in life, regardless of our inability to make informed ones. Now we needed to find a way of satisfying any continuing desires without the risk of hurting others. Suddenly I stood up and walked away, ignoring Nathan's pleas to finish what I had started.

I turned and said, 'It's wrong, Nath. You're gonna be a dad real soon.'

'Fuck you Jack!' he angrily retorted. I did not take offence at his anger. It was just an immediate reaction to a reality slap from me. He was a good guy too and knew he was making bad choices. I left before Nathan woke the next morning. This was not the end of our friendship, but it was certainly the last time we would ever share an intimate *physical* moment again.

CHAPTER FOURTEEN

The next two years provided a bit of stability for me. Nathan and I continued to be close friends, but only ever socialised as a group of four and of course now there was Lucas, their little boy to consider. Maria and I had once again moved house following a surge in the housing market, resulting in a good return on our previous investment that provided us with some funds for a four-week holiday in Australia. Things at work remained challenging but there was light at the end of the dark tunnel as I was now enrolled on the two-year head teacher training course and applying for new deputy head positions in order to escape Ms Filsbury.

The new house was our dream home: a late Victorian terraced house in an exclusive area of the city. Needing a lot of renovation, it was the perfect family home. When we chose this house there was a glimmer of hope that Maria shared this view too, but I had now come to terms with the fact that I would never be a dad. I accepted this because of my love and respect for Maria. I have always felt that childless couples could become incredibly selfish and materialistic. Maria and I always seemed to be wanting. My finances were planned out for the next six months and it all revolved around renovation plans and the purchasing of fancy furniture. There was no room for travel or excitement. I had my flash new Audi TT convertible and I was somewhat content. The return on the previous property had provided us with enough money to pay the experts to renovate the house, although initial estimates had been a little ambitious and the money soon ran out. The house already looked great, with only a few rooms left to decorate. The kitchen, bathroom and living room were complete and, courtesy of Maria's eye for style, they were looking incredible.

The garden had been landscaped thanks to my father and my close friend Michael. I would have liked to take some credit myself but I was not one for getting my hands dirty. I was more of a manager, directing and overseeing the project. This was somewhat frustrating I think for my dad but expected of me all the same. Thankfully this garden was low maintenance and would not suck up my entire Sundays in the spring and summer. The cute Scottish guy next door also gave enough reason to spend some time outdoors.

The young couple had moved in just after us and Rob was particularly friendly. He would often be pottering around shirtless in the garden, providing a welcome relief to the chore of weeding. Incredibly pale and lean, he would stand peering over my wall chatting about the excellent progress we were making on our house. Rob was classically handsome. A chiselled face and floppy hair made him cute eye candy although his somewhat gangster style of fashion at times made me chuckle. The remaining neighbours were all of an average age of sixty-five, so providing little competition for Rob. Strangely enough I kept my distance from Rob despite his frequent requests to call over for a drink. I guess I knew I could not be trusted to be just friends and felt it was better to focus solely on Maria.

Maria and I were back on track in my eyes. Of course, for Maria we were never 'off track'. She was never aware of any issues or problems. These were exclusively my burdens to bear. Any changes in my personality she put down to my moody nature or stress at work. But for me the past twelve years had been so difficult at times and so lonely. I had the girl I believed to be my soul mate at my side constantly, but I felt alone. I had wonderful friends and family at hand and yet I was lonesome. I was lonely because I was experiencing trauma by myself. I could not share my intimate thoughts with anyone; who could possibly understand? Every weekend my mother would ask what was wrong with me and why I looked so miserable and yet I could not even tell her.

'He's a moody bastard that's all!' snapped my father, unhappy that I was causing so much worry for my mother. If only he knew how much I needed him at that point. So unable to express myself honestly, I took on the persona of a stressed-out career guy and for a short time I actually believed it. In reality, I was suffocating and sinking and it was only a matter of time before this persona would crack.

The trip to Australia had been amazing and made me appreciate what I had in life, rather than focusing on what I wanted. Of course Maria's crazy routines and intense planning of day trips drove me insane but overall I felt at the time that the trip had brought us closer together. We had experienced some amazing moments together, such as whale watching in Sydney and the visit to the koala and kangaroo sanctuary in Brisbane. On reflection, we were just two great friends travelling the world together. In the four-week trip there was no intimacy and no sex. We never even questioned each other about it. There were times when I was horny and would try to make a pass, but Maria was too tired or the hotel accommodation was sub-standard and she did not feel comfortable. I convinced myself that after twelve years of marriage it was normal for a couple's sex life to become less important, but I was still only thirty years old and still horny most days so why was I not getting any sex? Nathan had complained about the same thing to me in one of our weekly chats on the phone.

'It's as if the moon has to be in some kind of fucking perfect alignment in order to get the green light!' he joked, as we both continued to moan about our partner's lack of interest. 'Thank God for porn and chat rooms is all I can say!' he went on to say proudly before asking about the websites I explored. Reluctant to say, I made my excuses to end our conversation short and hung up. Within moments he was texting to ask me the same question again. I replied explaining that I doubted he would be interested in my choices as it was of a *particular* genre.

'Try me!' he eagerly, and rather rapidly, responded. I took a deep breath and typed, 'www.men4men.com'. No reply. Had I now crossed a line with Nathan? Was he disgusted by my choice of viewing pleasure?

'Whoa! Check out the dicks on these guys. INSANE! Good choice Jack.' Shocked and confused, Nathan's comments disturbed me. Here I was confused and alone and yet my best friend was seemingly going through the same thing, but refusing to talk about it and now a frigging father to a little boy and another one on the way. His actions were only adding more confusion and heartache because now I was beginning to wonder if all men felt the same. It was not about being gay, it was just about being a guy. Only we did not talk about it in the same way as girls. In exchange for information, Nathan shared a web-link with me, a web-link that would be the catalyst to my phase of deceit that would go on to change my life forever.

DECEIT

CHAPTER FIFTEEN

I patiently waited for two weeks for the opportunity to explore Nathan's web-link. Maria was out for her usual mid-week catch up with two of her old friends from university and I was entertaining *Montreal Men* for the evening. Logging on to the website using the username and password Nathan had kindly provided for me, I was full of intrigue as to what sordid cyberspaces he explored when Jess was away. The concoction of nerves, intense intrigue and a full week of feeling horny were resulting in the shakes as I attempted to re-enter the password for the third time. This was the first time I had ever visited a chat room of any description. I had always felt talking to real guys would be less erotic and my preference had always remained around fantasy. But here I was on this cold and miserable evening chatting with Ricky from Dallas. Stage name, 'Cum4U', Ricky was a paid performer for whom you would donate gold coins in exchange for personal viewing pleasures. Donate a small amount and he would perform for a group of paying perverts. Increase your spending and get the sexy Ricky all to yourself in the private chat room. Nathan had already told me that he never donated any gold coins. He just enjoyed the group chat with other frustrated men where the model, although fully clothed, continued to grope and feel himself in the hope that one of those excited, vulnerable men would click the 'Give Gold' button. Well, I was one of those guys. I did not want to be fucking teased. I was too busy for that and besides, Maria was sure to be home by ten. I wanted to see some hot arse now!

Frantically searching for my bank card I found myself creating my own account. I did not think Nathan would be too happy about me running up a huge bill under his name. Enter! I was in. I did not want to splash out too soon so I went for a group option the first time. Four lonely, sexually frustrated guys all watching 'Cum4U' undressing and licking his lips. The chat room allowed all four participants to interact with the model and with each other. At first it was just as I had imagined – crude, perverted and seedy. Clearly these other guys were probably mid to late fifties, no doubt married and full of curiosity, with receding hair lines and expanding waist-lines. They were probably sitting watching the screen, breathing heavily whilst rubbing themselves as the young, financially challenged part-Latino guy (who was probably straight) followed the demands of his clients. Why I felt able to judge these other guys and make assumptions I do not know. After all, here I was doing the same thing and the last time I looked, I was not a middle-aged, overweight pervert. I think it came down to preconceptions and social opinion about the users of such sites. Chat rooms were relatively new and there was a lot of negative media attention around these sites and the link to paedophilia. The first night I could not overcome my own judgements and I found that no matter how much sexy Ricky shook his hot hips, the chat amongst the viewers was seriously turning me off. I clicked exit, logged off and took to my bed where I lay reflecting on Nathan and what all of this meant. When Maria returned just after ten I pretended to be sleeping for fear my frustrations would be taken out on her. I did not like the way these desires for men made me feel and how it affected my mood and my ability to interact with Maria. I had developed a split personality in an attempt to lead this double life, but I was not always successful at it and I frequently found myself speaking to her in a way that made me feel ashamed. The trouble was that I just could not see a way out. Now I had an accomplice – someone encouraging me to partake in sordid activities. Someone who was making it easier to justify my behaviour and thoughts.

With a little encouragement from Nathan in one of his texts, I decided to log on once again to *Montreal Men* and this time try to be more positive. No sign of Ricky and those hips but there was a cute blond guy from Quebec standing-by to strip and strut for us cybersluts. I paid my gold and at first enjoyed Daniel all to myself. He was a bit slow to undress which annoyed me as each dollar gave only one minute of viewing pleasure. If he continued at this rate I would have needed a bank loan to pay for this impending wank! Tanned, muscular and hot, Dan was an Internet dream. His abs were incredible, which briefly depressed me, until he was down to his tight black boxers and he regained my full attention. I was a little distracted by the pleasant conversation that had started up between myself and my fellow chat room whore. He called himself 'Horny101' but on first impressions he seemed kind of 'normal'. I tried to convince myself that this was how innocent victims of Internet psychopaths got into trouble by being so naïve and so decided I should exit the room.

Ping! The sound of a new line chat from Horny101. *Hey man, by the way, where you from? Welsh boy here....* Now I was paying full attention to the chat and completely ignoring Daniel's performance, though intrigued as to what the hell he was doing lying in that position!

Are you seriously from Wales? Me too!

I'm just outside the Capital, along Furlong Road. A wave of fear suddenly came over me. Here I was on a Canadian chat room talking to someone who lived five minutes from where I was currently sitting. Was this guy stalking me? Had he hunted me down? The moment passed and I pulled myself together, now conscious of the twenty dollars this tanned but seemingly dull beauty had cost me.

Hey let's chat on MSN. It's free and this guy is fucking making me impotent! messaged 'Horny101'. It made me chuckle and I could feel my guard dropping. I knew the dangers in cyberspace but I was not a stupid schoolgirl, so was pretty sure I knew what I was doing. What I did not fully comprehend were the consequences of that decision.

We exchanged MSN contact details and agreed to chat in about ten minutes after we had both taken a much-needed pee stop. I had taken a sick day from work following a tooth extraction and so had the day pretty much to myself. The sun was beating in through the small window of the study and the cat was enjoying the rays as he lay along the ledge. I grabbed a coffee and logged in to my MSN account where there was already a contact waiting to be approved. He was keen. At least this chat was not going to involve any gold coins; that had to be a major plus point! Same screen name 'Horny101'. Moments later the chat started and it seemed to flow so easily. He seemed like such a nice guy. A builder with his own business he did not make any reference to sex or any kinky shit, which was a pleasant surprise. I found myself explaining my personal situation to him and he was incredibly supportive and understanding. He had gone through a similar thing himself in his younger days and so assured me it was not abnormal and I was not a bad person. After all my shit with Nathan I needed to hear this. Now in his early forties he explained how he was living at home with his elderly mother. Since coming out in his mid-thirties, after divorcing his wife, he had never successfully found love with a guy.

Four hours had passed. Chris was so easy to talk with. This was the first person I had ever been able to fully disclose everything to. I had 'met' this guy only hours ago and yet he knew all my dirty little secrets, all my thoughts and desires, my worries and above all he knew the one secret that no one else knew, not even me. He knew that I was gay! And for the first time in my life I admitted to myself that I *was* gay. He helped me to get to this point. His kind words and ability to empathise enabled me to finally see things clearly. Chris supported me in recognising that by admitting I was a homosexual it did not mean I had to lose Maria and it did not mean I was a bad person. This was fucking insane. For thirty years I had lived in a world of internal confusion or mind-fuck as I have come to phrase it. Battling my emotions, fighting myself with right and wrong, and here was a complete fucking stranger helping me to see with a clarity I had never experienced before. For thirty years those who loved me most failed to sense my turmoil, failed to detect my trauma, and yet here was a FUCKING stranger standing by my side when I finally stood up and said, 'I am gay!!' Not my parents, my loving wife, my closest friends but a possible crazy psycho from the net. Well that kinda sucked. But of course Chris could help me to this point because he was not real. He was an Internet person only. No face, no identify and therefore I could retract all that I had said and he would not be able to tell anyone. It is much harder to face a person you love and tell them the kind of things I had shared with Chris. I could now understand how people are able to confide in therapists who are complete strangers. There is no emotional tie to these people so the thoughts and feelings come oozing out.

I accepted I was gay and I cried. I cried because I hated myself. I cried because I did not want to be gay and I certainly did not want to lose Maria or my family.

Hey Jack, being gay is what you are but it doesn't mean you have to leave your wife or that you have to tell people. Not if that's not what you want. I needed to hear these words so much, because inside my world was crashing down around me and the fear was at a peak. *Just find a way to manage your feelings. Hey I have to go but how about we chat again tomorrow?*

I sat in the study for a further three hours in complete silence, staring at the four walls around me whilst the cat desperately tried to get my attention. 'Oh fuck off Jackson!' The cat felt the force of my emotion and left the room, head down, tail between his legs. I kept playing the same words over and over in my head, *I'm gay. I'm fucking gay. Oh my fucking God I'm fucking gay!*

I screamed out and threw my coffee mug at the freshly painted wall in the hallway and fell to the floor sobbing. I did not want this. I did not know what it meant for me now and I felt stupid that I had not realised it before.

The vibration of my mobile startled me, snapping me out of my self-indulgent moment. It was a text from Maria: *I love you very much Jack. Hope you feel better. I will come home early to cook your favourite xx.* I may have undergone a moment of enlightenment that day under the supervision of Chris, but my feelings for Maria were no different and I had no intention of living my life as a gay. As my new friend had told me, admitting I was gay did not mean things had to change. He was right. I just needed to find a way to manage this.

I talked with Chris most days for the next three weeks whilst 'working' in the study. I would keep my MSN window minimised on my desktop whilst prolonging the completion of my lesson plans. I would eagerly wait for each new message from Chris. Things had progressed a little and his form of therapy had now progressed to including some sexual banter. I had already decided I did not find him sexually attractive when he first sent me a picture via MSN. Although only in his early forties, Chris looked much older. Maybe he had lied about his age or maybe he had prematurely weathered from his choice of trade. He was working the rocker look; long thinning hair, pierced ear and loving the denim. I was a little disappointed when I first opened the picture file. But talking to him was easy and he did excite me when talking suggestively. Chris had now linked his MSN to a web-cam but I was not happy to return the favour. He was most definitely an exhibitionist and now enjoyed chatting to me whilst sat in only a black T-shirt. He did not need much encouragement to start masturbating on screen and the climax of his performance was pretty impressive. He frequently sent me video files via MSN with similar material and this excited me immensely.

Thursday evening and Maria was working late – PTA meeting. I logged on to my MSN account and saw a message that Chris had sent earlier that day: *Meet me later? Text me when and where....* My hands immediately started shaking but the blood was pumping to my groin. I was excited but nervous. I was intrigued but anxious. I grabbed my phone and began to text. I put the phone back down on my desk. Phone back in my hand, I continued the text. I was now entertaining a battle of conscience in my mind. Good and bad were at war and I was getting impatient for the result as I threw the phone down once more. I thought about the videos he had sent me and my excitement threshold was smashed. I snatched the phone back, completed the text and pressed enter. It was done. In thirty minutes I would meet Chris for the first time in the car park at my local gym. I did not know what was going to happen but what I did know was that I wanted *something* to.

CHAPTER SIXTEEN

Sitting in the car park I repeatedly questioned my actions. This was good progress because now I was aware to some extent of what I was doing and in particular what I was doing as a gay guy. I still do not believe I was fully aware of my actions or the implications. I think I was depressed and confused and this was a form of escapism for me. Chris had been quite instrumental in helping me to move out of my state of denial so the least I could do was meet the guy in person to thank him.

The granite grey van pulled up alongside me. The description and location of my car clearly had been good enough as he found me with precision. I glanced to the side and saw Chris beaming back. I was very familiar with his look from the large number of video files he had sent me over the weeks. His hair was now shorter though and what was left of it was waxed into spikes. I wondered if he had made a special effort in an attempt to impress me. This made me a little nervous as I was not overly attracted to him and the last thing I needed was some old guy with a crush on *me*. He beckoned for me to jump into his van and pushed the door open for me. The opening exchanges were awkward and involved a lot of nervous laughter. I expected someone of his age to be more experienced and therefore take more of a lead but I doubted the likelihood of this happening. Sitting facing out onto open fields, we talked about everything from likes and dislikes to music and films, celebrity crushes and family life. I had by this point already decided that Chris was not attractive and that I did not want anything to happen. He was easy to talk to but nothing more. He invited me to his home on Friday evening as his mother was staying with his sister. Despite my lack of interest in him I encouraged the moment by asking what we would do should I take him up on the offer. His reply erected my cock surprisingly. I lacked experience and hearing a guy talking dirty to me face to face was hard to resist.

I swooped in fast for a kiss but closed my eyes so that I could imagine the recipient was a hot young thing with floppy blond hair, piercing blue eyes and a body chiselled and ripped. Chris' hands were all over my body. He grabbed a little too firmly at my chest as he groaned with pleasure and licked my neck, which disgusted me somewhat. I disliked the taste of his kiss which clearly indicated he was a smoker. But I was enjoying the concept of being with a man and the situation itself was erotic. I was a little self-conscious of our public location. During our first embrace a few cars either side had moved on and so I wondered who and what had been witnessed. I was taking a real risk here. I had friends, colleagues and neighbours who all frequented this leisure facility. Was this really how I wanted to be discovered? As Chris bit my ear and rubbed the shaft of my cock over my shorts my ability to sense my surroundings declined. I recalled his talent from the videos he had shared and so now began to explore in reality.

'I need a piss!' Chris romantically whispered in my ear as he jumped out of the van and into the field. A surge of guilt rocketed through me whilst left sitting in the cold interior of his work van. I knew it was wrong – progress. I knew by doing this I was gay – progress. I thought by doing this there would be no implications – serious lack of progress! I had been carried away by the words of Chris, '...*have to find a way to manage this...*' At the time I believed that was exactly what I was doing – managing my problem, like a sick patient manages his illness or a reformed alcoholic manages his addiction. I caught sight of Chris' large penis as he finished in the field and again I was hard. As he returned to the van I took one quick glance around my arena before pulling his sports shorts to his knees and playing with his manhood. The foreskin reclined with ease and he was quick to be aroused. His balls were large and hung low and I felt *so* aroused as I caressed them gently in my hand. His moaning intensified my own pleasure as I satisfied my hunger.

'I won't be able to cum sorry. I don't feel comfortable here.' I took this as a challenge and I picked up the pace and varied my technique using my knowledge from my porn collection! I moved back up to his lips and kissed him deeply and passionately which made him throb even more. He pulled his T-shirt up a little, revealing a piercing I could have predicted would be there. The pink nipple that housed it was erect and longing to be caressed. As my tongue teased it I masturbated his thick dick with great intensity. His pleasure was clear, his climax imminent. I remembered the impressive finale of his onscreen wanks and so pulled his shorts up a little to catch the main surge. His legs kicked and spasmed in ecstasy and his cheeks were infused with colour.

'Jesus Christ, you're good! I think you were born to do this!' Chris joked with laughter.

Judging from the wet patch on my shorts this had clearly been a moment of great pleasure for me too but the pre-cum was not enough to encourage me to continue. I did not really want Chris to return the favour despite how horny I was feeling. His comments of praise and satisfaction were becoming annoying quite quickly and I wanted to make a quick getaway. I left him in his cocoon of delight, making promises to call him later or see him on MSN. I knew then that I was lying. This was the last time I would meet or speak with Chris. He knew too much about me and I needed to remove him.

With a good gym work out behind me, I returned home, showered repeatedly, deleted all the video files Chris had sent to me, deleted and blocked his MSN contact and changed my SIM card to the spare one I had lying around. I was now a player in this game of deceit and I was going to be taking the lead. I was not proud of what I did to Chris. He was a nice guy who really helped me, but at the time I felt he did it only for the end result, which I too willingly gave to him. I told myself that he had only offered support in order to encourage me to have sex with him. I was also fearful of the information he knew about me and what he might do with this. Sadly I will never know what his true intentions were.

Lessons clearly not learnt and two days later I was exploring a new UK chat room. Clearly deceit was now my new kingdom. 'Biguy2000' was my code game and 'bisexual' was now my new identity. There were so many guys who seemed to be excited by the prospect of meeting a married guy, virginal to the gay scene. The talk was dirty, intense and exciting. Hundreds of guys sharing fantasies, desires and contact details. Offers for phone sex, cam2cam exchanges and sex meets were made. Multiple young guys referring to themselves as 'curious' and endless men stating their preference as 'bisexual'; it was denial at its best. Before a guy has the confidence to admit he is actually gay he will often assign himself different labels. Stage one guys state they are curious. Often they have a girlfriend. They say they have never touched a guy, but often think about it. They are difficult to chat with beyond simple flirting as they are still deeply submerged in fear. Stage two guys refer to themselves as bisexual. These guys are either single or in relationships, but have some gay experiences which they will admit to. They often lack experiences with females but prefer to continue to refer to themselves as bisexual. They are often more masculine and feel it is more manly to say bisexual than gay. Still in denial, they have made more progress than their 'curious' counterparts. Stage three guys are gay and proud!

'Bi-man21' had caught my attention on that day. He was friendly but a little pushy. He lived nearby and was quick to exchange telephone numbers, (that original SIM card would prove to be useful). Everything seemed to be in a rush. I knew so little about him but was waiting for him to pick up the phone as I finished dialling his number. His voice was sexy. He seemed a little frantic and hyperactive at times, but still I was enthralled. No picture, no background information, I was making arrangements to meet him at his place later than evening. I was planning on a long gym session so this would prove a suitable cover to Maria. Moments later, a text came through from the guy whose name I still did not know: *Don't come over. Sorry!* This seriously pissed me off and so I called once more. He let the phone ring for a long time before finally submitting. His justifications for the text were baffling, a sign of his own internal confusion. I took pity on him and felt the need to help him in a similar way to how Chris had helped me. Acting a little too forceful I encouraged Dan to let me come to talk with him. I explained a little of my background and this seemed to put him at ease. I detected a slight English accent and a youthfulness to his voice.

It was just after 8 p.m. as I parked my car in the next street and walked slowly towards the address Dan had given me. I caught a glimpse of a young, cute guy looking at me through a downstairs window and moments later the front door flew open. So quick to beckon me in, Dan was clearly fearful of what others thought of him. I wondered if this was his first time, but then questioned why he was not referring to himself as curious only. Maybe curious was without intent. Once intention comes into play you move to bisexual. If Dan had invited me over, he clearly *intended* for something to happen. He guided me through the narrow passageway of the old Victorian house down into his ground floor flat. One small room was all he occupied. A grubby old couch and a single bed in the corner. I declined the offer of a drink on quick inspection of the lack of hygiene in the small kitchenette. Awkwardly, Dan sat alongside me on the couch making some attempt at small talk. He intrigued me. He seemed so nervous and yet was confident in his appearance. Tight curly hair kept short, an athletic frame and the same height as myself. The contrast between his dark hair and green eyes was very sexy. I placed a hand gently on his thigh and was impressed at how firm they felt which was explained by the fact that he played football regularly. A little surprised by the news of his girlfriend, my understanding of his confusion was improving. Here was a young guy living away from home. A football-playing straight dude with his own WAG and yet tempted by the body of a man.

'I'm not gonna have sex with you!' Dan blurted out, unannounced.

'Hey I am happy to talk...' And with that Dan was straddled across my hips and kissing me with eagerness. He ripped off his top and pulled mine off with equal haste. His body was golden in colour and hairless like a lab rat. Skinnier than I had anticipated but no less pleasurable to caress. His intense kissing left me breathless though the friction from his stubble was becoming a little unbearable. He stood up, pulled open his Levi's and forced my head into his groin. For someone with little experience he was proving to be a surprise. With little effort his threshold was reached and his knees shook as he climaxed. The cum dripped slowly down his hairy thighs and seconds later his dick was flaccid in my hand. He was frozen to the spot. No movement. No attempt to dress himself. No words of thanks. I pulled his jeans up and looked up to ask if he was okay. He was crying. I gently wrapped my arms around him and he sobbed like a baby. I was overcome with emotion and struggling to speak. *He* was riddled with guilt and I had been the cause of this and I felt ashamed. I knew he was confused before I arrived and yet I still came. Maybe I thought I could help him or maybe I wanted to take advantage of someone more confused than myself. Whatever the reason, for that moment I held him close, reassured him and passed on the wisdom Chris had given me.

Dan composed himself and showered but asked me to wait until he had finished which was a good sign. I had expected him to throw me out in a rage of guilt and panic. But he was a good guy; I could see that. We talked a little more before he politely asked me to leave, continually apologising for not having returned any sexual pleasures. I was not concerned about this. I genuinely wanted to help him. We agreed we would be 'fuck buddies' or 'friends with benefits'. As I drove off to what would now need to be a shorter gym session I felt a sense of contentment. I had found my way to manage my desires – in the sexual pleasures I would enjoy with Dan.

Sadly that was the one and only time I shared a passionate moment with Dan. You see Dan was more confused and fucked up than I had realised. For three weeks I messaged him repeatedly with no reply. I called multiple times and searched the chat room daily. I knew he was not the type to lead me on so I took the step of visiting his home where it all began. Hesitantly, he opened the door, revealing a battered and bruised face and a broken arm. Dan had been out 'cruising' one night in a nearby parkland notorious for gay encounters. Sadly the guy Dan had chosen was a 'gay basher' out to cause only pain and harm. He had been left for dead before another passer-by had taken pity on him. He refused to let me into the house and repeatedly apologised for what he had done.

'For fuck's sake Dan, *this* is not *your* fault!'

He started to sob once again but still refused to open the door. I gave him his space and left. I continued to hear from Dan from time to time. The usual mixed messages of wanting to be intimate with me and then total denial of any gay desires. He continued to mis-manage his late night needs and frequently found himself in difficult situations. Contracting a sexually transmitted disease, losing his girlfriend after being caught in a compromising situation with another guy and an obsession with pre-operative transsexuals were all part of Dan's adventures, making my life seem a little more 'normal'. A year later I had completely lost contact with Dan. This time I chose not to go and explore and only hoped and prayed that he had found his way in life, preferably with a little less drama.

CHAPTER SEVENTEEN

Icontinued my quest to find the perfect fuck buddy and the next to try to satisfy this need was William. Another guy claiming to be bisexual, I should have seen the warning signs. After the usual online flirting and exchange of mandatory photographs, I agreed to meet Will at his home. Concerns about my own personal safety when visiting a guy in his own home never crossed my mind. I was just focused on one thing and maybe that overshadowed any concerns I may have had. The usual cover story – another session at the gym. Why was I not looking like Chris Hemsworth by now? I was also struggling to focus on my work and I had little desire to spend time with Maria or my family.

Arriving at Will's home I was impressed by the house and what this indicated about his salary and lifestyle, albeit a shallow reflection. Driving onto the new estate seemed familiar and I quickly made the connection. I had celebrated a colleague's birthday at her house somewhere on this same estate. My sense of direction has always been horrendous, so I had no idea where my current location was in relation to this but it did make me feel a little self-conscious. I quickly put together my cover story should I face questioning the next morning at work. Why would people be suspicious anyway? I was married and there was nothing unusual about visiting a male friend. Right? *Knock! Knock!* Left waiting a while, I wondered if Will was a fraud or having second thoughts. The door finally opened and a rather cute, smiley face was looking back at me. He was clearly relieved that I was not a freak and his smile widened even more. His face was sweet and he had a very friendly demeanour. I felt at ease straight away, but clearly he was going into panic mode as he invited me into his home. The pace of his speech was increasing and the pitch rising. He was asking questions before giving me the chance to answer previous ones.

'Hey Will, calm yourself!' We both started to laugh and he touched my upper arm as a gesture to thank me for being understanding.

'I don't normally invite guys over to my place,' Will said sheepishly. Maybe I was being naïve but I believed him because he was certainly not acting calm and controlled. I did not discuss *my* history of chat room 'meets' but I did reinforce that I was married and what I was looking for. Will explained he was bisexual and that no one in his family or even friends knew that he liked men. After further questioning it seemed Will had *no* experience whatsoever with women and so therefore he was clearly a full blown gay in total denial, probably driven by family pressure. He had pictures all over the lavish five-bedroom property which I quickly noticed on my tour. The pictures were of him and his 'girlfriend' or 'fag hag' as gay guys would refer to her. She was providing the perfect cover for him, although sadly she was not aware of his tendencies and chose to believe his strict religious beliefs were the reason she had not enjoyed an intimate moment with him! Oh the lies that gay guys will tell in order to keep their secret untouched. Returning to the lounge we sat side by side on the sofa opposite the rather impressive TV that dominated the wall. This guy clearly had money and being a little older than me I joked to myself how he would make an excellent sugar daddy. Preoccupied with making myself laugh at my own jokes, I failed to see Will making a move without warning and without romance. He forcefully pushed me back onto the sofa so that I was lying flat out and then proceeded to mount me. He was like a ticking bomb with a clear goal in a limited amount of time. I was overwhelmed with the attention and so went with it. His breathing was so heavy and his actions so hasty. He was licking and biting profusely but I didn't like to dampen his spirit. I have a belief that when guy A is less attractive than guy B, guy A will always be so grateful and therefore act attentive. Will was no monster, but I figured I was better looking and probably better looking than most of the guys he had shagged in the past! Therefore *he* was acting grateful and it felt good!

Within minutes we were topless, shirts thrown to the floor. His skin was pinker than I expected with a brush of fair hair in a diamond shape on his chest. His arms lacked any definition but his shoulders were naturally broad. For a brief moment we forgot the open curtains and the live peep show we were providing to the punters. Will jumped to his feet and pulled the curtains closed with a motion that almost brought them to the floor alongside the shirts. I was not holding out for a prolonged session judging by the speed at which this guy was moving. I knew the drill by now. He would force my head into his groin and expect some oral pleasure. He would cum within minutes due to the overwhelming excitement of the occasion and then apologise to me for being unable to satisfy my needs now that he was riddled with guilt. Well that had been the pattern with Nathan, Chris and Dan, but strangely enough not with Will. He was all about pleasing me. He beckoned me to follow him to bedroom number one. Here he undressed me at speed and with each layer of clothing removed, his breathing became louder and shallower. He was in ecstasy and I was feeling like a gorgeous stud. The sight of my body was doing this to him and it felt great. His hands caressed my entire body to the tune of his groans and moans. He paid particular attention to my chest, complimenting me on my physique before running his tongue the entire length of my torso to my belt. I was the hardest I had ever been before. Seeing someone so turned on by your body is a turn on in itself and I was milking this for all it was worth. This was new territory for me. He pushed me hard onto the bed and yanked at my belt to open it. No joy. I rescued him from further fumbling and pulled open the buckle before handing back to him. One quick flick and all five jean's buttons had popped open. I lifted my head off the pillow but he pushed it back in one swooping move. This guy was insatiable! G-Stars around my ankles, he licked and bit the shaft of my cock through my tight black shorts. Not one for teasing, I grew impatient and pulled the shorts down and pushed *his* head into *my* crotch. I was now in the driving seat and *this* time I would not be leaving in my usual frustrated way!

Technique clumsy, action needing refinement; I wasn't overly enjoying myself. Maybe because normally I took more of an active role. Being so passive was not really exciting me. I pushed myself upon to my elbows and then threw Will onto his back so I could take on the role I was more familiar with. Pulling Will's jeans off I had to bite my lip to prevent an outburst of laughter when I revealed a kinky jockstrap. The concept was sexy – on a 6-foot muscular footballer maybe; but on the skinny frame of a middle-aged guy sporting the early buds of a pair of man boobs, this was seriously not appropriate. I controlled my emotions and removed his poor choice of underwear quickly. Will was having a blast but I could not help but feel that I was just going through the motions. I did not feel turned on at this point, despite the fact this was the first time I had been in a guy's bed naked.

When we seek sexual gratification we have an excitement threshold. If we don't *up* the excitement level from time to time we become somewhat immune to the pleasure and therefore not really turned on. I needed to change the game plan. I decided to venture lower and began to give Will oral pleasure below his now rather firm ball sack. I had never been here before and judging by the sounds Will was making, I was the first explorer for him. It worked! Once again I enjoyed the pleasure of a very firm erection.

'I want to fuck you!' I whispered into his ear in a voice I did not recognise. It was deeper, hornier and determined. I sensed fear from Will and wondered if he was a gay virgin like me. He may have been a virgin but he was certainly prepared. Pulling the drawer to the left of the bed open, he revealed a box of condoms and lube. I pretended not to notice the dildo that sat lonesome in the back of the drawer. This was a new situation to me but instinctively I seemed to know what to do. From behind, I slowly caressed Will using the warm lubricant for the first time. With each stroke of my fingers I felt his cock pulsate which in turn helped to pulsate mine. I gently pushed myself against Will knowing that this act was going to change everything. There would be no stopping me now if I performed such an intimate act. Will's groans were sounding different, less pleasurable and he asked me stop.

'I have not done this before. I don't think I can. It won't go in!' The flattery in the comment helped to soften the bitter disappointment. I had built myself up and now not achieved the goal set. This was not going to end in this way.

'Get behind me then!' I replied with little thought. Images from porn movies filled my mind. I had always wondered how this would feel as the guys in the movies seemed to be enjoying a level of excitement and pleasure I had not experienced in my life. With a final firmer push Will entered me and I screamed. The pain was excruciating and not at all like in the movies! I jumped to my feet yelping and ran to the bathroom cursing and swearing.

'Are you all right Jack?' Will asked timidly.

'Do I fucking sound okay to you?' I snapped back, panicking at the sight of blood on the tissue. I composed myself and returned to the bedroom where Will was now sitting on the edge of the bed, dick limp and face fallen. 'Hey, must be cos you have a monster cock, Will.' Of course he did not, but the guy was upset and I needed to lift the mood a little.

'Will you hug me Jack?' he asked. Hug? Hug? I had never hugged a guy before. Normally one or both guys were full of guilt at this point and ready to run. Will rolled over and I snuggled in behind, forming a neat pair of spoons. We were actually a perfect match for hugging. I nestled into the soft skin of his back and reprimanded myself for the earlier judgements I had made about Will. He was actually proving to be a really sweet guy, caring, attentive and genuinely in need of a little love and not simply a quick fuck. But I was forgetting my own plan of action. I was not looking for love. I had that already from Maria. I wanted pure, sexual gratification. For some reason this hugging felt good. I felt at peace. I felt contentment.

The contentment resulted in an unexpected sleep and only the sound of the neighbour's car door slamming woke me an hour later. 'Shit Will, I gotta go!' I did not like leaving in this way as I knew it looked like I was a professional whore running out on his client but Maria would surely be wondering about my whereabouts.

'Come for dinner on Tuesday? I will cook.'

'Will, I'm married remember!'

'It's just dinner Jack. Bring the wife, if you like.'

'Oh ha bloody ha Will!' I hastily drove off down the quaint little street where the blossom petals fell onto the windscreen. The evening's events replayed in my mind as usual, as I desperately tried to make sense of what it all meant. Was I still a virgin? Did one push even count? Dinner on Tuesday? Was I now dating? Was I actually having an affair?

Tuesday came so quickly and the lack of questioning from Maria was making this all too easy. She seemed to except my lengthy gym routines, probably because she had no reason to doubt me. I arrived at Will's house feeling somewhat peculiar. Will's excitement was written all across his face and he was practically jumping around like a puppy. He looked a little different the second time around. More handsome than I had given him credit for the first time we met. His dress sense was different too – a little younger, more trendy. He was only in his late thirties but being part of a conservative Christian family his appearance was sometimes more mature than necessary.

'Here Jack, sit at the table. It's almost ready.' I watched him adding the finishing touches as I sat alone at the long oak dining table in the adjoining room. He looked so happy. So proud. I wondered if he had any friends or if I was the first to show any real interest in him. There was no reason for this to be the case. Will was your Mr Nice Guy. 'I hope you like chicken and pasta,' Will asked, as if not remembering the conversation we'd had whilst hugging, about favourite foods and films etc. He had cooked my favourite meal. I should have been impressed but I was somewhat apprehensive. This was all a bit quick, all a bit much. He was acting like we were two lovers who knew everything about each other. I focused on enjoying the food and chose to stop over-thinking Will's every move. We chatted about work and I now understood the source of Will's spending power. He was vice CEO of a low-cost airline, though I did ask him to justify his poor choice of company car!

Throughout the meal, Will continually ran his foot along my leg making me incredibly horny. With dinner finished I followed Will to the kitchen and pushed him against the wall. The play was rough and the volume loud. I pulled his trousers to his knees and began to pleasure him just to the point of climax before slapping him on the arse and leading him to bedroom number two. Feeling incredibly excited, Will pushed my face into the quilt whilst fumbling around in the drawer next to him. I wondered why every room was prepped and ready for action. Will penetrated me with greater ease than the first time, though it took some time before the pain subsided into pleasure. The feeling was electrifying, with waves of delight shuddering down my spine. The small hairs on my chest stood erect and my skin flushed with colour. The touch of Will's hot breath on the small of my neck intensified the feelings as I climaxed quickly. Still inside me, Will hugged me from behind as my body fell limp and exhausted. This was the first time I had had penetrative sex with a guy. One solitary tear fell down my crimson cheek, landing on the back of Will's hand.

'Oh my God, did I hurt you Jack?' The softness of his voice and the tenderness of his hug induced my wave of emotion. My tears poured out and my heart ached like never before. Inside a small part of me died: my self-respect. I had cheated on Maria. I had cheated on her with a guy. I was a bad person and I hated myself.

Patiently, Will held me close to his chest. He did not offer any wise words or make pathetic attempts at justifying our actions. He just held me. Held me until the moment had passed. Now feeling embarrassed, I excused myself to shower. I washed myself repeatedly and cried continuously, desperately trying to avoid Will hearing my whimpering. As I dressed I never spoke one word to Will or even looked at him. I was too ashamed. I could sense him looking at me, longing for me to say something, to ease his own anguish and offer him reassurance that this was not goodbye. I had nothing left inside me to give. I replaced the wedding band on my finger as another tear fell to the floor and whispered in a barely audible voice, 'I'm sorry.'

The drive home was about twenty minutes along the same route I took each day from work. I paid no attention and was in some sort of cruise control. I knew I could not face Maria in this way so pulled over into an empty car park en route. I did not allow myself to cry. I knew I needed to take control now and being an emotional wreck was going to be counterproductive. I had made some bad choices that evening but I was still sure it was Maria and the straight life she offered that I wanted. She had even given me a glimmer of hope about starting a family, when we had chatted about extending the house over breakfast that morning. I was not going to throw that away now. Three deep breaths and I was ready to adopt my alter-ego. The split personality was certainly proving to be invaluable when Maria returned home thirty minutes after me. I even managed a few giggles at the stories she told me about her day. The face was smiling, but the soul was dying. I felt ashamed as she hugged me goodnight, although relieved that the hug had no sexual intention.

I have often felt that being a gay in denial is like being possessed by the devil. You feel ashamed at some of the activities you engage in. The shame comes from not being able to be honest about them with others. Yet despite the shame you continue to indulge in such affairs. As easily as you talk yourself out of being gay or doing gay things, you can easily talk yourself into doing them again. The voices of good and bad inside your head are deafening. And when you are horny, the volume increases. Despite my best efforts to ignore Will's pleas to visit, I succumbed. Every time I saw him I tried to explain that we could only ever be friends and that I was in love with Maria. Yet every time I saw him we ended up in bed. We had sex in all five bedrooms of his house and most of the other rooms too. And this continued for four months. I realised that Will was somewhat a part of my life now and denying him or my feelings was futile. Instead, I recalled the wise words of Chris once more and devised a way of *managing* the situation with Will rather than *denying* it.

I created a whole story around Will that I shared with Maria using my previous experience with Gareth as a template. He was my new friend from the gym and to make the story even more realistic, Will even joined my gym. This alarmed me somewhat as we had not talked about it and I liked my personal space when working out. I wondered if his intentions were to keep a closer eye on me as he often displayed a jealous nature, but I chose to hope he was merely thinking of me. Will lived near to where I worked so seeing him was easy. I had secured a new job and so was not putting in the same hours at my current school as I knew I would be leaving in a few months anyway. This enabled me to leave work early a few times each week and pop over to Will's for a much-needed release. I was surprised how he was always available to see me and wondered if he was so keen that he was calling in sick or rearranging his shifts to suit my needs. He was proving to be a great fuck buddy just as I had hoped. No strings, no emotions, just full on sexual pleasure with someone who was now also a good friend.

That was until on one hot July evening when Will uttered the words I had never expected to hear, 'I love you Jack!'

I froze to the spot. Unprepared for such an occurrence I could not even move my lips. This was not a reality check or even a slap. This was a fucking reality bomb blast. Sure, I had feelings for Will, but it was not love. It was not remotely anything like love. He was a friend who I fooled around with and nothing more. My mind raced back to his previous behaviour: his eagerness to cook my favourite meals, the change in his sense of fashion. God damn it he was wearing the exact same T-shirt as me at the gym the previous day, having seen me wearing it the previous week.

'Will this has to stop right now! For fuck's sake I told you I love Maria. I won't ever leave her for you. I'm not fucking gay like you!' Back in full denial I was losing control. My words clearly cut deep, revealed in Will's sunken eyes. But he refused to let go.

'I know you love me too Jack, *you* just don't know it yet. And when you do, you will leave Maria for me. For sure. And I will be waiting for you when you do.' His words made my blood run cold. He was so calm, so collected and he let me walk out of the door and down the path without a further word. He had total confidence in my return.

One month passed with no contact from Will, much to my relief, although I did miss hanging out with him and I certainly missed his cooking. I had started a sexual relationship with Richard, a rather posh former public school boy who lived on a private farm near to my parents' home. He was young, athletic, incredibly handsome and stinking rich. Well his family were. We enjoyed many happy times in his private indoor pool – a sexual first for me. Richard was openly gay, though totally straight in appearance and persona. He expected nothing from me and asked nothing of me. He understood my personal situation and accepted it entirely. It was a welcome change from Will who now seemed to have let go. If only. I thought I had seen Will sitting in the car park of the gym on Monday evening but had put it down to my paranoia. But on Thursday there was no denying that he was indeed watching me arrive. I quickly changed and made my way to the weights room, a little disturbed by Will's actions.

Half way through my workout I caught sight of Will on the floor mats in the corner of the room, facing in my direction. He just stared at me the entire time causing me to stumble at one point from a lack of concentration. He never attempted to speak to me or approach me but he watched me continuously. I could not take this any longer and so made the move towards him.

'Are you following me Will?'

'This is my gym too remember, Jack. Don't be so paranoid.'

'Don't fuck with me Will. You live thirty minutes away from this gym with two other gyms next to your estate. Why the hell are you still coming here?' My blood was beginning to boil, but I was aware of the densely populated room at this point.

'I'm waiting for you Jack. Just like I said.' An insane coldness swept through my body. His words were not threatening, but his eyes were menacing. I walked away.

'Oh Jack. That prick you are seeing on the farm – it won't last!'

This was like something from a fucking psychopath thriller. What was next? Jackson found boiling in a pot in my kitchen or Maria kidnapped? I knew Will and I knew this was a stupid attempt at scaring me. It was an act. Will was a good guy, but he was losing the plot.

'Screw you, Will. Stop fucking following me and stop bloody wearing the same clothes as me you sad fucker!' I knew my words were hurtful. I intended them to be. I was in panic mode and I needed to hurt him to stop him from loving me before he did something crazy like tell Maria. I knew deep down he was not that type of guy, but my God he was following me to Richard's farm so anything was possible.

Richard did not take well to knowing this and decided to call it a day with me. His hopes of a future in politics could not risk stories of crazy stalkers. I did not really care anyway. I had become immune to any emotions around my sexual activities with men. It was just something I had to do. It meant nothing and therefore who it was with did not really matter. The excitement of the first meet was now the driving force in reaching my excitement threshold. Plenty of guys on the net to choose from, I would tell myself, and now that Will was sorted, there would be no stopping me.

CHAPTER EIGHTEEN

I was growing tired of these quick fix sexual encounters born out of the Internet. There had been numerous encounters of all types since Richard; from hot rugby guys to married older guys. All failed to satisfy my cravings. Even the more daring encounters on the hard shoulder of the motorway did nothing to quench my thirst, so much so that I was coming across as just plain rude to my potential meets. Gone was my charismatic conversation, making way for a more direct approach of, *Wanna fuck?* What was happening to me? Why was I now so cold and so immune to emotion? What had happened to turn me into the predator that I now saw in the mirror? My plan for one sexual fuck buddy was now a distant memory. It could never satisfy my ravishing hunger. I wanted quick fixes only. Minimal chat and no after sales!

Craig was a perfect match for this criteria. Equally direct, I knew there was no chance of him becoming another Will. His opening line, *Top or bottom?* I liked it! Straight to the point, (pardon the pun). He even sent a naked pic within minutes and this was the rush of excitement I had longed for. Incredibly hairy, he was a masterpiece of perfection. Although clearly tensing his abs, his body was impressive and the thick mat of hair was a surprising turn on. The baseball cap was a cute touch too. I felt he was out of my league, but he appeared keen. Despite all the positive attention I had received over the past few months it had done nothing to build my confidence. The wave of flattery from Craig caused me to make my first mistake – agreeing to meet in public. I had never done this before. The normal drill was to meet at the guy's place or at worse, in a car park. There was never any socialising. For some reason this time I had forgotten the code as I pulled up to a local coffee shop about fifteen minutes from my home. I saw Craig waiting in his car opposite and felt my legs trembling with excitement; I loved the thrill of the first meet so much.

I walked across the car park, pretending not to notice Craig sitting in his car. His battered used Ford Fiesta did nothing for me so he was lucky he had his looks! When he came in moments after me I was a little taken aback by his youthful appearance. He gave a cheeky grin in my direction as he leant against the counter and placed an order. I quickly tried to think of some topics we could discuss before he joined me. This was new to me. Was this a date? There was no need to have stressed about conversation starters; Craig was anything but shy or silent. He was the most talkative guy I had ever met. I think he may have just wanted a friend to talk to but that was not what I wanted and I could sense myself drifting during some of his more lengthy stories. I tested the water with a little bit of flirting to which he responded well. He was openly gay and gave no thought to reaching over to touch the back of my hand when I paid him a compliment. I was tangled in the moment too, somewhat forgetful of the wedding ring I was sporting and the risk I was now taking.

'So do I look the same as my photo?' I asked, knowingly fishing for a compliment.

'Oh way better Jack! I'd fuck you for sure!'

The response certainly took my breath away! This guy was now more to the point than me and the rubbing of my thigh under the table was certainly enticing. The two elderly ladies next to us were not impressed and the look was curdling the milk in my latte!

'You wanna go back to yours?' I asked hastily.

'We can't Jack. My housemates are in tonight. How about yours?'

I had already explained my personal situation to Craig but he knew Maria was out this evening. I imagined running my hands across that hairy chest and feeling those full lips on my body. He was so cute in that baseball hat and his handsome face was enough of a prize to lead me to making my second mistake.

Following behind my car, Craig and I were on the way back to my house. My marital home. The place I shared with my wife. What the hell was I thinking? I had never even contemplated such a thing before, so why now? Of course! I was trying to surpass my excitement threshold. This was new territory for me; what could be more exciting! I ran through every possible scenario – a neighbour seeing us, Maria coming home and catching us, Craig becoming a stalker and knowing where to find me. But when you have the horn on, these issues can be solved so easily! I entered the house with Craig close behind, thinking nothing of his excessively loud voice as he greeted the cat in the porch. I quickly closed the Roman blinds before being taken by surprise as Craig pushed me to the leather sofa. Seconds later his jeans were around his ankles and his hands were forcefully pushing my head into his groin. So much for needing a friend to chat to. His thighs were incredibly masculine. Thick and hairy and clearly the result of frequent weight training sessions. I ran my hands up to his peachy arse which was equally hairy. He pulled his T-shirt over his head, knocking his baseball cap off and revealing a shockingly rapid receding hairline. And

I just thought it was a cute fashion accessory rather than a symbol of his denial to accept his impending baldness! What he lacked in hair on his head, he made up for on his chest! It was like nothing I had ever seen. Thick waves of black hair that provided a nesting ground for his nipples, which were nowhere to be seen.

He was now sprawled on my sofa; the same sofa I shared with Maria. Cushions flew across the room as Jackson watched, unamused, from the doorway. I scanned along the whole of Craig's athletic body but could not stop myself from imagining Maria sat there and my head started to spin. Maybe sensing my distraction, Craig pulled me on to him and now I was straddling him, naked from the waist down. His kisses were immense. His thick tongue flickered like an electric eel. His firm, manly hands grabbed at my chest and his moans were intensifying. He grabbed my cock and rapidly started to pleasure me at the same time as stimulating himself. He was a sexual artist. I could not take any more as my body spasmed in ecstasy. Craig jumped to his feet and proceeded to shoot his excessive load across my chest and onto the sofa. The sofa I sat beside my wife on! I closed my eyes as guilt set in with the realisation that I had now broken the code and changed the rules of engagement. Somewhat startled by the sound of running water I ran upstairs to find Craig lathering himself up in my shower.

'Christ Craig, Maria could be home anytime! You need to leave.'

'Maria? You wife's name is Maria? Does she teach at Weston School?' It suddenly occurred to me that I had not actually used her name despite spending the night explaining my unique situation.

'What? You know her? What the fuck!' I had to steady myself as I suddenly felt both nausea and fear consume me. I was not sure I wanted to hear the answer to the next question.

'How do you know her?' I asked reluctantly.

'Oh I'm a teaching student at the same school, but we haven't really talked.' The colour drained from my face and my gut wrenched.

'Hey, it's okay Jack. I won't tell if you don't! Just remember me when a teaching vacancy comes up in your school!' His attempt at humour at this time did not impress me and I pursed my lips to show my lack of contentment. He leant in and kissed my lips gently and gave a playful slap on my bottom before leaving. I sat on the edge of the bath feeling numb. I had risked everything for a quick fumble. I had put both myself and Maria in a compromising position. I could only pray that Craig was the good guy he appeared to be, who would honour his word and keep quiet. But this had taught me a lesson. It was the trigger that would stop my Internet cruising as I once again decided I needed to focus on rebuilding my life with Maria.

The first opportunity I had I logged on to my gay dating sites and erased my profiles. I felt a strange sense of relief, as if my life sentence had been quashed. The final step was to erase my fake email account which proved useful when signing up to my endless porn sites or receiving sexy videos and pictures from my Internet buddies. *You have one unread message* appeared as I logged on and searched for the 'delete account' button. There was no point reading the message. I was now a reformed character. Curiosity got the better of me and after being seconds away from ending this run of deceit, I opened my mail. The message was from Ryan. Luckily there was a picture included because the name failed to trigger any memories. Opening the picture

I soon remembered this guy. We had briefly chatted a few months back and had intended on meeting, until he explained his love for ganja which had led to me somewhat losing interest. In fact, we had had a heated debate around this topic. Despite my moral standing I could not help but find this one attractive. Maybe it was the overly large smile, or the cheeky banter, but this guy was now halting my road to recovery.

Hey Jack, remember me? Ganja guy! Haha. I have been going through a really rough time the last few weeks so not been in touch sorry. You fancy coming over to catch up?

No, no, no, no! I was not doing this anymore. I had changed remember. I truly believed that was how easily I could change. I was going to focus on Maria now. No more Internet, no more guys. Yet this guy needed me it seemed. Surely I could just pop over for a chat? Make sure he was okay and then leave. That was all it would be. If only I had realised that this 'quick visit' would change my life and the life of Maria *and* my family beyond belief. Ryan would end the life I had known for the past thirty years forever.

CHAPTER NINETEEN

I recognised the street as I pulled up outside number twenty. From Ryan's directions I had guessed it was near my mother-in-law's house, but I had not realised it was this close! It was not a problem though as I was just acting as a good Samaritan on this occasion. I would just check-in on Ryan, make sure he was doing okay and have a little chat, before excusing myself and being on my own little way. The neighbourhood was not in the best part of the city and the small group of drunken middle-aged guys sitting outside the house opposite looked like they might provide a potential risk to my beloved Audi. The area had changed a lot over the years and was now a bustling ethnic minority community with a converted church at the top of the street now providing a place of worship for the increasing Muslim population. Sadly the suburb was of low socioeconomic status and had lacked investment in recent years. This helped to reinforce the preconceptions I had built up about my marijuana-loving new best friend.

I patiently waited in the front porch, having rang the doorbell twice. Judging by the excessive number of doorbells, the converted Victorian house was home to many. As I nudged the gate closed it fell from its rusty single hinge, causing a small fuss which failed to draw attention from the half-soaked crew opposite who were too busy negotiating the tops off their cider bottles. Distracted by my own commotion I failed to hear the door opening behind me until Ryan spoke in the strongest Welsh accent I had heard in a long time.

'All right butt. Ow's you 'en?' I wanted to laugh but the grin that followed was enough to make the thickest of chocolate bars melt. His smile was incredible and spanned the entire diameter of his face. The perfect smile for sure. He was a lot taller than I had anticipated and much cuter. I think I struggled to conceal my delight. He was like a Cheshire cat grinning back at me and neither of us were saying anything. 'Well, you gonna stand outside my 'ouse all day or you coming in 'en?'

Oh my God I had regressed to my giggling schoolgirl phase once again, as I ducked under his arm and into the passageway. The smell of damp was a little over-powering as we tramped up the narrow staircase to the first floor. Stepping into Ryan's flat I could not help but be impressed; it was a little piece of bachelor heaven. A stark contrast to the communal area and the street in which it sat. Ryan was the proud owner of a little gem.

'What the hell?' I was little surprised by the sudden gnarling at my heels courtesy of Boxer, the little puppy Ryan was babysitting for his friends. The dog gave a welcome distraction to Ryan's constant grinning. I half wondered if he was off his face from a recent dose of weed before I arrived. Whilst wrestling Boxer and trying to sit I could not help but notice the golden bling draped on Ryan. A gold chain I could accept but this coupled with a few gold rings was a little chavtastic for me. I focused on the smile instead and the interesting conversation he was nervously trying to generate.

His quick wit was so amusing and I laughed in a way I had not in a long time. For every topic he had a humorous comment or story and his gentle teasing of me was also enticing. Maybe he was hiding behind a smoke screen but this guy seemed more than okay and clearly he did not need me to talk to. My work was clearly done. I was not needed there and so I began to make my move to leave.

'Hey, don't I gerra kiss before you go 'en?' This was cheeky and yet so expected and it made me blush a gentle shade of pink. Leaning forwards, I placed a soft peck upon his cheek. 'Not what I was thinking. How about you try again?' His little game was fun and my crotch began to throb. They say a guy thinks with his dick. Well this must be true because all that bull shit about doing my good Christian work was now a distant memory as I started to passionately kiss Ryan. Seconds later the tops were off and being flung across the room, quickly followed by the jeans which were being chewed by Boxer. An explosive embrace that moved quickly to the bedroom that was less than five steps away. No words, no humour, no justifying, just pure unadulterated hard-core action. The voyeur in the corner was slightly off-putting but gave a short gap of rest whilst we both broke down into laughter as Boxer proceeded to lick my bare white butt. The disruption of flow was my saving grace and gave me a much-needed pause to think about the consequences of my actions. Ryan noticed my change of mood and simply hugged me. We fell back onto the bed that was not as comforting as it looked. The wooden slats were worn, indicating that this bed had seen plenty of action over the years; a thought I did not want to entertain right now.

Lying on Ryan's chest I felt a great sense of peace. For months my deceit had caused great anguish with a constant flow of guilty traffic racing around my head. Torn between doing the 'right thing' for me and the 'right thing' for Maria, this moment of tranquillity was much needed. I felt a real connection to Ryan and a strange sense of familiarity. Previous encounters had normally resulted in a frantic collection of clothing, random excuses to leave and little emotion. With Ryan things were different. I felt so comfortable lying naked on top of his bare body, running my finger along the outline of the dragon tattoo on his chest. We talked for hours about every possible topic. His past experiences with women helped me to make sense of my own situation with a little more clarity. He never once judged me or tried to tell me what to do.

'You're a good guy Jack. I can feel that!' Ryan's words were so comforting, so healing. Although he was very sexy, this was about the personality. His charm was addictive and I was not ready to go cold turkey just yet.

'How about we run away together?' I said in jest, waiting for a witty response.

'Sure, why not? How about Jamaica!' We both broke out in hysterical laughter. Not because it was particularly funny but because we both at that very moment *really* wanted it.

'I need to go Ryan. Sorry!'

'You'll be back! We need to sort out Jamaica!' Ryan replied playfully. I could not contain my smile and as I looked back at Ryan before I left, I knew this was something different and that indeed he was right. I *would* be back for sure.

Every day for one month I saw Ryan. The cold January nights were not enough to keep me away. I used every combination of excuses to free myself from Maria, giving me the opportunity to sneak away to Ryan's, even if it was only for thirty minutes. I finished work early, shortened my gym sessions and disappointed my friends with last minute cancellations; anything to be able to spend time with Ryan. This time it was not just about the physical relationship, although that was incredible. It was the emotional connection. It was the way in which he helped me to understand my situation and provided support, often comforting me when it all felt too much. He did not just sympathise with me but was able to empathise due to his own colourful past. He understood what it felt like to be ashamed of who I really was inside. He could relate to the constant confusion and the burning desires continually eating away at me. He recalled similar stories of encounters with high school bullies and awkward conversations about sport with straight guys. Having someone to share these feelings with was incredibly enlightening.

Whenever I had met guys in the past I had always been very clear about my intentions: I love my wife very much and will never leave her. This is just something I need to do. I never strayed from this line. I even used it on Ryan after our first intimate moment. But something was changing. Something was very different because, for the first time in my life, I was starting to imagine my life without Maria and a life with Ryan. I had never prepared myself for such a thought. Never once even contemplated leaving Maria for a guy. I was falling for Ryan and falling quickly. Our post-sex jokes about running away to Jamaica were now less humorous and more appealing. Ryan was like a meteorite that had collided into me without warning and at full speed. My whole world was now upside down and my anguish was at a peak. I had always been so definite about my life plan and this was a diversion that was not planned. The next step in *my* manual was to become a dad. I had always believed it was my destiny to care for a child. This new alternative lifestyle I was considering would rob me of that. This was a thought I could not bear. I had only ever wanted to make everyone happy but now no one was happy; least of all me. Maria was aware of the growing distance between us and was hurting. We were not engaging in any sexual activity and she was putting it down to the stressful situation I was facing at work. Ryan was incredibly insecure and felt he would never truly win my whole heart. He was desperately fighting the temptation to pressure me to make any decisions. And what about me? I was a mess. So confused, so unsure and so lonely. The pressure I felt was incredible and it was suffocating. I could not breathe. I was spiralling out of control in my head and for the first time in my life I was lost with no way of finding my way back. I needed help and there was only one person who really knew me and who could be trusted: Nathan. Sadly this leap of faith, to call upon my best friend, would only further add to my agony and result in even more tears being shed.

CHAPTER TWENTY

Maria and I had booked a short trip to Iceland for our February holidays some time ago and I couldn't think of a possible way of avoiding this. I was concerned about spending so much time together and how I would deal with not seeing Ryan. This was our first trip away since my deceit had truly taken a hold of me. The adventure was magical in terms of the amazing scenery and experiences we enjoyed. We were united by our common interest in wildlife. I had forgotten everything that was going on back home and for the first time in a long while I enjoyed our time together. We were like two best friends travelling together, having a blast. Our friendship was never the issue. It was the lack of intimacy that was.

It had been around nine months by this point and whilst I was taking a much-needed hot shower after driving the snowmobiles over the glaciers, Maria decided to change this with an unexpected appearance behind me. I knew this had taken a lot of courage from Maria as she was terribly, and yet unjustifiably, self-conscious of her body. A sweeping moment of thrill washed over me as I enjoyed the touch of her soft breasts on my back. The soap lathers provided a silky satin sheet that felt so good. We kissed passionately for the first time in months as she ran her hand down the side of my body and over to my groin. It was soft. It was the softest I had ever seen it and it was showing no signs of changing state. I was devastated. This had never happened to me before and I felt utter shame and embarrassment. Maria attempted to brush it off as one of those things, but I could see the anguish in her eyes. She knew this was not good. Nine months of no passion and now no signs of being able to successfully arouse me. As she stepped out of the shower and left the room I sat on the edge of the bath and sobbed. I knew what this meant. It was over. I clearly felt no sexual chemistry and it was because I was gay. Whatever I had done to trick my body into thinking otherwise for the last thirteen years was now not working. I needed to talk to Nathan more than ever.

Maria and I never spoke of that moment again and just enjoyed each other's company for the rest of the short trip. Arriving home I called Nathan immediately and asked if we could meet. I think he sensed it was something serious and so he tried to put me off. Sometimes he spoke to me more like a business associate rather than a close friend.

'Let me check my schedule and get back to you Jack. Things are hectic with the kids and catching up with family.'

'I appreciate that Nath, but I'm really struggling here. I don't think I can cope.' My voice shook with a genuine fear and my pleas were flushed with desperation.

'How about the second of March?' asked Nathan without a hint of emotion.

'What the fuck? Are you for real, Nath? You live twenty minutes away from me and it's only fucking February. Are you seriously telling me you cannot "fit me in" until next month! For Christ's sake I need you!'

The reply was as cold as his first response, 'Don't do this Jack. I need to go. I'm sorry!' He was gone. I had not even told him why I so desperately needed to talk, but I guess we were close enough that he realised and he just could not handle it. This was my first attempt to reach out to someone and it had failed. I was devastated and cried hysterically. I needed to end this. I could not bear the burden any longer. I begged God to end the pain, to take my life and end my misery and the misery of others around me. I screamed his name repeatedly and punched at anything in close proximity.

'Why are you doing this to me? I can't deal with this. I beg you God. I don't know how to face this.' I looked at my face in the mirror; it was red with anguish and tears rolled down my cheeks and onto my chest. I hated myself so much. I could not look at myself; I felt sick to the pit of my stomach. More screaming, more punching, glass shattering, blood pouring. In the broken glass I saw my own reflection of agony and I wept some more. The multiple slashes across my hand were only superficial but dramatic nonetheless. I wanted the blood to pour out and every drop of life to exit with it. But I knew that would be too easy and too selfish. I was stronger than that and needed to pull it together and face this properly.

Any sign of blood was now a distant memory; the crime scene was now clean and free of evidence. Of course there was the broken mirror and multiple plasters on my right hand to explain but that would be easy. I felt a strange sense of direction now. I knew what I now needed to do. I needed to make Maria so miserable that *she* would leave me. Then with Maria out of the way I could run away somewhere with Ryan and not have to tell my family the truth. In years to come I could tell them I was gay if things in the world had changed. It all seemed so clear now. So clear and yet so naïve. Nonetheless I started the process of trying to make Maria hate me. I was so confused and hurting so badly that I was truly unaware of my actions. The only thing I knew for sure was that I had to get out of the current mess one way or the other. I became even more distant and less interested in Maria and our relationship. I was aware I was not supporting her and in fact not really listening to her. I was incapable of doing so. I was not myself. We had always been such good friends in the past, but now I felt resentment whenever I spent time with her. I had stopped looking for a way to make us work. After thirteen years I was handing in the towel.

Valentine's Day was upon us and I wondered how I would manage to be civil let alone romantic. Ryan had also changed his tactics and was no longer prepared to be the 'bit' on the side. He was demanding more and was unaware that this additional pressure was further suffocation for me. I knew Maria despised forced romantic events such as Valentine's Day so managing to escape would not be too much of a challenge. I often wondered if she had already stopped looking for *me* at this point. She did not care that I was off to the gym, which made it so much easier to leave. Maybe if she had known it was our last Valentine's she would have played it differently. Could she have changed the course of events? Unlikely.

For the first time Ryan and I were now on a date *and* on the most romantic day in the lovers' calendar. After months of hiding our feelings away in the confines of his room we were now displaying our relationship for all to see. Actually, that was probably how Ryan had interpreted it. I was too self-conscious, too riddled with guilt and too uptight to actually enjoy the moment. I was only doing it to pacify Ryan's growing impatience of the situation. *He* was like the cat that got the cream. He was so happy to be sharing this moment with me. A candle-lit Asian feast was the setting. Ryan could not stop himself from grinning with delight. This was his first ever Valentine date he informed me and at that moment I could see the absolute pleasure in his eyes. I had not known him long but he had never looked happier. I desperately tried to relax but felt convinced that the straight couples that surrounded us were staring. I wondered if any of Maria's friends could see me and were puzzled as to why I was sharing such an intimate moment with someone else. A someone else who was a guy! I tried to act like we were just a couple of mates having a drink but the ambient soft glow candle burning between us was somewhat in conflict with that idea. For sure it was the quickest I had eaten a meal and I certainly was not entertaining the idea of sipping on some cheap wine all evening. Ryan did not seem to pick up on my haste. I think he was just grateful to be sharing the moment together.

Driving back to his place I reflected on what the hell I was doing. I was now flaunting my gay lover in a public place on the evening prized by couples in love. I believed I had lost the plot and knew that this was something I would not be doing again. There was no room in my life for two partners and so one would have to go. Weighing my options up I considered I was not strong enough to pick Ryan and hurt Maria so badly. It was disappointing that I did not maintain this choice when Ryan managed to convince me to come up for a quick drink. I think he sensed he was losing me and so was preparing his battle plan. One drink had been my intention but as I pulled up my boxers and slipped on my T-shirt, I realised that that was never going to be what happened. I knew I was pushing things with Maria though as my gym session was fast approaching three hours!

'Sorry to rush off Ryan, but I need to get back.'

'Yeah don't worry Jack, I know the drill now. We fuck.

You leave. And I feel like shit. Like a cheap whore!' he angrily snapped back at me.

'Hey, you knew exactly what you were getting involved with. For God's sake I just spent Valentine's with you whilst my *wife* is sat at home waiting for her gym-obsessed husband to return.' I was really pissed at his lack of gratitude for my kind gesture that evening.

'Yeah well I can't do this anymore. It's about time you made your choi...'

'Don't you fucking dare give me ultimatums Ryan. I will leave Maria. Just give me time.' This was the first time these words had ever passed my lips and I actually felt like I meant them.

'I think you have had long enough Jack. We both know you won't actually do it!' His words were hurtful. After months of playing the understanding lover, he had now reached his own threshold and was playing his final card. I simply grabbed my keys and walked out without a word and without as much as a glance back at Ryan.

Sitting shivering in my car, from the mixture of the cold night chill and the adrenaline pumping through my body, I resented the way in which Ryan had spoken to me. Where was my angel who had helped me understand my feelings and shared in my anguish? Where was the patient, caring empathetic friend who knew the pressure I felt inside? I guess he had his own wants and needs and now these were starting to surface. My resentment turned to anger as I punched the steering wheel with both fists. I caught a glimpse of Ryan in the upstairs window, clearly looking upset too. My own anger turned to pity and I just wanted to race back upstairs, throw my arms around him and tell him that he had my heart. But I was weak and I was fearful. The thought of telling Maria was unbearable and knowing I would lose my family was too intolerable to consider. I started the engine and drove off, taking one last glance back up at Ryan. Returning home, Maria did not even question by whereabouts. Did she trust me so much? Or did she no longer even care?

For two weeks I desperately fought the burning desire to speak with Ryan. With every journey home from work I longed with every atom in my body to take a diversion and stop by his home. My heart ached so much and despite my greatest efforts I could not stop thinking about him every moment of every day. With my mind so preoccupied with Ryan I was still unable to give any thought to Maria and her desperate attempts to 'find' me. I snapped at her every enquiry, growled in response to her questions and refused her emotional advances. I knew it was wrong, but I could not stop it. I saw her pain, but I could not help her. I felt her fears, but I did not know how to alleviate them. Or maybe I simply did not want to. Returning home after a quick bite to eat to 'celebrate' her birthday, Maria started to question me with greater persistence. She refused to accept by flippant brush-offs this time. She craved to know the root of my unhappiness, the reasons for the change in my gentle nature. I tried to avoid the need to answer but Maria was not tiring and like a lion stalking its prey, she refused to let go. Two a.m. had now come and gone and the questioning continued. She never once asked if I was having an affair. Her concern was genuinely about my mental state yet I still responded with such anger.

'Fuck off Maria! I don't know what's wrong with me, okay? Maybe your fucking nagging is driving me insane!'

She didn't need to respond to that hurtful sentence. It was all in her eyes and written across her fragile face. She was shocked and sickened. I had let her down and she could not look at me. She simply got off the bed and, taking the chenille blanket with her, left the room silently sobbing. I fell asleep within moments. I failed to lie there replaying the events, regretting my words or worrying about the future. I simply fell into a peaceful slumber. Five hours later I was up and showered and ready to face the day ahead. Was I suffering with temporary amnesia or selective memory loss, because the evening's events were having no effect on my mood? Was I now such a cold bastard that I did not even care that I had hurt my wife so much? Apparently so. There was no sign of Maria in the house and yet that did not concern me or worry me in the slightest. As I drove to work I thought only of the final day ahead before the long Easter break. Sitting in the head teacher's office completing some paperwork, I thought only of what delights I could eat for lunch. BEEP BEEP BEEP BEEP. The sound of my mobile text alert startled me from my preoccupation with my food.

I can't do this anymore Jack. I don't know you anymore. I am staying with my mum. I am ashamed to say that I practically cheered. I know now I was in some kind of deep denial about what was going on. I think it was just a sense of relief, as the intolerable balloon of pressure was finally pierced somewhat. I simply smiled, placed my phone back on my desk and carried on working.

One hour later reality hit home. Not the reality that my wife had just left me, but the reality that I could now be with Ryan. I texted him asking if I could call over after work and that I now knew that I really wanted to be with him. *Maria's gone!!* I coldly added onto the end of the text. I hid all my emotions from my colleagues as I carried on the day's business and as the hours passed, the excitement was soaring. Seeing Ryan waiting at the door when I finally reached his house was electrifying. I knew that smile would heal some wounds and the warmth of his gentle hug gave all the reassurance I needed that this was something he wanted too.

He did not recap on past events or make me pay my dues; he just softly whispered, 'I am sorry about you and Maria. I know you love her so much. I will do all I can to help you through this.' No doubt deep down he was so happy to have finally won, but he was at least tactful in displaying his winning glory.

'I need to call my parents,' I unexpectedly proclaimed.

'What the hell? Are you serious Jack? You're going to tell your parents you're gay? Today?'

Ryan's reaction was of a man running scared. Was he now having doubts?

'No! You idiot haha. I will just tell them Maria has left me. I think that will be enough to take in for one night.' Was I telling my parents because I needed their support or because by telling them it made it more of a reality? The phone seemed to ring endlessly which built up the anxiety even more. I was sitting on the edge of Ryan's bed whilst he was watching TV in the next room. The smell of bacon sandwiches wafting up the stairs from the flat below made me feel a little queasy. It was then I realised I had not eaten in hours.

'Hello, Mum?'

'Hello luv, how are you doing?' Her voice was always so chirpy and welcoming which always made me cry when I knew I could not give her the response she wanted.

'Maria and I are over Mum. She left today!' My voice was somewhat distorted by my gentle whimper, but I think my mother failed to pick up on this.

'Shut up you daft sod.'

'Mum, she's gone. We are ov...' Unable to finish my sentence I detected panic in my mother's voice. She was desperately trying to think about what to say whilst dealing with her own emotions at the same time.

'Well what's happened? I'm sure you're over-reacting as usual. That girl is besotted with you.' There was now no denying the anguish in her voice too. She questioned and questioned and pushed and pushed. I tried all methods of avoidance, but the inquiries kept coming.

'Has she found someone else? Have you found someone else?'

'No Mum. For God's sake we are just over!' I snapped back angrily.

'Well it just don't make sense. I'm sure you will get back together. Just give her some space.'

'We won't Mum.'

'You don't know that. You will...'

'No you don't understand – we can't,' I interrupted, sounding defeated now.

'What do you mean?'

I interrupted her again, took one deep breath and released the words I thought would never be spoken to my mother.

'I think I am GAY!'

Silence. 'Hello?' Silence. 'Mum?' Silence. She had hung up. I had just spoken the bravest sentence I could ever conjure up and she had bloody hung up. I screamed out hysterically and Ryan came flying into the room. My fears were true. I had lost my family and all because God had made me in a mutated form of himself. For ten long minutes I cried intensely. The guy holding me so tightly was all I had left in my life now. For ten long minutes I had lost my family until my mobile rang. It was my mother, sounding barely audible.

'I... I... I'm sssorry.' My mother's tears were clearly streaming. A mixture of shock, upset and shame for having hung up on her son who was in turmoil. But I knew it was only panic that had elicited her initial reaction. Ryan stepped out of the room to give me some private time with my parents.

'Mum, it's okay. It doesn't matter,' I replied reassuringly.

'But why do you think you might be gay? How do you know?' insisted my mother, no doubt clinging on to some sense of hope that it was all just a misunderstanding.

'I just know Mum. I'm sorry.' My tears began another journey down my pale face, falling onto my trembling hands. I could hear the disappointment in her voice. Was this the moment she hoped would never come? Were all those doubts from the past now piecing together into her worst fears? Was this about me or about her? Maybe she just feared the road I was now turning down and the repercussions I might encounter. Barely comprehensible my mother explained that everything would be okay and that her and my father wanted me to come and see them the next morning.

All night I sat wondering what kind of conversation my parents would be having. I imagined my father being ashamed and unable to express himself. I assumed he might be blaming my mother for over-protecting or smothering me in love as a child. Possibly my mother was fighting back, blaming my father for not having formed a better bond between him and I. Or maybe they were united in the realisation that in fact this was no surprise and there had been many incidents over the years that they had both chosen to ignore. What is for certain is that they probably did not get much more sleep than I did. Ryan was incredibly sensitive and supportive that endless night. No words, just a prescription of hugs, kisses and smiles. As four a.m. came and went, I felt surprisingly great. The immense weight of shame, guilt and fear had been somewhat lifted. A great sense of peace washed over my entire body and for the first time I felt able to breathe once more. No matter what the following day might bring, for now I cuddled into that moment.

CHAPTER TWENTY-ONE

As I embarked on the thirty-minute journey to my parent's house I rehearsed the conversation I would probably be forced into having. My body was trembling from head to toe. I am not sure if this was fear or apprehension but whatever the cause it was resulting in waves of nausea, unbelievable stomach cramps and cold sweats. It may have been totally inappropriate to tell your mother you are gay over the telephone, but it was certainly easier than looking into the eyes of your disappointed parents. It was not too difficult to predict my mother's reaction to seeing me; I had already had a snippet of this last night during our phone call. My father, well that was a different matter altogether. A man of few words, it was likely he would just sit and refuse to engage in any disgusting conversation about being a gay. I even considered whether or not he would be angry. It was certainly a possibility. After all, this was the guy I once saw wielding a pick-axe at my sister's boyfriend and the guy I once saw knock out his brother-in-law for wasting his week's wages on gambling. He was also very fond of Maria and so emotions could be soaring. I pulled over into one of the lay-bys as I suddenly started to lose control of the rhythm of my breathing. Why had I thought this was going to be so easy? I took a quick look at a photo of Ryan on my mobile and remembered my incentive for doing all of this. I had to be strong. The worst part was over. I had said those three difficult words, 'I am gay'. Actually, what I did say was, 'I *think* I am gay.' One little insertion, whose impact would soon become apparent.

Walking into their home felt like stepping into a courtroom where I was about to be tried and hanged. My crime – loving men! I took a final deep breath as I pushed the oak wooden door into the living room open. My mother was in her usual chair next to the window that overlooked the well-maintained garden.

'There he is, mammy's little soldier!' As she lifted herself from the chair her bottom lip began to tremble and I could see the pain she was feeling. It was not her own pain, but a sympathy for the pain she imagined I must be feeling. Throwing her arms around me I felt an overwhelming sense of relief. She did not speak, yet the lack of words was no less comforting. I closed my eyes briefly to savour the moment and then felt my mother pulling away to make room for my father. He hugged me so tightly, in a way I had never known him hug me before. He was not an emotionally expressive man and this was a big gesture for him, which I still cherish now. My mother's hug was predictable. I never doubted her support, but my father's reaction was so unexpected and I felt a little guilty for doubting his ability to support me. The hug seemed to last forever and, for only the second time in my life, I heard the sound of my father's tears which evoked an outburst from me. A jewel of love which impacted on me tremendously and helped to form the foundations of a much improved relationship between us in the future.

'Let's have a cuppa shall we!' said my mother on cue. She was always on hand with a nice cup of tea in times of crisis and boy there had certainly been many in this family over the years. A typically British thing, there is nothing like a cup of tea to calm the nerves and detract away from emotionally charged situations. As my mother made the tea I sat in her chair trying to look remotely interested in the latest spring bloom in the garden. I felt a sense of paranoia as I caught my father looking at me. I wondered what was going through his mind. Was he judging me? Did he admire my bravery? Or was I repulsing him? Sure, he had said all the right things but that was his duty as a parent. What was he really thinking I wondered?

My mother returned to the room and placed my mug on the side table next to me before ruffling my hair as if I was a kindergarten pupil. Despite being almost thirty-two, my mother had failed to notice that I had grown up. I was still her little soldier whom she needed to remind about the dangers of crossing the road. She still liked to ruffle my hair and tell me how handsome I was. I actually loved this about my mum. It was so incredibly endearing and provided the strong emotional footings that I was grounded in. It was because of her that I am sensitive and perceptive to the feelings of others and unafraid to express my feelings and emotions. The spontaneous crying in response to dire TV shows has also been an unwanted by-product of such love however!

'So what's this all about then son?' It was a very weird and unexpected question from my mother. It was as if we were discussing something topical from the news or a minor dispute with a neighbour. It sounded flippant and a total underestimation of the true extent of my thirty-year-dilemma. My response was to cry. I cried because I realised she did not really understand.

'Oh come on now luv. There's no point in crying.' Although an emotional mess I still observed the frantic exchange of glances between my parents, each looking to the other for something wise to say, for a way to handle this new territory. It was the first time I had witnessed my mother appearing lost. It was then that I could see that it was my father who was dealing with this so much better than my mother and I replayed in my head how she had hung up on me yesterday. Clearly my father had given her clear instructions on how to behave today, though already the cracks were appearing and her own inability to accept my revelation was starting to show. She was battling with what she really wanted to say and what my father had advised her to say. My father was normally the type to hide behind his newspaper in times of 'difficult' conversations, but he too sensed my mother's hopelessness and came to the rescue like a white knight.

Pulling up a footstool he sat alongside my mother and they both grabbed my hands as my whimpering continued. 'It's okay son. We don't care what you are. Gay or straight we don't care. Do we luv?' My father diverted this question to my mother, but she managed to avoid it with an interruption of her own question.

'But what do you mean you *think* you are gay? So you don't really know then?' And there it was. The implication of that little additional word. It had given my mother hope. Hope that this was just some terrible mistake. Hope that her only son was not gay. Hope that one day I could tell her I was going to be a dad.

'I just *know* Mum,' I whispered back.

'Yes but if you say you *think* you are gay, then maybe you are not.' I sensed some level of excitement in her voice.

'You knew you were straight right before you ever did anything with a man? You didn't have to question it, you just knew. You didn't wonder if you were attracted to men. You just knew it. It's the same for me. I just know I am gay.'

My mother sobbed at this response and I found myself comforting *her* now. My father looked confused and I could see he was building up to a sentence that was intended to be tactful but would no doubt be anything but.

'So if Victoria and David Beckham walked into this room naked, who would you look at?' questioned my father. It was the most bizarre and unexpected question I could have imagined, but I truly admired his efforts. I paused for what seemed like a lifetime. The prolonged response gave my mother further hope as she imagined I must be weighing up the advantages and disadvantages of the Beckham couple. Of course I was not. I had immediately picked David, but was trying to dig deep to find the strength to say his name.

'Daaaavid!' I cried out as the water outlets that were my eyes opened up once more.

I could not bear to look at my father having said these words, but he simply placed my hand inside his and softly said, 'It's okay son, he's a good looking lad!' It was brilliant! A real gem of a moment and one that makes my friends laugh every time. It was so needed too to lift the choking atmosphere that surrounded me. I am not sure if my father had intended to be so comical, but nonetheless it was a perfect response.

For two long hours we talked. Mainly about my *thoughts* of being gay, but also about other matters which seemed trivial now. Of course, this was not all just to do with me being gay. There was also the little problem of the break-up with Maria.

'Have you told Maria?' asked my mother suddenly.

'No, I can't. What would I say? She would be devastated!' I replied remorsefully.

'Well, you don't have a choice luv. It won't make any sense to her otherwise. Why don't you go and see her tomorrow?' I felt a little pressure here and I was not sure of my mother's motive. Had she lost all hope now and so just wanted the truth out there or did she think that by seeing Maria I would realise that I was not actually gay? Either way I knew she was right and so I sent a text to Maria asking if we could meet the following day. If that day had been a challenging hill to climb, then the following day would feel like an unsurpassable mountain. For now, I would just bask in the pleasure of knowing I had not lost my parents despite my greatest fears.

Arriving back at my own house was very upsetting for me. I felt a cold chill running through the Victorian terrace. The cat was sitting in the hallway looking withdrawn as if he sensed the impending break-up of his family. The living room was dark as no one had pulled the Roman blinds up and there was still a small collection of cups and plates dotted around from two nights ago when we had last shared this home together. Sombrely, I walked into the kitchen, partly hoping to see Maria standing there ready to tell me that everything was going to be okay. There was no sign of her. Reality hit hard. Maria really was gone and there was no turning back now. I could never retract what I had just said to my parents. The kitchen felt so cold, so empty. Nothing had changed; nothing had been removed. But it felt strangely empty. Soulless. The cat litter was long overdue for a change and I realised that Jackson had been abandoned all night. He had been my cat since I was a teenager. In his younger days the stocky black and white tiger would bring me gifts of rodents and small birds, often still alive. Incredibly loving, he had the most endearing charm. Maria had come to love him too and so I wondered how we would sort out any custody battle. Did people go to court for the custody of a pet?

Before facing Maria, I needed to talk with my younger sister. Adela and I had always been so close and it was important for me to get her acceptance. Maybe I was just diverting from the pressing matter of Maria or maybe I just needed greater inner strength which I felt Adela's acceptance would give me. I made the call. I knew I should be telling her face to face but the meeting with my parents was all I could manage for one day.

'Hello?'

'Hi Adela. It's me, Jack. What you up to?'

'Are you okay Jack, you sound kinda breathless?' Adela asked.

'Yeah I just ran up the stairs,' I replied with a lie. Clearly the build up to my revelation was taking its toll on my breathing. I suddenly felt weak and my knees started to buckle. I quickly grabbed the wooden banister rail to steady myself before lowering myself onto the stairs. I hated this hallway. It was one of the few places left to finish in the house and the parquet flooring and small stained glass window always reminded me of a church.

'Yeah we just got back from the cinema. We were sat next to these two guys.'

'And?' I enquired nervously.

'Well it's odd, init? They must be gay. I just find it weird that's all!'

Silence. 'Jack! Jack?' I could barely breathe let alone speak. I was just about to tell the one person I considered to be my rock my deepest, darkest secret and she had spoken that sentence. I was devastated. I could not do it. I knew it was only a matter of time before my parents told her, but I had lost the strength to reveal it myself.

'I gotta go. Sorry sis. There's a delivery at the door.'

'You are such a weirdo sometimes, Jack.' She started laughing hysterically. She was a playful character and so innocent. She just said what she thought, sometimes without realising any implications. There was not a hurtful bone in her body and I knew that. However, her tactless comment had knocked the wind right out of me and I needed to end the conversation quickly.

I sat back on the wooden steps and stared at my surroundings. Three years Maria and I had lived in that house and I still felt no connection to it. Nothing. No emotion, no sense of comfort from my familiar surroundings. Maybe it was the ridiculous monthly mortgage payment or the constant expense of renovating a turn of the century property. It was a stunning house and the location was beautiful. A tree-lined middle-class suburb, it suited our lifestyle well, but there was something missing. It was children. The house was meant for children. The sound of children laughing and running around was needed in that kind of house. Maria and I were like two lost souls wandering around in such a big house.

My longing for children had never waned and I now saw that this was something I would be giving up forever. As a gay guy I would never come to father a child. I would never get to hold my child in my arms for that first time and tenderly kiss its cheek. I would never get to organise the first birthday party in the dining room next door or call my parents to tell them about the first step, the first tooth or the first word. I felt a pain like no other. Why had I not realised this before? Choosing to be gay was not simply about losing Maria, it was also going to be about losing my entitlement to fatherhood. Was I stupid not to have seen this? I knew gay guys could adopt but for me it was not the same. I wanted to see a little version of me. I wanted a child that was made *by* me. And even if I did adopt, was the world really ready for true acceptance or was I being selfish and bringing a child into a difficult situation just to satisfy my own wants and needs? My heart felt so heavy sat inside my chest. My blood ran cold through my body and my stomach wrenched. Running quickly to the kitchen I vomited into the sink before the tears and wailing commenced once more. I was devastated. With every fading thought of being a dad came another wave of nausea and wretching. Coughing uncontrollably, Jackson had now wandered into the kitchen to see what the latest drama was. I was sure I sensed sympathy in his eyes. A fifteen-year bond between us; maybe he felt my pain as he brushed his soft fur against the back of my legs. It was comforting and calming. I took a sip of water and slowly walked into the living room.

I needed to gain my strength if I was to have any chance of meeting with Maria the following day. This strength came from the acceptance of others. With Nathan out of the picture and Adela on hold, I knew without doubt that my Aunt Jess would give me what I needed since we had always been so incredibly close. I respected and admired her so much, maybe on account of her own difficult life. Yet without doubt she could be there for another person in need without fail at any time. She was incredibly wise and liberal and had the most diverse group of friends and acquaintances. She was a real life Good Samaritan. I picked up the phone praying for a more successful conversation than the last one with Adela.

'Hey Jack. How are you? I was just talking about you to Sam. How are you doing?'

'Not so good to be honest. Maria and I are over.' I was surprised with the ease at which these words came out. I think it was the way that Jess made you feel. She never expressed any tone of judgement in her voice. Very little would shock her.

'Can you work this out?' she softly asked.

'Ummm, not really. There is a reason why we can't.' My voice broke a little on the last word but I managed to hold it together.

'Oh, have you found someone else?'

'No,' I responded gently.

'Are you gay Jack?' It was so unexpected and yet so needed. Having someone else say those words was much easier and I responded with a simple yes. I waited to hear the words I longed for.

'Hey, it's okay Jack. I don't care what you are. I'm not surprised in some ways, but I never suspected it. I love you so much and you know that. It makes no difference to me at all. I just want to see you happy.' It was the ray of light I knew it would be. Jess never failed to give those in need some comfort.

'I'm just worried about my mum. She doesn't seem to be fully accepting it,' I said.

'Jack. You mean the world to your mam and nothing will change that. Just give her a little time. She loves you so much, as do all of us.'

For twenty minutes my aunty talked and listened, reassured and supported. Her sympathetic ear enabled me to feel at ease and so all my barriers came down. I felt able to tell her about Ryan, someone I had failed to mention to my parents. Again, she showed no judgement and was in fact a little happy to know that someone was holding my heart.

'What about Uncle Sam? I can't face telling anyone else. Not yet,' I added nervously.

'Oh you leave Sam to me Jack. You have nothing to worry about there. He loves you too.'

Jess was clearly an ally and someone I would come to depend on over the next few months. No doubt my mother would also turn to Jess for support and I could rely on her to help my mother come to terms with the changes ahead. With my spirit intact I took to my bed and prepared for my big day ahead with Maria.

CHAPTER TWENTY-TWO

I think I slept for no more than thirty minutes. I rehearsed every possible way to tell Maria the truth behind my recent change in behaviour. The truth about who and what I really was. I imagined every possible reaction from her. Anger, shock, disgust, disbelief. I could not really begin to predict the outcome. I had never shown any signs of being gay, musical taste and sense of fashion aside! I knew she would be shocked for certain but how her emotions would play out I had no idea. And what about her mother? Oh God I had not even thought about *her* reaction. This was her daughter whose heart I was about to break. She would be angry for sure. For now I needed to focus on Maria only. Unable to eat a morsel of food I decided to head over to Maria's mother's house a little early. Ryan had called to wish me luck and although I appreciated the effort I could not help but sense glee in his voice. Sometimes I wondered if he appreciated the utter devastation we were about to unleash on others. Or was this just a competition for him, for which he was now the crowned winner? Deep down I knew this was not true; it was just the tactless timing of his phone call. I did not need any distractions now. This was all about Maria and I. No one else.

I saw the blinds twitch as I pulled up. I had been visiting this street for thirteen years now so I knew many of the neighbours. Byron, the next-door neighbour, was the first to greet me and, unaware of the latest events, he thought nothing of keeping me talking for over five minutes about the importance of the correct size spanner for a job. I was not remotely interested but avoided the temptation to be rude. He was a lonely man who had no children and few visitors. The blinds twitched a little more and it was then I realised Maria's anguish in waiting to see me and so I made a polite exit from the elderly neighbour.

Coyly, she opened the door and I was shocked by her appearance. She looked bloody awful and I was responsible. Clearly she had been equally deprived of sleep. Her hazel eyes that normally sparkled whenever she saw me were now sunken and unresponsive. Dark circles outlined their location. Her skin was red and blotchy, clearly the result of many hours of crying. This was before I had even broken the news. I panicked slightly and took a small step backwards. I longed to get back in my car and drive off and never face the situation, but I knew this was it and this was not my option to take. I at least owed her the truth. To see her so emotionally drained was heartbreaking. Whatever my unhappiness had been over the years I had always made it my mission to make her happy and to protect her. I was unable to do that and in fact I was the root of the problem. That was soul destroying for any husband.

'Come in Jack. You have a key anyway. Why didn't you use it?' Maria spoke so softly without even looking at me. Did I disgust her that much?

'Sorry, it just didn't seem appropriate this time. Where is your mum anyway?' I enquired nervously.

'Don't worry – she's out with the dog. Lucky for you because right now she probably wants to kill you.' Maria broke out into a small giggle at this point. She knew I would be worried about what her mother thought and so could not resist teasing me.

'Do you want a cuppa?' she asked.

'Oh God. Don't you start with the tea making. My mother drove me insane with this yesterday.'

'So *they* know about us then?' Maria replied with a sting of sarcasm. Maria had always found it difficult to form a relationship with my parents and always seemed to feel they would blame her for any problems. She sat on the couch opposite and I sat in the single chair overlooking the street. The atmosphere was tense and it felt like we were two strangers waiting in the doctors' surgery. I sat there fiddling with my wedding ring which seemed to be growing increasingly tight! I hadn't noticed that Maria was now whimpering and as the first tear struck the floor I felt frozen to my seat. My wife was sitting opposite me crying and yet I could not move. I felt paralysed and helpless. I was unable to offer a shoulder to cry on or any words that could be remotely comforting.

'Just tell me Jack! What's going on?' Maria sobbed. Again, frozen. My mind was empty. I did not know how to start the sentence. I was blank. I grew increasingly restless and my feet began twitching too. A single tear rolled down my cheek. Maria could never bear to see me crying and immediately she jumped up from her seat and came and sat at my feet and hugged my leg. For the first time ever, it was not comforting. I did not want the physical contact. It would make saying the words so much more difficult. She gently rubbed my knee and looked up at me. There was a pleading look in her eyes. The girl was in agony and longing to hear my explanation. My heart was pounding and my mouth was so dry. A few more tears fell though, silently. I was not sobbing but the sadness and fear I felt was greater than ever. My palms began to sweat and I felt light-headed. I knew I could not prolong this for much longer. I dug deeper than ever and whispered the words I knew would change Maria's world forever.

'I... I... I'm, um... I... I... think I'm gay!' The last and most significant word was just about recognisable. I was now crying louder and harder than ever before. With the release of words came the final explosion of the pressure balloon. A magical sense of relief sprinted through my entire body and my head cleared instantly. I had finally said the sentence that had haunted me for decades. I had not yet looked at Maria but I still could feel her arms wrapped around my legs.

'It's okay Jack. It's okay.' Looking down at her she was smiling, although the tears were racing down her flushed face. I wondered if she had misheard me or if she was in denial. What did she mean, '*It's okay*'? How could it be okay? It was anything but bloody okay.

'I think I'm gay Maria!' I thought I should try repeating myself just to make sure she was clear.

'Yes I heard you Jack. I thought you were going to tell me you had met another woman,' she smiled. This was not the reaction I had even contemplated. She actually seemed relieved that I was gay and had not been having an affair with another woman.

'But it would be better if I had Maria. At least there would be a way back. Being gay means there is no return for us.' This hurt me even though I was saying the words, yet Maria looked untouched. There was something bizarre going on and although it was certainly less traumatic than a screaming match, it was hauntingly unnerving. Of course what I had failed to detect was the hope in the sentence I had given to Maria, ' I *think* I am gay.' Fuck! Had I not learnt my lesson from my conversation with my parents? However, it was making this so much easier to cope with and so, like a coward, I went with it.

'We can still work this out. I read about a couple where the husband thought he was gay and they had counselling and are still together now!' The light in her eyes was back a little and she was more animated. I thought about telling her about Ryan, but knew that would crush her. She had had enough trauma for one day; she just didn't realise it yet. Whatever was going on in her head, her reaction was so loving and supportive. She did not judge me or overly question me. She demonstrated how deep her love for me was. She was ready to forgive me and accept me whatever I was and whatever my secret thoughts about men were. Her heart was pure, her motive sincere, but her sense of reality was fractured. She was running scared and desperate for any way of holding on to me. It all made sense to her now. My recent moods, bad behaviour and sudden outbursts and it was not her fault. She could now see this and instead of blaming herself for her failings and losing me to another woman, this was just about me and therefore she could help me just like she always had. If only it would have been that simple. If only Maria could help me. Help us. At least then she would not have had to suffer the incredible pain that was waiting for both of us in the coming months. But for now, her intentions were comforting.

CHAPTER TWENTY-THREE

The day had seemed endless and had certainly taken its toll on me. Returning to the house alone a second time was no easier. I had been driving around aimlessly for hours in an attempt to avoid the need to go back to the soulless house that had now become my bachelor pad. I had stopped by at my parents' home to explain how things with Maria had unfolded. More tears. More questions. It was not something I could face today and my father could sense this.

'Why don't you go home and relax son and stop over-thinking things for a few hours. You look bloody shattered.' I was so grateful to my father for offering this escape route as my mother's questioning was beginning to intensify.

The surprise at not seeing Maria standing there waiting was no less painful. Ryan had asked me to stay over but I had told him I needed to be alone, just for one more night. I was incapable of thinking about anyone else right now. I knew this was difficult for him too and how he longed for a hug of reassurance, but how I was feeling was tenfold more painful and no amount of hugging was going to heal my wounds tonight. There was no denying the impact the change of atmosphere was having on my feline friend. Jackson had barely touched his food for two days now. Maria was always more attentive towards him. I tried to be a good substitute. As I gently stroked the back of his neck his claws softly scraped along my left arm – a sign of his affection and appreciation. It seemed pointless cooking for one, so I simply lay down on the sofa and wrapped myself tightly in the chenille blanket. The scent of Maria was comforting and my eyes slowly closed as I drifted off into a far more peaceful place.

The sound of the neighbour's dog opposite startled me around five a.m. My neck was incredibly stiff on account of sleeping on the four-foot couch, though I was grateful for the amount of sleep I had been granted. The cat was pacing around and in desperate need of his night-time prowl. Walking to the master bedroom I felt an overwhelming sense of loss. It was strange to me as I was the driving force in this relationship break-up, but nonetheless I had never been a single adult. Maria and I had dated since teenagers so this was new territory for me. The lush white linen in the master bedroom looked so enticing yet it felt somewhat inappropriate to sleep in our marital bed. I sat on the end of the bed and hugged the single velvet cushion. A longing to see Maria crept inside me and remorse was suddenly choking me. I missed the way she had always looked out for me, had always hugged me when I appeared troubled and had always been my biggest supporter. Now she could not fulfill this role. That hurt. But this was what I wanted so why was I now at war once more? Was it just seeing Maria that had made it more difficult? Yes, that was it. I needed some space. Space to come to terms with my emotions.

I called Ryan and asked him to book some time off work. I still had some of the Easter holidays remaining, which made the idea of a spontaneous trip possible, and Ryan was more than keen to get away. Destination – Cyprus! Departure date – tomorrow! I sent two simple text messages. One to my parents telling them not to worry and one to Maria explaining that I was taking a break with my friend. My parents reply – supportive. Maria's response – seriously pissed! She talked of how selfish I was being at a time when our marriage was in crisis and how my behaviour was totally uncharacteristic of me. A thirty-minute conversation later and she was calm. She could now understand my need to get away and agreed that she probably needed the space too.

'Hey Jack, whilst you are away though I want you to do one thing for me. I want you to join this forum for gay married guys. I have joined the group for wives.'

'Are you frigging serious Maria? A forum!' I angrily snapped back. It had been challenging enough discussing my inner most feelings with my loved ones over the last few days and the thought of doing this on some weirdo forum was seriously aggravating.

'Jack. This is the least you can do. Go find yourself in Cyprus or whatever it is you plan on doing, but at least look at this forum. Don't you think you owe me that?'

Maria was right. I had just ripped this girl's heart out of her chest and then trampled all over it. Looking at the website was a small penance to pay. Needless to say, I was not going to do this whilst on a romantic getaway with Ryan. That was hardly going to make him feel secure knowing that I was looking at ways to 'cure' gay husbands. I would look at the site that evening after packing.

As I packed the last pair of swim shorts I giggled to myself, realising that this had been the single most spontaneous thing I had ever done. I was Mr Scheduled, Mr Planned. I had been writing 'to do' lists and timetables for myself ever since I was ten years old. Allowing myself ten minutes to eat breakfast and two minutes to brush my teeth, everything was to precision. My mother would often joke about the perfect timing of my every arrival. If I said I was coming at one o'clock, then one o'clock I would be there! My grandfather joked with me about my 'windows of time' and how everyone was timetabled a fixed amount of time. There was some truth in it although it was never a conscious thing. I think the job had made me that way. My working day was timetabled to the last minute and so on weekends and holidays it was difficult to break the mould. Since I had been doing this as a child I guess I was predisposed to this kind of lifestyle! Well Mr Planned was making way for Mr Unexpected and it felt fucking great! For the first time in my life I was doing what *I* wanted, when *I* wanted and with whom *I* wanted and fuck everyone else. Constantly worried about the feelings and comments of others I had surrounded myself with pressure. Now I was basking in being a selfish git. A couple of boxes of condoms and the packing was complete. I was incredibly excited and just thinking about the endless nights of passionate sex made me seriously horny. The master of filing away feelings and thoughts, I had clearly popped Maria into the deepest folds of my mind.

The doorbell rang and I prayed it was not Maria planning an outburst on the doorstep in an attempt to halt my trip. Hesitantly, I opened the door, which was a little swollen on account of the heavy rainfall over the last few days. Thankfully it was Adela, looking a little teary eyed.

'Hey what's up sis?'

'Oh Jack, Mum told me about you and Maria. I should have been there for you. I am so sorry.' I knew my family gossiped so I should not have been surprised that Adela had been told and part of me was relieved that I did not actually have to say the words yet again. I was just pleased to finally see my sister and bathe in her support. Jackson had brightened up too and was delighted to be receiving the attention of another. Adela was not so keen on his advances and so after just fifteen minutes Jackson was being pushed out into the now overgrown garden. Briefly I considered mowing the lawn before the great expedition but the thought slowly evaporated as the kettle finished boiling. Adela was my favourite air-head and it took only moments for one of her stories to ease the atmosphere and make me laugh hysterically. She was telling me about how the radiator had fallen off the wall at work and she had been left fighting the water screaming for help. Picturing my sister completely drenched, make-up running and her hair slapped to her face was hysterical. She was so self-conscious about her appearance that for her this would have been traumatic. Luckily for her she was dating a plumber and so the only one who needed to see her wet T-shirt entry was him. Oh and one or two of the partners at the company where she worked!

'So Jack, what's happened then? Why the break-up all of a sudden?' It was then I realised my mother had only told Adela part of the story and there was no escaping the need to complete the story now. Pushing the cinema story aside, I knew deep down that Adela had no issues with gays. When her best friend's boyfriend had revealed the same secret last year, my sister had been very supportive, not only of her friend but also of Brandon, the gay boyfriend.

'Jack, it's okay. I think I know already,' Adela said softly as she gently grabbed my arm.

'Did Mum tell you?' I questioned.

'No. Just something Karl said last night made me think. He was always convinced you were gay!' I was a little distracted by her last sentence. I had always thought I acted pretty straight, so the thought that her boyfriend

Karl had 'detected' my gayness was a little troubling. 'Jack, I don't care. I just really want you to be happy and you haven't looked happy for a long time.' Her tenderness was so soothing and for the first time I did not cry. I was not quite ready to tell her about Ryan, but took great pleasure in recalling her tactless story of the two guys at the cinema and how her timing had been impeccable. We both laughed at this before Adela was on her way. I felt a great sense of inner confidence now knowing that those I cared most about were aware of who I was and were accepting of it. Of course, I had not told my grandfather yet but it was going to take a hell of a lot more confidence before that conversation was going to happen. Bags packed, it was time to focus on the adventure ahead. I completely forgot my promise to Maria about a certain forum!

The journey to the airport in London had been so much fun. Roof down, music up loud. We sang along to the upbeat tracks and Ryan made me giggle at his endless impressions of famous musicians. Memories of my recent 'outing' were distant and fun was the name of this game. The flight had given us time to plan our trip which would be centred around sunbathing, drinking and sex! Ryan did not try to deny the emphasis on the sex part, which made me blush yet feel desirable. I wondered how it would feel to make love to Ryan in a guilt-free zone. There was no deceit now. There was no need for hasty exits or random excuses to be able to meet. Would it be any less exciting I wondered? Would Ryan lose interest now the chase was over? As he leant in to give a sly peck on my cheek as we landed I figured he had quickly addressed my concerns.

The holiday home was far from luxurious and clearly the Internet was prone to exaggeration! The twin beds were not sexy and the off-white linen was not inviting. Classically

Mediterranean in design, the white tiled floor leading out onto the terracotta terrace was quaint. I am not sure if the manager of the complex had even finished showing us around the place before Ryan and I were stripped and in the hot shower. It felt so good touching his chest that was lightly dappled with blond hair. It had been a while since we had been intimate, but my excitement levels had not faded. Ryan grabbed my buttocks firmly and kissed me deep and passionately. His cock felt so hard pressed against my abdomen. I felt each pulsation which was growing in intensity. He bit the lobes of my ears and licked my neck which excited me immensely. His passion was incredible and his attention to detail most satisfying. Unaware of the small open window which overlooked the pool area, my moaning intensified. With every push inside him I felt waves of ecstasy swimming through my bloodstream. The heat from the shower mixed with the warmth of the Mediterranean evening air outside was overwhelming. The sweat was pouring from us both but this only amplified the passion until my final groans and spasms signalled my hunger had been fed. Pushing me to my knees, Ryan forced his cock into my mouth and screamed out as the sexual frustration he had been experiencing during my absence over the last few days had finally ended. It was only in that post-coital moment that I realised that Ryan and I had just had unprotected, bareback sex. Although a wave of panic washed over me I felt a sense of glee. Was this another level of trust or just another level of stupidity I had reached? We slowly washed each other's bodies, enjoying the opportunity to fully explore every part without the need for haste. Time was no longer our enemy and the chance to hug, to kiss and to gently hold each other took us to a new place. Too often the passionate embraces had been massacred by sudden departures. Ryan tenderly caressed my face as we lay down on the bed and drifted off into a deep sleep. He held me tightly, like a mother and her newborn child.

The five-day trip was a whirlwind. I felt energised and fearless. No one could hurt me now and I was afraid of nothing. My family had accepted my revelation and the wife was out of the way. Things with Ryan were strengthening each day. I had only previously experienced a sexual relationship with a guy and so experiencing the whole package was something quite special. I did not care about the glances the straight couples gave us in the restaurants or the jibes the rugby lads shouted over at us on the way home from drinking. I was feeling invincible and with Ryan at my side I did not give a shit what the world thought of us, including the elderly couple in the apartment next door who had no doubt heard my screams and groans! I was sticking two fingers up at the world. I could not have asked for a better character than Ryan to share this moment with. He made me laugh constantly with his antics.

Life was about fun with Ryan. From almost drowning in the sea due to the enormous waves, to the crazy nights of binge drinking, it was all about seizing the moment and seizing it with a smile. He even managed to get me skipping arm in arm down the main street after one too many shots on the final night. It was an incredible finale to an incredible day. We had been entertained on the beach most of the day by the sight of a lesbian couple making out in what they thought was a hidden location. Both rather large, and sporting equally gargantuan breasts, the couple had distracted us from the intense Cypriot heat, resulting in rather unsexy panda eyes and flamboyantly red arms.

We certainly attracted a lot of attention that evening on account of our crimson glow. It did make the sex a little painful later that evening, but we were so horny from the alcohol and constant sly groping of each other that this discomfort was not going to stop us.

Falling back onto the soft pillows we drifted off to sleep. Ryan turned towards me and effortlessly whispered into my ear, 'I love you Jack!'

CHAPTER TWENTY-FOUR

The return to reality was a bit of a shock as I pulled up outside the house to find Maria's car parked there. The personal space that I had been temporarily granted was now once again being invaded. I had been so naïve to think a thirteen-year relationship was ever going to end so easily. Hesitantly turning the key in the lock, I could hear Maria's movements upstairs. Jackson was sitting on the top step looking smugly at me. He clearly favoured Maria and I suspected in my absence that she had been overindulging him in treats in an attempt to win back his love!

'Jack? Is that you?'

'Yes!' I snapped angrily. I resented her being here. I said I needed space. Was my trip to Cyprus the sum total of my entitlement? The drive from London had been tiring and sleep had not exactly been a top priority during the short break. I was feeling irritable and impatient, not the best combination when dealing with your broken-hearted wife.

'What's with the attitude Jack? You're not the one who has just found out your husband is gay and has run away to be with his gay lover!'

'What the fuck? Maria why are you even here right now. I said I needed space!' I retorted angrily.

'Well loads of the women on the forum say it is very common. I have described your behaviour and they say there are classic signs that...'

'Like what?' I interrupted.

'Well the secret texting, the sudden revelation, the running away to Cyprus with a friend *I* don't even know and then the fancy new underwear you have been buying.' The last of that list made me laugh out loud, but I guess there was some truth in that even if those recent purchases had subconsciously been about being gay.

'I have been searching through all your computer files and emails. You have been chatting to guys and viewing gay porn sites for quite some time Jack.' Maria almost looked smug, like a newly appointed detective who had just solved her first homicide. The smugness had distracted me from noticing the lack of emotion or upset in her voice or on her face. I suspected she was in survival mode and trying to remove herself from the situation.

'Some of the pictures on your computer are pretty disgusting too, Jack. No wonder you have been struggling to accept your new-found orientation.' Maria was now being strangely supportive, although totally misguided as those photos that disgusted her were what defined my orientation. 'And what did you think of the forum for the gay husbands Jack?' Not wishing to partake in any more lies I replied honestly.

'No idea – I have not had a chance to look.'

'Yeah I figured. So I have registered on your behalf. The home page is on your PC now and your log in details are on a Post-It next to it,' replied Maria as she grabbed her pink pashmina and car keys. She was acting incredibly strong and a woman clearly in control. It was kind of sexy (maybe in a different context). As she reached the lounge door she turned and firmly said, 'I'm moving back in on Sunday Jack. You have four days to work out in your head what you want, but either way I am moving back in. This is my house and my things are here. I have to go back to school on Monday and I want to be around my own things when I do. If you don't like that then you can move out!'

There was no time for any response. She was gone. I had not considered the need to move out. I assumed I would remain in the house. And shit – what about work? There was no way I was ready to return to work and tell my friends and colleagues. I would call my boss later and explain I was taking some time off due to personal circumstances. For now I was in need of sleep and plenty of it!

Five hours later I woke up. The light from the neighbour's car turning in the road startled me. The sun had said its goodbyes and handed over to the moon for the night shift. Slowly rising from the bed I stood up to close the blinds. My sexy Scottish neighbour looked up from the street and gave what appeared to be a sympathetic wave and so I assumed Maria had explained the current situation. I only hoped she had not told the whole story otherwise my enthusiastic wave back could be misinterpreted for a schoolboy crush! The street was so silent. Most of the houses were occupied by elderly couples or couples with young children. The street formed a natural timeline telling the story of its aging residents. There was no place here for a gay. This was middle-class family life at its best and I no longer fitted the mould. I imagined the look of disgust from Mr and Mrs Griffiths in the house opposite when catching a glance of me moving my gay lover in or the gossiping between the residents of number 47 and number 49 after being kept awake by my endless nights of hot passionate sex with countless hunky fuck-buddies. My imagination made me giggle but deep down I knew there was some truth to this. I was not ready to move in with Ryan and the constant questioning from my parents was unappealing. I would call Aunt Jess later and ask if it was possible to stay there. I had not seen Uncle Sam since he had been told, but Jess's last text assured me that he was totally cool with it and just looking forward to seeing me.

Second cup of coffee and feeling like a hobo wandering from room to room I ended my travels in the study. I was feeling a little horny and contemplated a little wander around some slutty sex sites. My growing erection was soon knocked down by the totally unsexy home page that appeared as the computer came out of its slumber. 'Gay Married Men' was the title and there were well over three thousand members, two hundred of which were currently online. The top five articles made for an interesting read. Some talked of the power of the Church in helping them to 'see the light' – delete! Others referred to therapy treatments proven to 'cure' men like us – delete! Had these people written these articles in the nineteenth century, for Christ sake? And what the hell was Maria thinking encouraging me to read such trash? Did she believe I was sick or lost and could be saved?

My growing anger resulted in the coffee mug being flung across the room and smashing into a million shards on the yet-to-be-varnished wooden floor below. Was she fucking desperate? Yes, of course she was. This girl had loved me for thirteen years. She had invested so much time, trust and belief in me. I was the man she had chosen to spend her life with. I was her provider, her supporter, her friend, her soul mate. So of course she was desperate and this realisation struck me hard in the chest. How incredibly admirable this women was. Not once had she passed judgement on me. Not once had she intensely questioned me in the quest for finding out some undiscovered truths. She had never made this about her but only helped me to find my way.

How could I not still love her for this? Lesser women have thrown their men out for smaller crimes. Of course Maria did not know the whole truth and I wondered where her threshold would lie then. There was also no denying that her actions were not totally selfless, even if she did not realise this. Maria had now turned thirty-one and no woman wants to find herself facing divorce at this age and being catapulted back into the world of singletons. She was probably incredibly fearful of a life of loneliness and unhappiness, should she lose me, and so who could blame her for fighting back strategically?

Scanning over countless profiles, it did not take long to identify the common identity they all shared. They were all in their late forties or fifties and had children. Chatting to a few of them online I could understand the reasons for the choices they had made. They had grown up in a world different to mine, even though only one or two decades separated us. 'Coming out' was not even a possibility for some of these guys. Marriage was all they knew. Some of them were still in denial, some were secretively living double lives, others had been totally honest with their wives and together they had faced the challenges ahead. Albert had been one of those guys. He was seventy-five and I was impressed he had mastered modern technology. We talked for hours and his story fascinated me, although the speed at which he typed was a little trying! Albert had been married for fifty years to his wife Rose. Before they had even married he had told her about his feelings for men. He explained how she had never judged him and her support had never failed. They had knowingly chosen to enter into marriage and to raise three children, totally aware of Albert's true sexual identity.

When I asked Albert if he had ever strayed and been unfaithful his reply was quick and honest, *Just the one time, and I regretted it every day after it happened.* Albert explained that he had been totally honest with Rose and again she had passed no judgement on him. I sat in the study staring at the freshly painted walls wondering if Rose was a fool in love or was she like Maria, a true angel?

Albert, you are a lucky guy to have someone like Rose. As I typed to Albert on the forum a warm fuzzy feeling filled me inside, giving me some hope that it was indeed possible to continue in my marriage.

Jack, Rose died 10 years ago. My heart stopped and my attention was all on that six-word response. I did not even know Albert but I felt such sadness and yet I did not understand why. I guess I felt they were a loving couple giving me a sense of hope. But now Albert was all alone. The one person who had guided him through his life battle with his sexuality was gone and now he explained he was too old to engage in anything with a guy. He just simply enjoyed the company of other men and tried to help those in similar situations on the forum. I found myself feeling comfortable enough to share my story with Albert, knowing he would empathise. I was surprised by his response: *Jack, I totally understand your feelings about Maria and I know your intentions have only ever been good but you have something that I did not – choice. As much as I loved Rose, I know that I was not the husband she deserved, not because I chose not to be but because I was incapable of it. I was moody and miserable even though I had a loving wife and family. This was because I was not being honest and true to myself. Don't make the same mistake as me Jack. It wouldn't be fair on you or Maria.* It was not the response I had expected to hear from a guy who had stayed married for over fifty years but I understood what he was talking about. Maria and I did not have children to consider, we were not in our fifties and we were not living in the 1930s.

Deciding I had revealed enough of myself for one night I prepared to log out of the forum until unexpectedly a message appeared in my inbox. The message was Torn212 and his profile pic revealed a young, rather sexy looking guy. We exchanged stories and tried to offer each other advice. Karl, (aka Torn212), was married to a woman and had one young child. His wife knew nothing about his extra-curricular activities with guys that had been taking place ever since they got together. Karl was so fearful of losing his loved ones that he had succumbed to society's expectation to marry and have children, but his soul was weak, (and his libido high), and so he sought sexual thrills with men on a regular basis. Karl described himself as a sexual deviant. In order to achieve sexual satisfaction he continually pushed the barriers. He often cruised around known gay haunts late at night, picking up random guys for sex in parks, the back of his car or at cheap hotels. His needs were growing and the frequency of these much-needed encounters was increasing. The risks he took were greater and his overall well-being and mental stability seemed to be declining. For the first time in a while I found *myself* giving support to others. It was a welcome relief to my own heartbreak and I really felt for Karl. I sensed he was a good person caught up in a tragic situation. I could not have expected his story to become even more complex.

I had been talking to Karl for two days and I think he found it easier to open up to someone of a similar age. No disrespect, but the majority of the guys were in the depths of middle age. It was easier to disassociate yourself from that group when you could see yourself as different. Karl and I could see similarities between ourselves and that made opening up easier. What Karl told me next made my world stop dead. A bolt of shock struck me so hard that I froze to the chair and was literally unable to respond for what seemed like a lifetime. Whilst out one night in a local park, Karl had hooked up with a young lad wearing sports gear and a hoodie. Karl was in desperate need of a release and so without hesitation he took the guy behind one of the deserted power supply buildings and allowed the young man to fuck him. The encounter was brief and rough. There was no intimacy, no foreplay. As the guy came inside Karl, he pulled out suddenly and rammed Karl's head into the brick-walled building. Karl had difficulty recalling the exact events because of the initial blow to the head but he remembered the anger in the thug's voice as he proceeded to kick Karl hard in the abdomen and chest. With each blow he shouted words of insult such as faggot, queer and shirt lifter until Karl finally passed out. The following morning Karl was found by the park keeper and taken to hospital.

His wife was beside herself with worry. Karl made up some elaborate tale of how he had been mugged and dragged into the park, but he refused to talk to the police. His wife was unaware that this area was a notorious homosexual hotspot. Karl had sworn to himself that that was the last of such meets. He had been scared well and truly and now wanted to focus on his wife. Sadly, three months later Karl had discovered something that changed his plan. Karl had tested positive for HIV. There was a lengthy pause after Karl revealed this secret. I suspected he was reliving the moment and was clearly emotional. My breath taken away, I could not respond. What words could possibly offer any comfort? I recalled my own stupidity in Cyprus where Ryan and I had enjoyed unprotected pleasure. I selfishly focused on myself now and panicked that I too was possibly in the same boat as Karl, out at sea without a paddle between us.

Karl's message alert startled me and brought me back to his needs. Karl was coping well and was now clear on what he was going to do. The forum had made him come to this realisation. He planned to leave his wife, who knew nothing of the HIV, this week and start a new life with Steve, a long-term fuck-buddy. They had been intimate for many years and now both of them were joined by a common identity: they were both HIV positive. I felt a glimmer of hope for Karl. I was sure it was not how he would have planned his life but at least now he had a sense of direction. Emotionally drained, I promised to speak with Karl in the morning.

Eight a.m. I sprung out of bed. For the first time since the break-up I had slept in the master bedroom. I think Karl's emotional rollercoaster of a story had diverted me from my own pain and the location of my night's rest was no longer a consideration. The master bedroom was *so* Maria. Clearly designed to her taste, it served as a painful reminder of her absence. The elaborate aqua green Laura Ashley wallpaper on the main wall had created a warm and homely feel. The cream sheep-skin rug felt good under my feet as I stepped onto the colder stained wooden planks. The mirrored wardrobes highlighted the tiredness on my face. Dark rings circled my eyes and my blotchy, dry skin was the result of countless hours of crying. I was so keen to talk with Karl so I booted up my PC and went to make a much-needed coffee. Returning to the study I noticed how the house was looking in desperate need of a clean. I could not face it that day and since I was about to be evicted in the next day or two I figured it was pointless.

Clearly familiar with this forum now, it was not difficult to remember my log in details. I was really hoping to see Karl online but there was no sign. One unread message sat in my inbox. It was from Karl!

Jack, I'm sorry to tell you in this way but last night I planned to tell Jane that I was leaving. Before I could even start she told me how she is 12 weeks pregnant. I am devastated. I can't go on like this. My wife and unborn child are probably HIV positive thanks to me and I can't live with that. I can't sit back and watch their health decline over the years. I hate myself so much. I am such a bad person. When you read this in the morning Jack it will all be over. Don't make the mistakes I did. Make the right choice now x

I re-read the message several times. I did not understand or I refused to accept its meaning. I did not know this guy but his story had touched me so much. I felt my sympathetic ear had provided the support he longed for but now I was helpless. I felt sick to the pit of my stomach. What had Karl done to 'end this'? Tears streaming, I frantically sent multiple messages to his inbox but by the end of the day they all remained unread. I felt anger for his selfish behaviour. He was a coward. I punched the wooden cabinet in front of me and screamed out. Why was I concerned about the behaviour of a stranger? The reason: I could see my own destiny. Choosing a life with Maria would result in similar circumstances and I could not allow this. I was not angry with Karl, I really felt for him. I was angry with the world, with God even, for putting us in these situations and leaving us to fend for ourselves. I never did hear from Karl again. I guess that I knew I'd never know how things ended for him or his family, but what I knew for sure was that *that* forum was not going to give me the answers I was searching for.

CHAPTER TWENTY-FIVE

A number of weeks had passed since I had first tried to confide in my friend Nathan. Apparently too busy to support me at the time, he had now finally decided to make an appearance. Maybe the fact that Maria had moved out was the cue he needed to show some loyalty or maybe the guilt of his abandonment was now too much to bear. Whatever the reason, I was just glad to see him. I noticed he was thinner than the last time we had met or possibly I was just feeling bitter and looking for flaws to identify. There was definitely no questioning the thinning hair. His eyes were as large and puppy-like as I previously remembered though they appeared less friendly than before.

The visit was short and strained. It did not provide any comfort or help me to find any answers. Nathan clearly resented having to give the time to me and continually looked at his watch. We did not really mention the 'G' word. We spoke in some kind of code, avoiding any direct reference to me being homosexual.

He sternly told me to focus on my wife and to, 'Stop this crazy nonsense!' For a moment I was not sure if I was talking to one of my closest friends or if I was being reprimanded by a head teacher. Possibly my personal situation was too close for comfort for Nathan. Maybe he saw the demise of his own relationship if he continued to dabble in all things gay! He was portraying the image now of a young man who had, in his younger days, had a time of exploration, but had now matured and was being a responsible man and father. I wondered how many other men had gone through this transition period. If you look back through history there are many examples of periods of time, such as the Roman era, where men 'exploring' other men was deemed 'acceptable'. When these men reached a certain age they became responsible adults and fathers. I wonder how many were truly able to give up their sexual appetite for men? For me there was something missing, a flaw in my genetic code that prevented the transition out of this phase and into the phase where I become a responsible husband and father. Nathan seemed to be looking down on me as if I was still immature and refusing to move out of this exploratory period. He clearly lacked compassion and his insensitivity was only making me more frustrated.

As he took another look at his watch I could not help but sarcastically say, 'Somewhere else to be, Nath?'

He fidgeted in his chair a little and replied, 'It's just the baby will be having a bath at seven. I don't like to miss that.' I was not lucky enough to know what those moments felt like and so maybe I was being selfish, but I was certainly experiencing the feeling of neglect and rejection from my closest friend. Could he not just be here for *me,* just this one evening? My life as I had known it was changing beyond recognition and I was on this journey riding solo once more. I *needed* Nathan now. There would be endless bath times ahead surely.

'I wait weeks to see you Nath and you spare me forty minutes. My life is well and truly fucked up and you don't give a shit!' Nathan was clearly angered by my outburst. His cheeks were now a subtle shade of red and his body language was defensive.

'You just don't fucking get it do you Jack? I have a family and responsibilities and no one is gonna fuck that up for me!' Was this a warning for me? Whatever the intention of his response I knew that I had lost my friend. I deserved better and I did not need selfish shits like him in my life. The guy who had made me laugh and smile for so many years was now the same guy who caused only hurt.

'Well thanks for stopping by Nath. Duty done, now you can go back to your family and feel less guilty about how you have not been there for your friend as his life fell apart.' I was well aware that I was being a little melodramatic, but I hated this guy right now. He should have considered the possible consequences when he let me suck his cock back in the good old days! I felt my tears embarking on yet another journey, but I was not prepared to let Nathan see this so I walked out into the kitchen.

'I'm sorry Jack,' Nathan called out to me softly, before the door closed and he was gone. He was gone forever this time. I never heard from Nathan again. Years of friendship gone. Endless experiences together now only memories. To lose a friendship is difficult enough but to lose it when you need it most is devastating. To some extent I understood Nathan's actions. It was born out of fear only. He was a good guy who just acted selfishly for what he believed to be the good of his family. There is not a week that passes by that I do not still think about him and the hurt is no less now than five years ago. I am only grateful that many of my other friends were able to provide the loving, supportive environment that I desperately needed in order to make it through that traumatic time. I also hope, for Nathan's sake, that he was indeed able to focus on his family and did not simply replace me for another plaything!

At eight p.m. the doorbell rang again. If the visit from Nathan had been anything to go by then this would be no less dramatic. My other closest friend was next to make his appearance – Michael. Actually Father Michael. Yes my oldest and closest friend was now a Catholic priest and on two months leave from his posting in Rwanda. There was no denying he was a true friend but this was going to be a massive test of our friendship on more than one level. Michael was not only one of my closest friends but he was also Maria's. For sure Maria would have filled him in on everything so at least I would not have to say those words again.

Stepping into the hallway I had forgotten just how tall Michael was. It had been quite a few months since our last meeting, on account of his overseas posting in Rome. He gave me a sympathetic smile and then hugged me. This was always comical because of the significant difference in our height, but I welcomed the gesture with great relief. I had half wondered if he would sprinkle me with holy water in an attempt to rid me of my demons! Taking off his hat, scarf and trench coat he moved into the lounge. Many a night we had spent talking in this lounge, the three of us. We had challenged world politics, suggested improvements to the UK social security policies and even gone head to head on religious and moral issues, such as abortion and female priests. Michael was the single most intelligent person I had ever met and now he was wearing glasses full-time he looked even more so. He was fluent in many languages and there was not a single topic on which he did not have some knowledge or at least an opinion. He had dragged me through my A-level chemistry exam and provided constant support during my further studies. As he leant back in the chair and folded his arms I could not help but notice his expanding waistline. They were clearly looking after him, which was comforting to know as I always worried about him.

'*So* how are you?' Michael asked assertively, looking over the top of silver-rimmed glasses.

'Yeah I'm okay.'

'Liar!' replied Michael quickly. I was a little taken aback by this response, but it made me laugh and Michael joined in, only *my* laughter quickly turned to tears. Michael did not move from his seat. He just softly smiled and rested his chin upon his hands, joined together as if to begin a prayer session. Despite having once had a strong faith, now was not a good time for me and I would not welcome it. He had recently completed a course in psychology and I think he welcomed this opportunity to test out his counselling skills. It was sometimes difficult to tell if he was in friend or shrink mode.

'I don't understand why this is happening,' I sobbed.

'Sometimes God has a plan that even the best of us can't possibly understand or explain.' Michael gave a little half smile as he finished his sentence. I think he was testing my tolerance of bringing God into this.

'Did you ever think I was?' I asked.

'Was what? Why don't you ever use the word, Jack. You mean gay, right?'

'I don't feel comfortable saying it Michael. Especially with you,' I snapped back. 'Surely *you* think it is wrong?'

'It's not for me to judge. There is nothing in the Bible that says loving another guy is wrong. It only refers to the sexual act. And just like with you and Maria, I prefer not to think about those things,' sniggered Michael.

I welcomed his response. Here was a representative of a religious organisation that I believed despised people of the same sexual orientation as myself and yet he was still able to offer me a supporting hand. He had always been more liberal in his thinking. His sermons at mass were incredibly captivating. There had always been conflicts in my mind between the Church's line of thinking on various topics and the scientific or more 'modern' views. Michael was great at creating a degree of synthesis between the two schools of thought. Yes he recognised what was written in the Bible, but he also acknowledged that it was written a very long time ago and by people who did not know any difference in the absence of science.

'All I know is that God made *you* and God never makes mistakes and therefore if he made you this way then that was his intention and so how can it be wrong?' This was the most powerful response anyone had ever given and one that has formed my own acceptance of my homosexuality. With so many homosexuals, lesbians and bisexuals in the world, could God really have made so many mistakes? Of course if you do not believe in God then I guess this is not a valid argument, but if you do not believe in God then you probably do not give a shit anyway! For me, a former Catholic altar boy, a guy married in the eyes of God, this was important for me to hear at the time. A lot of my anger had been towards God in the early days and this helped to pacify me somewhat.

'But why would God let me go through all of this and hurt so many people if this had always been his intention?' I enquired.

'Jack we are not puppets. God gave us free will and we make our own choices. You may not have the choice about your sexuality, but you have the free will to make the choices around this.' I was fascinated by his answer. Normally any reference to *choice* would elicit dramatic outbursts from me as I felt I had done everything possible *not* to choose to be gay, but what Michael was saying actually made sense.

'So are you saying I have the choice to stay with Maria?'

'This is not about Maria now Jack. We are talking about *you!* You made the choice to marry Maria but I believe you were not 'able' to make that choice because of factors beyond your control. You didn't realise or accept that you were gay at the time and therefore it was not an informed choice. This is the basis of entering into a marriage.' Was Michael giving me a 'get out of marriage' card?

'So are you saying leaving Maria is okay?' I asked.

'No Jack. That is not for me to say. That is your choice to make. I am talking about your *ability* to have entered into this marriage and your *ability* to continue to be in it.' His body language was so characteristic of a shrink. One leg crossed over the other, hands folded inside each other and back upright but relaxed. The soft smile made him approachable. 'If you are to stay in this marriage not knowing or understanding your sexuality, are you *able* to make Maria *and* yourself happy? Are you *able* to raise a family within a loving relationship?' I pondered Michael's words, waiting for *his* answer but there was not one. The questions served only to stimulate my own thoughts.

We talked for a couple of hours about my sexuality, minus the deceit, and at times it was less than comfortable. I was not sure if I felt uncomfortable because he was so close to Maria or because he was a priest. His intentions were good and that was the main thing and it was certainly a refreshing change from how Nathan had handled things. His warm hug before he left was soothing and I took a deep sigh as if to signal that I had survived the interrogation.

'Michael, before you go. *Did* you ever suspect I was gay?'

'No Jack, never. My mother said she always knew. She was just waiting for you to realise in your own time.' He smiled and left, leaving me to wonder how his mother could have possibly known and yet my own wife and mother were clueless. Were they just too close to me to see or was his mother just trying to act smart? When I have told people over the years about my new-found sexuality you get two groups of people. The one group are totally shocked and say they never suspected a thing. The second group are more smug and say they always knew it, like it was some TV trivia question they knew the answer to. Well I wish bloody group two would have spoken up sooner and said something, because it may have saved a lot of heartache for a lot of people. Actually, I am not so sure this group do know anything more than group one. Yes they may see certain traits, behaviours, but nothing more and there are plenty of straight guys that display similar behaviour: the metrosexuals I believe they are called. It was irrelevant to the bigger picture and so I resisted the temptation to dwell on Michael's parting words.

CHAPTER TWENTY-SIX

Eviction day was upon me and I had failed to pack a single item or secure my new accommodation. I was avoiding the need to think about this and to make any decisions. Although I had been in regular contact with Ryan I had not actually seen him since Cyprus. He understood *this* was something I needed to go through alone and he just needed to sit tight. Unfortunately, it was not working out this way. With absence the heart was not growing fonder, it was simply filling up with uncertainty and confusion. Not seeing him made it easier to focus on Maria and the hurt I was imparting on her. I was not sure if I had the strength to see this through. My love for her was stronger than any feelings I had for Ryan, but I knew I could never be truly happy with her and I had already demonstrated my inability to make her happy. Surely things had gone too far now?

At midday, Maria arrived. I had hoped not to bump into her but my lack of organisation made the encounter inevitable or maybe it was subconsciously planned. She was looking less assertive than at our previous meeting. Wearing more casual clothes and glasses, she looked miserable. Her dark brown hair was pulled back into a ponytail. She clearly was not looking forward to having to face me. As we met in the hallway she burst into tears and my instant reaction was to hug her. I hated seeing her that way, especially when I was the cause. The hug was so tight and lasted so long. It was surprisingly comforting yet conflicting with my intentions. I felt her kiss my neck softly as her tears slid down her face and onto mine.

'Jack, please!'

'Shhhhhh,' I whispered. I felt her pain. I felt the weight of her heavy heart and it was killing me. Her skin was so incredibly soft and the smell was always so fresh. I had missed that feeling so much. I pulled away fearing that my strength was depleting. I sat on the edge of the brown leather sofa in the lounge and dropped my head into my sweating palms. I felt Maria wrap herself around my legs and squeeze me so tightly. Her dependency on me was clear and I saw how sunken her eyes were, as if I was draining the life out of her.

Kneeling up, she ran her hand up my chest and on to my face and held my left cheek softly as she looked deep into my eyes and pleaded, 'Please don't do this. I love you so much!' As she spoke these words I saw my life with Maria flash before my eyes. From the first kiss to the first night of sex. From our first date to our wedding day. I loved this woman so very much and would never want to intentionally see her hurting like this. I opened my legs slightly and moved her body closer to mine. Continuing to hold her close to my chest I whispered gently in her ear, 'I'm not going anywhere Maria!'

CHAPTER TWENTY-SEVEN

Pulling over at the small park at the top of my street I sat inside my car, staring vacantly at the rain falling outside. There were a few of my neighbours and their children, who had been caught out by the sudden April downpour, and were running for cover into the newsagents on the opposite side of the street. The deserted gardens now looked peaceful and tranquil – a stark contrast to what was going on in my head. I felt so alone, so confused. I knew I loved Maria but I knew about my sexual needs for men. Could I have both? No! I did not want a life full of deceit. Could I be strong enough to resist the physical contact with men and focus solely on my wife? Probably not, but I desperately wanted to try. I owed Maria that. I had made the excuse of needing to go and see my sister who lived close by so that I could go and call things off with Ryan. I was not looking forward to this and was not even sure if it was the *right* thing. I just knew it had to be done. When Ryan opened the door his face lit up as if the postman was delivering an unexpected parcel. This was one gift he definitely was not going to enjoy unwrapping. Ryan seemed to sense my mood and his expression changed rapidly. He was a little emotionally challenged on account of his tough upbringing and endless failed relationships and his mechanism for coping was to put up defensive walls. The walls were clearly rising as I followed him up the stairs and into his room. Ryan was sitting in the corner of the sofa, one leg cocked up, eyes fixated on the TV.

'So why don't you just say what you came to say,' snarled Ryan dismissively. He was clearly a very perceptive guy and had already prepared himself for this moment. I stood in the doorway unable to say it because I did not even know myself what it was I wanted to say.

'I just can't bear to hurt Maria like this. I wanna be with you but I just can't!' I broke down at this point and prayed that he would come and rescue me from my anguish. No such luck. Those barriers were up and locked and there was no way of penetrating them now.

'Fine. Just go then!' Ryan angrily snapped back. For a brief moment I wondered why I had even considered being with this cold and damaged twat, but as I glanced over to him for a second time I caught the sight of a single, solitary tear making its slow journey down his left cheek. There was no sound, no change in expression, just one bead of sadness. Ryan would not even look at me but instead chose to continue to look interested in the TV drama playing in the background. I am not sure what it was I was looking for Ryan to do or say. Maybe I just wanted him to fight for me. I remained fixed to the spot pulling at my fingernails, which was one of my less attractive traits when feeling nervous. My eyes travelled the whole length of Ryan's body as if it were my final look. I wanted to make sure that this memory was going to be as complete as possible. His short blond hair had been recently shaved which was always a turn on. He had such a neat little head and the short look framed his handsome face perfectly. The oversized jumper swamped his slim frame and I found myself wondering how I would cope with never seeing or touching his body again.

'Why can't you just fight for me?' I yelled out in desperation.

'Why should I?' he replied softly and calmly, with no movement and no expression. 'If you truly wanted to be with me then we would not be 'aving this conversation. I won't beg for anyone.'

I was a weak guy. My heart was being pulled towards whoever put up the best fight and Maria was clearly winning. My biggest weakness was my ability to deal with the hurt I may be causing to others. Maria's was unbearable to see but Ryan was making this easy with his lack of emotion. I knew I could no longer stay rooted in the doorway; this was the final scene and the show needed to come to a close. I looked over at Ryan as the tears streamed down my reddened face.

'Ryan,' I whispered, but there was no reaction from him. 'I do love you.' Ryan slowly turned his face towards me. His face was flushed and the tears were streaming. His eyes were lost and for the first time since meeting him, I saw pain and sadness overwhelm him. I took one step back into the room towards him, knowing that he desperately needed a hug from me. I stopped. I knew that this would only complicate things further. I wanted to be with Ryan but suddenly my wedding vows engulfed my mind and I used every ounce of willpower to turn back around, open the door and walk right back down the stairs and out into the street. Looking up at the window where Ryan always stood to wave goodbye whenever I left, I saw only a reflection of the houses opposite. No Ryan. He was clearly heart-broken and I had been the cause of this. So many people hurt by me and my actions. I felt ashamed.

Fifteen minutes later I arrived back at my house to be greeted by a glowing Maria. Any feelings of pain for giving up Ryan I had now neatly parcelled away. I had become an expert in hiding my true identity and so the short drive back had given me the time I needed to brush myself down and pick myself up. Maria had already called her mother to explain that we had sorted things out. I wondered if her mother had pointed out to her that her husband was gay, or maybe the delight in knowing we were back together had distracted her from that most significant point. Maria had showered since I had left. Her hair was so silky and long and made her so look so beautiful. Her face was less blotchy and her alluring green eyes had some sparkle back in them. It was incredible to see the sudden change and immediately it took some of the pressure off my heavy heart.

She threw her arms around me and asked, 'Are you sure about this Jack?'

'For sure,' I responded gleefully. At that very moment I felt happiness. I was not considering Ryan or reflecting on the months of deceit. I was sorry that we had gone through so much pain and upset in recent weeks, but now I truly believed this was the right thing to do. If Albert could love one woman all of his life and resist the temptation to be gay then so could I. To see the happiness on Maria's face was a big enough incentive.

An hour or so later I called my parents. Of course my mother was delighted that I was once again playing happy families. It is a little concerning that no one thought to mention the little fact of my homosexuality and ask how I was going to manage this. Denial I guess, on everyone's part. Aunt Jess was a little wiser and although she was happy that I was happy she did ask me to reflect carefully on what it was I truly wanted. I knew I sounded elated on the phone and therefore how could anyone knock me down at that point? Having seen the turmoil I had been experiencing recently, who would want to add further anguish and pain through the questions they were asking? I wish they had though, however difficult that conversation may have been. After endless texts and phone calls, all the people important to us were now aware that we were back on track. Not all were aware of the full story and so it made explaining things a little easier.

Maria and I snuggled up on the sofa to watch a movie. It felt so good with her spooning me from behind and feeling her soft breasts on my back, as she nestled into me with a great sense of relief and contentment. I am not sure either of us really watched the movie; we were just happy being reunited. In the bedroom before sleep I lay on the bed in my boxer shorts and savoured Maria smiling back at me in the mirror as she pampered her face with various creams and lotions. Each time I glanced across to the ornate mirror I caught Maria staring back at me. It was as if she needed to keep a constant eye on me to prevent losing me again. It made me grin because I felt wanted, needed even. It was as if I had been a kidnapped child, lost from its mother and now finally reunited. Just like a mother and child, there was nothing sexual. We did not have sex that night. We just held each other close all night, never once breaking contact.

Maria was stronger than me and so she returned to work the next morning leaving me cuddled up with the quilt. I probably looked the most peaceful I had done in months. I had assumed I would not be ready for work as I had planned to be moving out and had therefore already informed my boss that I needed one week additional leave for stress and anxiety. When I woke at ten a.m. I noticed the sun blazing in through the bedroom window. It was one of those beautiful spring mornings, where the sky was piercing blue with dustings of white clouds sprawled across it. It sounded so peaceful and *I* felt so peaceful too.

The sound of a text alert startled me a little from my moment of awe. It was a message from Maria that read, *I couldn't be happier right now. Thank you xx.* Reading the message I suddenly felt a sense of panic. It felt as though someone was wrapping their hands around my neck and I could not comprehend why. Pushing the feeling aside I distracted myself by feeding the cat and tidying the kitchen. The kitchen was already spotless but I had an overwhelming desire to keep busy, like an expectant mother nesting in the later stages of her pregnancy. As I sat to eat a morning snack my heart was pounding with the occasional palpitation thrown in for good measure. I tried to ignore the physical anomalies and instead threw myself into daytime TV. My mind began to wander to Ryan. I imagined him sitting crying all night and the pain he must have felt, but with each thought I forced myself to block it out and focus on the TV screen alone. Ignoring these thoughts took every element of strength. I felt possessed. Every memory and thought battered my head despite my greatest efforts to push them aside. Every guy I had encountered, every night of deceit, every misdemeanour now haunted me. It felt as if the room was full of the ghosts of all the guys I had been intimate with, each one calling me a fool. *'It will never work you idiot. You're gay!'* the voices shouted out. The room started to spin and my coffee mug fell out of my hand and onto the darkly stained wooden floor below. The sound of the smashing china startled Jackson, but I was unfazed.

From nowhere I felt an overwhelming desire to view porn and so I ran to the office room upstairs and searched for the most shocking and explicit pages of pleasure. Incapable of reflecting on my behaviour I proceeded to masturbate myself as the graphic scenes resulted in waves of great excitement. I pulled at my cock with great anger and force, longing for the moment to end quickly. I was clearly aroused on the outside but internally I felt only nausea and disgust. Unable to cum I yelled out with uncontrollable anger and rage. I hated myself so much. Only one day ago I had promised to turn my back on these homosexual feelings and yet my desires were still taking control of my life.

The moment eventually passed and closing down the pages of eroticism I opened up my search engine and looked for therapists in the local area. I understood the 'cold turkey' phase that recovering alcoholics went through, but I was not expecting a similar experience with giving up my drugs. I wanted to know what this meant. An appointment with an actual therapist was never something I had considered. My experience with Father Michael had been pressing enough. But I needed answers and I needed them quickly, so I confirmed my appointment for later that day explaining that this was an emergency. I knew that if I did not see someone today, I never would. Maria had already encouraged me to speak with someone neutral and so was delighted when I informed her in my reply to her fourth text! She welcomed the gesture and saw it as me being proactive in managing my emotions. We had of course decided we would make a go of things, but I had revealed some damming personal thoughts and feelings that were going to need greater discussion if they were ever to be more successfully managed.

Driving up to the clinic in the sleepy village just outside the city centre I contemplated turning back. I think deep in my heart I knew it was going to open up more issues rather than solve problems. My hands were physically shaking as I locked the car and walked up to the entrance along the cobbled pathway. The village was so picturesque. The old cottages were dotted around a central green square with endless willow and blossom trees scattered about. It was a stark contrast to the inner city. The clinic occupied one of these cottages, which gave the impression you were visiting your great aunt rather than a counsellor. The tiny doorway led into a small reception area where a mature, larger lady sat flicking through the latest copy of *Hello* magazine. She peered over the top of her silver-rimmed glasses that were attached to a beaded chain around her neck. Her cropped, silvery hair was immaculately styled and judging by the quality of clothing she was wearing, she was clearly a woman of wealth. No doubt her rich husband was the CEO of some major import/export company and this was a little hobby to keep her occupied. Confirming my name her face dramatically changed. The sternness was transformed to friendliness by a single smile that revealed a fine set of teeth that had been privileged to good dental care over the years.

'Hello Jack and welcome to *We Care* clinic. Dr Ruth will be with you shortly. Please do take a seat.' I was totally fascinated by her voice. There was no accent to detect and she addressed me with great formality and perfect pronunciation. Every word was so beautifully emphasised. Sitting 'reading' the various coffee table magazines I could feel my stomach churning and my legs beginning to shake. It was disheartening to know that I was paying for such an experience. It was similar to the feeling of waiting for a dentist. Just as one article caught my attention, Dr Ruth appeared and ever so softly whispered my name. Incredibly tall and slim, she appeared most welcoming. She signalled for me to follow as we proceeded to make our way through the narrow hallway, up the winding stairway and into an upper room. This room was decorated in a similar style to the waiting area. There appeared to have been a conscious effort to avoid decorating in a clinical way. There were no stark white walls and minimal stainless steel furniture. Instead the cottage oozed familiarity and comfort. It gave the patient the sense of being at home with the bright daffodil yellow walls, blush grey carpet and a bountiful supply of tactile cushions. These cushions served as great distractions during awkward questions or as a barrier to hide behind when revealing something more difficult to say. The pictures on the walls bore inspirational and motivational phrases that were a little tacky for my liking, though the intention was creditable.

Crossing her legs, Dr Ruth began the session. 'So Jack, try to make yourself comfortable. Why don't you start by explaining your current situation and then we can go back and address some events that have brought you to this point.'

Her voice was incredible. So soothing and mesmerising. I was not sure of the instruction she had just given me as all I had heard were sounds. Nevertheless my response was instant. My defences came down, my body relaxed and I slid down in the chair slightly. The green fluffy cushion provided a comforting hug as I began to explain my situation. I may have been reluctant to have had this conversation initially, when Maria had suggested it, but there was certainly no stopping me now. I talked for the entire hour without a single word from the therapist. She gave the occasional nod, smile or sympathetic look, but she did not need to question or probe as all the necessary information just came flooding out. I opened up to her more than I had opened up to a single other person. I did not hold back any truths. It was incredibly cathartic and healing. I felt as though I had taken that great load off my shoulders and handed it over to Dr Ruth. When I caught sight of the doctor looking at her gold bracelet watch I knew it was time to stop talking. I felt momentarily as if I had been healed and cured of this 'disease'. Dr Ruth had not communicated her opinion, thoughts or judgements; of course this was not her role but her final closing sentence had a profound effect on me.

'Jack, I understand all that you have told me. You have been incredibly brave, open and honest. You clearly love your wife very much and you have all the information you now need to make your next choice.' She paused at this point and lent forward slightly, uncrossing her slender legs that sat inside high quality tailored trousers. 'But does Maria? You have only given her part of the story and expected her to make *her* choice based around this. Are you prepared to tell her the whole truth?' It was incredible. It felt like a revelation, but one that would not become clear just yet. It was also a costly sentence I thought as I handed over fifty pounds to the lovely receptionist on my way out. I pondered on my experience with Dr Ruth as I sat quietly in my car admiring the scenery one last time before making my short journey back home.

When Maria returned home later that day I felt unable to spend the whole night together. My mind was totally occupied with what had come up in therapy earlier that day. Asking permission, so as not to panic Maria with sudden departures, I took myself off to the gym where I pushed myself like a GI, in an attempt to exhaust myself and leave me incapable of reflecting back on the events earlier that day. I kept myself to myself and my eyes fixed to the floor so as not to be distracted by the homoerotic thoughts that could be elicited by perving on my fellow

215

fitness freaks. My muscles ached like no other time before and my body yelled out, begging me to stop and return home. The session was a success. Returning home I felt exhausted and unable to engage in lengthy conversations. Maria sensed this and only spent the night hugging me and sharing stories from her day at work. She was still wearing the same smile and that filled me with a much-needed boost. Before closing her eyes she turned to face me and softly kissed my left cheek.

'We are okay, right Jack? Nothing from your therapy session that I need to be worried about?'

The kiss in return appeared to alleviate her fears but inside me was only the sound of a ticking bomb. Slowly drifting off to sleep I felt sure I heard a voice whisper in my head, '*Sleep well tonight Jack for tomorrow the world will unleash its cruellest hand upon you both.*'

CHAPTER TWENTY-EIGHT

The night's sleep had been far from restful. All night I had tossed and turned with the words of Dr Ruth resonating in my inner ear. It was true. Maria did not know the whole truth and this deceit would slowly undermine us. But how could I tell her? How could I find the words? Surely she had already suffered enough pain courtesy of me.

The bright light from the street lamp outside blazed through the thin, cotton blind which added to my insomnia. The illumination made me feel like I was under the spotlight; the detective that was my conscience questioned me intensely, beating me down by continually repeating my misdemeanours. I looked across at Maria who slept so peacefully. Her face still seemed to be smiling and her mind was at rest. I imagined the angelic images she thought and the hopes she dreamt of. I wanted to join in her tranquil land for one final night. I watched her sleep for hours, taking note of every curve on her body, every line and scar that told a story and admired every inch of perfection that made her. I ran my fingers through her dark brown hair and took one last smell of the coconut oil she used to condition it. In some ways I did not want her to wake. I wanted her to remain in this land of fantasy where dreams and thoughts conquer pain and reality. I wanted her to live the life she wanted with me behind those closed eyes. I knew deep in my heart what I needed to do and was ready to embrace it. The seven hours of clock watching had given me all the time I needed to collect my thoughts and gather my strength.

When the alarm rang at seven a.m. I finally closed my dreary eyes to avoid the need to engage with Maria as she innocently rose to face the day ahead, unaware of the pain that awaited her. I briefly considered telling her before she left for work but I felt so ashamed. A coward. I played the part of a sleeping dog so well as she kissed my cheek and whispered she loved me. I savoured the words, knowing that it would probably be the last time she would say them to me. As the door closed softly I rose from my pit like the snake I had become. I could not bear to look at myself in the glass panel of the wardrobe as I slithered into the bathroom. I was not thinking about anything, merely following a protocol. My exit strategy. Cold. Calculated. I could not let Maria take me back not knowing the truth, yet I could not hurt her by telling her my darkest secrets. And Christ I would need an HIV test before I could even be intimate with her! How could I explain the lack of physical contact during the weeks I was waiting for the result? What would I do if the result was positive? How could I even be sure my days of deceit were even truly behind me? I was not planning to leave Maria because I was cold and did not care. I had no choice. I thought I was acting selflessly, but maybe in reality it was entirely selfish. I battled with myself to remain calm and controlled as the war continued in my mind.

I did not know where to begin. I was not even sure what I was doing. I walked so slowly down the wooden stairs that were yet to be smothered in soft carpet. I felt a sense of sadness that the house was still unfinished. For three long years this project had occupied our every holiday and sucked every spare penny I had. I was giving up on the house like I was giving up on us. I took a rest on the final step and sat down, absorbing the images around me. The unfinished hallway with its cracked walls and damaged woodwork felt as cold and empty as my heart. I imagined the sound of a little child running around and screaming with excitement as I arrived home from work. Taking my shoes off and walking across the deep pile cream carpet, the child would race to me and call me daddy. Except I knew now that there would be no child running around this house with me. There would be no child ever who would call me daddy because I was saying goodbye not only to Maria but also to that dream. The house would sit unfinished and unloved. The home that was to house my extended family would stand empty, unoccupied, just like my life. I had given up Ryan and now I was turning my back on Maria. At least it was clear now. I was not choosing between Maria and Ryan anymore. I was choosing to save myself. I was choosing to be honest with myself and others, even if that meant a life alone. Believe me it was not a choice in the true sense of the word like the choice you have when you visit the candy store. It was similar to the choice you would have if on death row and choosing death by lethal injection or by electrocution. Admittedly, you are picking what you want but your fate has already been decided just like I now knew that my sexuality had already been predetermined. But I had kicked and thrashed my arms around for the last thirteen years in an effort to avoid my destiny and yet here I was strapped to the chair and being asked for my final words.

Tears ran down my tired face. A gentle jog at first, but as reality fired its shot the tears now raced. I cried for myself and the pain and shame I felt inside. I cried for Maria and the hurt I had and would cause and for the loss

I felt in walking away from her. The sobbing came from deep in my soul and the pit of my stomach wrenched and ached as I wrapped my arms around my body, as if to simulate my mother's hug. My heart felt as if it was being torn in half, as the beating intensified and the blood soared through my veins like an express train. I felt lightheaded as I reached out to grab my phone to call someone. The low sugar levels made me feel incredibly weak and I stumbled forward bumping my head on the wooden sill. The phone crashed to the floor as my knees gave way and I fell to the floor. The wooden blocks did nothing to soften the fall. I felt such self-pity as I sobbed with my face pressed on the cold floor, my body sprawled out like a starfish. I was not physically injured but emotionally I was broken. I remained in this position for an hour, the tears continuing to fall and forming a pool of misery around me. Stretching out I grabbed hold of the phone and called my Aunt Jess. She barely understood my mumbled cries but she instinctively knew what to do. Within an hour she was at my home and helping me pull myself together. She wiped my tears and held me close and for a moment I felt protected. I did not need to tell her what I was planning, she just knew. Her face was always so warm and welcoming and despite her own problems in life she could always be relied upon to be there when needed.

'Everything will be okay Jack. I promise.' Her gentle voice was so soothing. Aunt Jess helped me to pack my bag and suitcase and each time she sensed my upset she would grab my hand and give a smile. I could see a reflection of my own pain in her large, exotic brown eyes. She was feeling my hurt because the bond between us was so strong. Her Mediterranean skin that was normally a beautiful caramel colour was now pale, an indication of her own discomfort with what we were doing. Packing was incredibly painful. It was the reality of knowing something had ended. A great sense of disappointment and regret. The thirteen years we had spent together flashed through my mind as I folded each item and gently placed them into my bag. So many happy memories and events, but so much hurt in recent months that now overshadowed these. Bags packed, Aunt Jess loaded them into her car and started the engine.

'I can't do this Aunt Jess. Not in this way.'

'Jack do what *you* need to do now. You have to think of yourself,' replied Aunt Jess so tenderly.

'I need to face Maria and explain. I will follow you later.'

Aunt Jess knew this was something I needed to do and so did not try to talk me out of it. She just kissed me softly and told me she loved me.

I wandered slowly back up the path and noticed the trees we had planted two summers ago had still not reached the top of the brick wall. I sat in the living room in complete silence and remained there for six hours without moving, drinking or eating. I only thought. I considered every possible way to break the news to Maria that I didn't *think* I was gay but in fact I *knew* I was gay and therefore we were over. I imagined her every possible reaction, but felt sure she would be as reasonable as she had been the first time I had spoken to her about my sexuality. It was the longest six hours of my life. The clock seemed to tick so slowly yet was incredibly loud. At 4.12 p.m. exactly the key turned in the front door and Maria stepped into the hallway. The sound of heels clacking on the weathered parquet flooring woke me from my deep thoughts.

'Jack? Where are you?' You could hear a sense of panic in her voice as she stepped into the living room where I sat on the edge of the sofa, hugging the knitted cushion and rocking slightly.

'Where is your suitcase and bag Jack?' The level of panic was definitely rising. I had forgotten that my bags had been sitting in the hallway since my return from Cyprus. Maria's face changed dramatically. Her eyes changed shape and the colour drained from her face instantly. The image of her face at that moment of realisation will never escape me.

'No no no no no no no NO!' Maria screamed out the last word. She did not need a single word from me. She just knew it. She felt it. The tears were flooding out of her eyes that now looked vacant. She fell to her knees wrapping herself around my legs so tightly and begging me not to do this.

'Why Jack?' she whined. 'Why now?'

'I'm sorry. I'm so so sorry Maria. I just can't do this. I thought I could, but I can't. I'm sorry,' I wailed.

For five minutes we remained in the same position. Maria coiled around my legs sobbing into my lap. My head resting on hers, tears washing her hair. With heartbreak comes sudden changes in emotion.

Maria leapt to her feet and screamed out to me, 'I knew going to see the therapist would do this!' Her anger was incredible but so short lived before the tears returned. Seconds later she was experiencing incredible rage. Grabbing the ceramic vases she smashed them to the ground below as she screamed out in absolute agony. I felt such guilt and a sense of hopelessness. I was no longer the person who could take away her pain. I did not know how to help her.

With the third and final vase in a thousand pieces Maria ran upstairs to the bedroom screaming the highest pitched cry I have ever heard. I could not tolerate the sound and pain so I followed her to the room upstairs that we once shared together. She was wrapped tightly around the quilt and crying intensely and uncontrollably. I could not find a single word to ease the pain. I tried to touch her but she pushed me away. More pleading, begging, shouting, wailing. It was the most traumatic event I had ever experienced. To see a loved one suffering so much is heart wrenching in itself. To see a loved one suffering so much and knowing you have caused it is incomprehensible. Never had I felt so shit about myself and so low. The rage returned and Maria flung the pillows across the room hitting the candles and glass holders across the room. Her hair was wild and her face so flushed as she staggered across the room lashing out at anything in her pathway. The plant pot crashed to the floor and the potting soil splattered the room. Grabbing both her arms I begged her to stop her outburst. She was unable to look at me and fought me with the last ounce of strength she had before her legs buckled and she sank to the floor. I wanted to help her but I needed to get out of the house. I could not cope with what was unfolding and I wondered how long I could remain strong. I could not cave in this time and promise Maria more false hope. With Maria more calmly resting against the bedroom wall, head in her hands, I stood up slowly.

'I'm sorry. I'm sorry. I'm sorry,' I repeated, as I crept out of the bedroom feeling horrified by the scene I had created. I had not reached the third step before the most incredible cry came belting out of the bedroom. It stabbed me deep in my heart and for a moment I died. I so desperately wanted to turn back around, run back up the steps to Maria and hold her in my arms, but I knew I could not. I raced forwards only, down the remaining stairs and out into the street. As the door slammed behind me I fell back against it to catch my breath. The screams and cries could be heard outside and I felt fear. Fear as to what Maria may do or how she would cope with this. Opening my car door I took one final glance back towards the house. I do not remember seeing anything but I will forever remember the sound of her crying. It still haunts me now when I recall that terrible day. I drove to the top of the street and turning the slight bend I parked up at what had become my usual thinking spot alongside the park. I lowered my head onto the stealing wheel and cried. What the hell was going to happen to me now? I was homeless, single and broken.

DISCOVERY

CHAPTER TWENTY-NINE

Three long months had passed and yet the pain was still so incredibly raw. Aunt Jess and her husband had welcomed me with open arms into their home and had provided me with the stability and love I so desperately needed. Uncle Sam had been totally accepting about the gay revelation and never did I feel judged or uncomfortable. Normally referred to as a little tactless at times, he proved to be one of my biggest supporters. He took the time to try to understand my feelings and what had led me to this point, often trying to draw on his own battles in life to support his stories of faith and courage.

Uncle Sam was an incredible man. Sadly he had been paralysed from the waist down following a medical blunder when I was only a small baby. I had only ever known him in a wheelchair, but having grown up with this I had never considered him any different. Sam was a very tall, handsome black guy with the friendliest smile you could picture and that smile never left his face. I had always been mesmerised by the size of his hands. They were like shovels and so many times he had scooped me up when I was young. Throughout my lifetime he had faced tremendous tests of faith and yet he prevailed and with a smile too. His existence itself was a miracle but his attitude was even more awe inspiring. His strong Catholic faith, together with the love of his dedicated wife, had given him the will to go on during the most trying of circumstances. He never complained or moaned or asked, '*Why me?* He was an inspiration, especially at the time of my accident. I could not help but feel a sense of guilt when I made a full recovery following a tiny insight into some of the challenges he faced. Sam really believed in everything I ever wanted to do and was a dedicated fan. He so desperately wanted me to succeed in life, but more importantly he wanted me to be happy. Hence he supported my current decision because he understood my professional success was not enough in itself and I deserved so much more. Their beautiful daughter Jasmine had responded as a typical teenager when Aunt Jess had explained. Her generation were so accepting and so welcoming of differences. It was considered *cool* now to have a gay friend or relative, like an accessory almost. If only the older generation could be so accepting!

My parents were a little fragile and struggling to come to terms with all the change. They were fond of Maria and were trying to deal with the loss of her from their lives. She was not responding to their texts that were intended to offer support, but it was apparently the only way she could deal with her trauma. Dealing with the family made the break-up all the more painful. I frequently visited my parents and soaked up their love and support which provided me with the strength I needed to face the challenges. But I also needed the space to deal with my own issues and losses, without having to be tactful of what they would be going through. I sensed my mother was not dealing too well with my sexuality but she did not allow this to poison her love. I understood her fears. She worried about me facing the world alone and the prejudices I might face. She feared the stereotypical gay lifestyle she had seen on TV or read about in the papers and the health dangers I would potentially encounter. Her concerns were real yet biased by the media.

Sophia, my elder sister was dealing with many domestic issues of her own and could not reach out to me and offer the love and support I needed. In stark contrast was the reaction from Adela. She was incredible and continued to be so. Her love and support was unquestionable and on many a night she would listen to my fears and offer a few gentle words of encouragement. Her love for me was undeniable and any personal feelings or sense of loss she may have been experiencing she kept to herself. She focused all her attention on me, not on Maria, my mother or what the wider world would be thinking, but solely on me and my immediate needs. I am not sure I will ever be able to express to Adela how much her love saved me at times.

Maria and I had not really spoken in the three months that had passed. It was still too incredibly painful for us both, though I missed her terribly. We had never spent more than a week apart and now this three-month separation had created a tremendous void. A few texts had been exchanged that ranged from upset to rage. Now recognising our differences were irreconcilable, Maria was on a mission to take control of her life. She wanted the house sold and divorce papers filed ASAP. I did not care much for the house or the ridiculous money that had been invested in the property. I only cared about helping Maria to deal with the situation, whatever that took. I had offered to give her the house and all its possessions and I did not stop to reconsider. I felt like the bad guy and I wanted a new role. I had not spoken with Maria's family since the night we had made those phone calls proclaiming false hope to all. Her mother was understandably livid with me and I was too ashamed to make contact. Maria's sister Emma had sent a text expressing how sorry she was and although angry because of the hurt her sister felt, she did not judge me or hate me.

And what about me? I was lost. I felt a great sense of loneliness and tremendous pain, indescribable shame at the hurt and embarrassment I had caused and an usual feeling of paranoia. I had stated my current personal situation at work and everyone had been incredibly supportive but working in a Catholic school I felt unable to be truly honest. Generally I was functioning as a normal, sane individual, going to work in the mornings and keeping it together for the day. Sometimes it was all a bit much and I would break down, occasionally in work, which only amplified the shame and embarrassment. Everyone had also assumed that Maria had cheated on *me* and left *me* for some reason. I had not fuelled this but my fear of revealing my true identity did not help me to deny these allegations either. And I still longed for Ryan. Despite the time that had passed the feelings had not lessened, although I felt he would not want me after the way in which I had handled the situation at the end.

It was now July and the long summer holidays were almost upon us. The cool evening breeze whistled around me as I sat relaxing in Aunt Jess' garden, surfing Facebook. The trees shuffled with each cool breath and the rustling sound created a tranquil ambience. I could not resist searching for Ryan Ellsworthington's page. His unique surname made the search a whole lot easier and it was not long until his profile picture filled my screen. It was just as I had remembered – so handsome and so alluring. I guessed, or rather hoped, it was an old picture as he looked so happy. Sadistically I still hoped he would be somewhat sad and longing for me. I clicked on 'send message' and proceeded to type a detailed proclamation of my love and justification for my actions. Delete. I could not do it. I could not cope with any further rejection and heartache. Yet I missed him terribly and I longed for some passion with him. As the light began to fall in the garden I began to type for the second time. I described my feelings from my heart and did not attempt to justify how I had handled things, but instead explained what I desired to happen next. Send. Whatever happened next, at least Ryan would know how I felt.

I need not have worried so much. Before I had even logged out, Ryan had responded. He expressed his sadness at how I had turned my back on him and the hurt he had felt recently, but without any doubt he still wanted to be with me. I was ecstatic and for the first time in months, happy! I slammed the laptop shut and ran into the house like a child on Christmas morning. The house was still empty so exiting was all the easier, with no need for lengthy explanations. I scribbled a note to Aunt Jess and ended with, *'Don't wait up!'* I knew she would instinctively know what this meant and that made me chuckle. She had been trying to encourage me to contact Ryan for some time as she felt he was good for me. This would surely please her.

I could barely contain my excitement as Ryan opened the door with that signature smile and eagerly beckoned me inside. We had barely reached the stairs before we embraced in a passionate kiss and an all over body grope. It felt insatiable. His every touch sent shivers down my spine that then ricocheted to my extremities. I felt electrocuted. As his tongue flickered mine my breathing became more intense and my excitement soared. I managed to pull myself away briefly so that we could move to the privacy of his room.

'Ryan I am so sorry for what happened...'

'Shhhhhh,' he whispered as he placed his index finger on my lips. He was forever the comedian and before removing his finger he repeatedly strummed my bottom lip which was noticeably fuller than my top. My laughter was muffled by my T-shirt that was now being hastily removed. His lips were all over my neck, as he erotically blew short breaths into my ear causing my knees to shake with pleasure. He was acting possessed and I loved it. His tender soft lips moved slowly down my quivering chest, savouring each part before locking onto my right nipple which instantly hardened. The pink colouration was now a deep red as the blood rushed to the surface. I was not overly keen on the biting but when I repaid the favour I could sense this was maybe a fetish of his. His skin tasted so good as I followed the trail from his belly button to his waistline. The fine blond hair provided the direction I needed to go.

With great haste I fumbled away at his belt but the nervous excitement hampered my progress and Ryan came to the rescue. Slipping my hand inside his underwear I pressed my sweating palms against his cock. Lowering his jeans I placed his cock back in my hand. I realised how impossible it would have been to have given this up for a life with Maria. I could not hold off any longer and so proceeded to pleasure him in the way I knew best. My mouth was salivating with excitement which heightened the pleasure for Ryan. His moaning was louder than I had remembered and this intensified my own erection. I used my tongue to reunite myself with each and every inch of his groin, teasing and tickling at each point. Pushing me off, Ryan was eager to indulge me. It felt incredible and I wanted everyone to know it. My arms and head thrashed with delight as the sensations rippled from my toes to my fingers. I rocked my hips in motion to add to the pleasure causing Ryan to gag at times but this he seemed to get off on. His masculine, strong hands caressed my inner thigh before gently cupping my balls. I needed to feel him inside me and so I turned myself over to lie upon my chest, rubbing myself up against the quilt provocatively.

Ryan was having none of this and whispered in my ear, 'I want to see your face!' With Ryan lying flat on his back I eagerly straddled him, looking intensely into his eyes as I lowered myself. It had been some time since Ryan and I had been intimate in this way and the pain was stronger than any pleasure. He was patient and tender as he slowly caressed the entrance, which pulsated in anticipation. Ryan assertively, yet gently, inserted himself, causing me to moan in pain a little. As I slowly moved my hips I gathered my rhythm and the ecstasy returned. It felt different this time. Less aggressive and animalistic and more passionate. It was not about what he was doing to me, it was the way he looked at me. We did not need words; it was all in our eyes and there was some form of communicative exchange taking place. Raising his legs slightly, the feeling was deeper. I pressed my knees into the bed and lifted myself slightly, pushing against his chest so that I could speed up each movement. His face was red and beads of sweat danced across his forehead before plunging down his temples and onto the pillow. His eyes never left mine as I seductively rocked up and down, his hands now firmly pressed on my hairy thighs. Ryan moved his hands across to my throbbing cock and slowly moved his hand up and down at the same rhythm that *his* cock entered my body. I leant back slightly and took hold of his balls in my left hand and caressed them softly which only intensified my own pleasure resulting in a spray of cum across Ryan's neck and chest. My own climax acted as a catalyst for Ryan and he began to force himself so deep and so hard inside me. The pain was just bearable but I longed for him to finish quickly. I kept my eyes fixated upon him as spasms of joy embraced him. He returned to a slow dance and each insertion felt great. My legs were exhausted and as I lifted myself gently I laughed out at my inability to straighten them. Lowering myself beside Ryan we kissed gently and coyly for twenty minutes or more without a single word spoken. I playfully rubbed his hair and coiled my legs around his. I felt safe once more and I no longer felt lost. This was my destination and now there was no reason why I needed to move on.

CHAPTER THIRTY

For three further months I hid my new love from others. Partly this was to avoid any possible confrontation where I might be told I was rushing into things, or worse still be judged, and partly it was out of protection and respect for the feelings of others, especially my grandfather. Aunt Jess was relieved to see me happy and was pleased to provide a cover story whenever my parents rang or called at the house unexpectedly. I had not officially moved in with Ryan but I rarely slept over at Aunt Jess'. I would occasionally eat with the family or run in for a quick change of clothes, but generally Ryan and I were inseparable and I could not get enough. I was obviously still battling with my conscience about what I had done to Maria, which was often amplified following one of our telephone conversations that were infused with bitterness. I did not feel it was appropriate to share with her my personal circumstances and so I tried to focus the conversations around her and her feelings.

'How are you? Are you okay?'

'Of course I am not okay,' she would snap. 'My husband is gay and has left me!' Her own harsh words would often disappoint herself and instigate an emotional outburst. 'I miss you so much Jack,' she sobbed, which never failed to make me cry. I was so worried about her. She sounded so tired and drained and I wondered where she found the strength to continue sometimes. Maria had befriended a group of women from one of the forums I despised. Although I disapproved of some of the information they were giving her, there was no denying that the commonality they shared was providing a sense of nourishment to her. Ryan was always so understanding during these lengthy and sometimes traumatic calls. He would sit there patiently whenever my mobile rang and often just grabbed my hand and gave it a little squeeze when he sensed I was under attack. However, from time to time he would become a little paranoid and would sit silently for some time after my phone call. It would take a lot of persistence to break down his emotional walls before finally uncovering his own insecurities. Of course this was understandable considering I had previously walked out on him for Maria. He was clearly doubting my ability to stay strong and was still not convinced of my acceptance of my own sexuality.

After five months it was time for Maria and I to face each other for the first time. She was keen to have me remove the last of my personal items and discuss the next step with regards to the house and divorce. Initially she had been very keen to proceed at speed but the reality of being single and homeless hit hard and Maria took several months to muster up the courage to face the difficult times ahead. I was incredibly nervous as I parked outside the house. The last occasion had been so traumatic and I could not cope with an encore. It did not seem appropriate to use my front door key and so I rang the bell. I stood within the porch area to avoid attracting attention from the inquisitive neighbours, who surely by now had clocked my lack of presence in the area. Maria opened the door with confidence and judging by her appearance she was certainly feeling positive and assertive about the future. Her hair was a little shorter than I remembered and the scattered

red highlights added a sassiness that caught my eye. She looked refreshed, relaxed and thankfully not emotional. I felt sure I could be out of the house within the hour. Walking into the living room felt strangely uncomfortable. This was *my* home yet why did I feel so detached from it? I felt on edge in a similar way to when visiting your in-laws for the first time.

'Would you like a cup of tea?' Maria asked assertively.

'A coffee please,' I responded.

'I don't drink coffee and since you don't live here now then there's no point in keeping it here!' That was the first of many bitter comments to come I thought.

'A tea will be fine thanks.'

Whilst Maria was out of the room I took the opportunity to scan the room like a detective at a crime scene, looking for evidence of change. Nothing obvious. I noticed the picture of me and my nephew had been removed and the candlesticks that were a wedding gift from a friend had been replaced by a far cheaper alternative. I took note of the space where the decorative vases once stood – a stark reminder of that frightful evening. Maria returned from the kitchen and as she passed my mug I could not help but notice the wedding ring was missing in action. Before leaving Ryan's that morning I had debated whether to wear my own ring or not. Not wearing the ring may look like I had moved on already, wearing the ring may have given false hope. When I finally did slip the ring on I could not help but notice the paranoia that consumed Ryan. However, I thought it was respectful to wear it. Clearly there was no need considering Maria's current finger status.

'Where's your wedding ring Maria?' I enquired.

'Not that it is any of your business Jack but I sold it. Along with my wedding dress.'

Ouch! The words were so damn cutting. It was not that she had sold them. I guessed there was little point in holding on to them, but it was the tactless way in which she delivered the lines. I had opted for the role of gentleman today and she was opting for bitch. My throat felt somewhat swollen as emotion took a hold of me in the same way as when men watch a teary film. The girl will sit there sobbing whilst us men are expected to cope with the strangulation that comes from the inability to be seen to cry. I was not going to let any more tears fall in this house and so I took one hard swallow and regained my composure. I needed to see this as a business meeting.

'So what did you want to discuss Maria?' I asked with the same assertiveness that she was displaying.

'Two things. Firstly, the house. I can't afford to live here on my own so we need to sell it and quickly!'

I noticed that behind that strict Victorian teacher demeanour Maria was struggling. This was her dream house and she loved it so much. The neighbourhood was also classically Maria – middle-class heaven.

'I can help you to stay here Maria. For the time being anyway until you are ready to move on. I will pay for half of everything.' It is amazing what guilt will do to a man. I was hardly in a financial position to be so generous but I was a good guy and I still cared so much for Maria. She had lost the life she once so enjoyed, courtesy of me. I could not also carry the burden of taking her home away from her. Maria accepted the generous offer and agreed we would re-evaluate the situation in about six months. We also needed to focus on finishing the house in preparation for a possible sale. I was not paying rent to Jess or Ryan at the moment but there would come a time when I would need to move to my own place or a bigger apartment with

Ryan. As cute as Ryan's place was, it was not meant for two grown men and the lack of storage was driving me insane.

'What's the second point you want to discuss Maria?'

'I want to get a divorce and then an annulment,' she replied coldly. She had taken on the role of the Ice Queen and it was unnerving.

'I think we have to be separated for two years before we can consider a divorce,' I cleverly responded.

'Not if I prove infidelity,' she snapped back quickly.

My heart temporarily stopped as I scrambled to catch enough breath to respond. 'What the hell are talking about Maria?'

'Well I know you were talking to guys online for many months and you ran away on holiday with a complete stranger. The same stranger I believe you are now dating? I think that's enough to start with don't...' Before she had even finished her delivery the Ice Queen had melted and all that pent up emotion was released. It was no less upsetting seeing Maria cry, but at least I felt less concerned now. The cold, calculated form she had taken suggested she was not dealing with things. It was not normal. Crying and bouts of anger were far healthier. I did not even hesitate to reach out and hug Maria and judging by how tightly she held me, she needed this. Through muffled cries she explained how much she missed me and the pain she was experiencing.

'I don't want to carry on without you Jack.'

It was incredibly tough to hear those words. To know that someone you still love is in such despair. It was the trigger that I needed to unpack my own emotions and together we stood embraced and sobbing. I enjoyed the feel of her soft pink cheek against my own and the familiar scent that oozed from her body. She was clearly losing a lot of weight I noticed as I wrapped my arms tightly around her torso. We did not speak. We just held each other close. We both knew that this was a hopeless situation and one that could not be reversed or changed, yet we enjoyed the mutual emotional support that came from the hug all the same.

Maria needed me to remove the last of my personal belongings so she gave me some space and drove to her mother's. It was a sombre moment. I could not help but be puzzled as to how Maria was aware of my relationship with Ryan. Maybe she had seen me driving to his home since it was at such close proximity to her mother's home? Or maybe my parents or a common friend had informed her? It didn't matter right now. There was an eerie silence in the dining room where countless memories of dinner dates danced around the mango table. A gentle wind whispered through the wooden French doors, blowing the white voiles that draped the oversized windows. The room was just how I remembered. Classically decorated. The expensive furniture and ornate Edwardian fireplace had made a significant impact on my savings two years prior. But there was no denying that Maria had impeccable taste. The plum coloured walls and dark-stained floors were elegant and majestic. Yet the room lacked soul and always had. It seemed staged, like my life I figured. I placed the last of my CDs into the cardboard box, giggling at the eclectic collection before me. In such a minimalistic room it was difficult not to observe the one missing piece on the oversized floating shelf in one of the alcoves. The wedding photo. The original silver frame still stood there but it housed no photograph. Empty. Like Maria's heart. It was difficult not to be upset by this observation. Was Maria trying to erase my entire existence? Did she regret our wedding day? Or was it all just too painful to remember?

Ryan was waiting for me when I arrived all teary eyed at his home. As we were now practically living together, he appeared to be more secure in our relationship. He now believed I was more accepting of my sexuality and that Maria was no threat to him. She was aware of our relationship and whilst she expressed that she felt I was rushing into things in one of her late night texts, she had not given me too much grief. My parents on the other hand were far less accepting. They were not angry or confrontational but just reluctant to meet Ryan. I knew it was my mother more than my father, but he was always so loyal to his wife and so they stood united. The truth is that I had not actually asked them to meet him. My mother had assumed this request was coming on account of Aunt Jess and Jasmine having met Ryan the previous month. The coffee date at Starbucks had been a great success and Ryan was a big hit on account of his wit and charm. I figured Aunt Jess had taken on the role of Ryan's PR manager, promoting him to my disinterested parents. Actually they were not disinterested. They were, 'not ready' as my mother stated and 'not willing to be rushed into things!' I sometimes wondered whose life had been turned upside down and whose marriage had broken down. Sometimes I found myself offering *them* emotional support and listening to my mother talk about how sad she was knowing I would not have kids or the upset she felt at my impending divorce. So many times I longed to scream out, 'This happened to me! This is my life that has been fucked up not yours!' I know that I underestimated their own pain and trauma. This had all come so suddenly for them. I had had many years to deal with the confusion surrounding my sexuality but this lightning bolt was unexpected for them. The son they thought they had raised was not the same in some respects. What was real and what were lies was now blurred. They probably questioned every event in my life. For sure they were blaming themselves, either for creating me in this way through the genetic coding that they passed on to me or through the way in which they had raised me. I could hear my father saying, 'I told you not to hug him so much!' They clearly needed time to figure out their issues and I was unable to help them with this one.

Ryan was incredibly sensitive to my feelings. Dealing with a break-up whilst simultaneously building a new one was not easy. Frequently our intimate moments were interrupted by random texts or phone calls from Maria. Ryan also had to deal with the fact that my family were not yet prepared to meet him *and* I was still dealing with my own loss and issues around being gay. Ryan never moaned or complained. He would sometimes go quiet and withdrawn, but following a little reassurance he would be right back on track. I felt so secure next to him. He was helping me to see the importance of the smaller things in life and these were making me incredibly happy. For too long my life had obsessed over materialistic things like cars and fancy clothes or ornate furniture and landscaped gardens. It had all felt like a rat race and one that was tiring me. Maria had been incredibly demanding at times in terms of wants and needs, and I had pressurised myself to be a good provider. With Ryan it was different. There was no fancy house or flash car. I had sold the Audi TT to make way for a more economically sensible hatchback now that I was facing an uncertain future. Life was about us only. Back to basics. It was not about expensive restaurants but cheap take-aways and DVD evenings cuddled up on the sofa. Most of my weekends in the past had been so prescriptive, providing little down time to unwind and relax. Now that had all changed. I spent endless Saturdays lying side by side on the sofa watching crap TV or Sunday evenings sharing a romantic candle-lit bath. My perspective on life was changing and I had never been happier or more relaxed. And the key to this change – laughter. Ryan had been blessed with a gift to entertain others. His impulsive wit and humour provided endless moments of elation. This coupled with his great looks made him the perfect man for me. However, we were incredibly different in many other ways and we came with our own distinctive baggage. With time I knew these differences would put a strain on the life we were trying to build and it was not long until the first of these ugly moments sadly occurred.

CHAPTER THIRTY-ONE

Ryan had arranged for me to meet with some of his friends at a sexy new bar in the city centre to celebrate the birthday of one of his close friends. This would be the first time I had really met any of his friends. This was on account of my own reluctance. I had not been ready to be introduced as someone's boyfriend, but now the time seemed right. We had been together for nine months and since we were planning on moving overseas together in the new year, I figured we were running out of time. I had already met Ryan's family and that had given me the confidence to meet his close friends. His family had been incredibly warm and welcoming. Although loud and brash, the differences between us did not seem important. They were down to earth people for whom family life was central. All Ryan's siblings had colourful pasts, as did his mother, but that made them all the more liberal and accepting. They could see how in love we were and that was good enough for them.

As we arrived at the bar we were greeted by three slightly over-intoxicated friends, Mel, the birthday girl, Jen and Clare, enjoying the cool September breeze outside. Although unable to focus on my face they were extremely friendly and already comfortable enough to kiss and hug me. Mel was very petite and almost oriental in appearance. She and Ryan had once worked together and remained close friends. They had taken on the role of husband and wife and were very hands-on, though in a humorous way. Clare was a bit older, but no wiser. She spoke very eloquently and appeared sophisticated in appearance. Jen was stunning and I took an instant liking to her. She spoke like the Queen but had the beauty of a princess. Her shimmering blonde hair and enormous smile were very sexy.

'He is soooooo handsome Ryan. Much better than the last one!' Mel slurred.

It was of course totally inappropriate but forgivable considering the volume of alcohol consumed! Ryan sensed my discomfort and quickly ushered me indoors where we met the remainder of the group.

This was clearly a straight bar with countless egotistic guys hitting on disinterested females who just wanted to party. I had not been to a bar in such a long time. It was not something that Maria and I enjoyed. I was mesmerised by the appearance of the 'straight' guys, so metrosexual, or honorary gay, as I refer to them. They are straight in terms of sexuality but they borrow a gay man's sense of fashion and style. It was difficult to predict a guy's sexuality in this bar. They all appeared well-groomed with elaborate hairstyles and cutting edge fashion sense. What had happened to the rough, gruff men with mismatched clothing and zero style? Was the world now being led by the homosexuals? Were we inspiring straight guys? It was difficult not to be distracted by the degree of hotness in the bar and Ryan noticed my salivating expression. I did not even know that such beautiful men existed and the fact they were straight made them so much more sexy in appeal. Everyone seemed to be the proud owner of a beach body, with army gun arms and impressive oversized chests. The tight, scooped-neck T-shirts amplified this further. I felt rather underdressed in last season's Diesel T-shirt and jeans. The arms I once considered large felt like twigs protruding from my sleeves. One guy in particular caught my attention. He was over 6-feet tall with black short hair that was ruffled in that out-of-bed style. His arms were like my thighs and the tail ends of an elaborate shoulder tattoo could be seen. When he glanced over in my direction, no doubt sensing the pervy gay man staring, I could not help but be struck by the beauty of his face. He looked handcrafted. The chiselled jawline was finely covered with stubble and his eyes were like two emeralds shining in the distance: the most intense green colour that pierced your soul. His tanned skin shimmered and the arse was a perfect double bubble.

'Would you prefer to join *him* and his friends Jack?' snapped Ryan, in a controlled yet clearly jealous outburst. In fairness the amount of dribble on my chin clearly signalled my lack of tact. I was not lusting after this dark and handsome stranger, I was just in awe of his beauty. I didn't want to be *with* him, I just wanted to *be* him.

'Imagine being that hot,' said a voice from the corner, who was salivating only slightly less than me. It was Charlotte, one of Mel's close friends. She and Ryan had only met once before. She was beautiful and of Vietnamese decent. Her petite angelic face was framed by a black silky ribbon of hair. Her eyes were like almonds and the smile was electrifying. She bore the same signature cheeks as myself; round and enticing. Her complexion was flawless and youthful and I felt instantly attracted to her, though not sexually of course! If I was to consider returning to the straight world this lady would be top of the list of potential wives.

Although a little coy and shy at first, Charlotte soon warmed up and was quick to order a drink from me which made me smile. I guessed she was normally reserved but the alcohol already consumed had given her a new-found level of confidence. She was funny and smart but she clearly irritated Ryan. He was actually getting jealous over the attention I was receiving from a woman, a woman who clearly knew I was gay and who happened to be at the party with her boyfriend Chris. Chris, whom I had never met before, was not at all bothered by the innocent flirtation taking place. He was more concerned about the hostility displayed by Ryan. We had only been at the bar one hour and already he was wearing a constant frown and drinking *way* too much for my liking. He had opted to sit alongside Amanda, one of the other girls he had a more established friendship with, but he would continually glare across the table at me. I was unsure as to what exactly my crime was. After all, I was making a good impression with his friends!

'Hey Ryan, come and chat with Charlotte. She is *so* funny!' I called across the table as I beckoned him.

'Don't fucking call me like your fucking dog!' Ryan slurred, clearly intoxicated at this point. I had witnessed something similar once before. As Ryan's alcohol consumption rose, the volume of his voice rose alongside his obnoxiousness. He was being a complete dick and everyone thought the same. A deathly silence circled the table broken only by the quick wit of Chris. He was an aspiring actor and incredibly funny. He bore an uncanny resemblance to a famous Hollywood funny guy. This surely drove him crazy by the time the fifth guy of the evening had made this connection.

'Do you fancy grabbing something to eat and then heading home?' I asked Ryan, making a second attempt at smoothing things over, but only half way through my words I was yet again distracted by the hot guy at the bar.

'Oh just fuck off Jack. Go and fuck you fancy new boyfriend at the bar. Go and suck on his big spray-tanned cock!' Each word was pronounced at a few decibels louder than the last and by the time we reached *'spray-tanned cock'*, we had the attention of most of the bar. I was mortified and frozen. I was not accustomed to such public displays of emotion. I had led a simple, quiet life up until this point. My desire to leave a good impression with his friends was now in pieces on the floor in front of me. And then for his encore, Ryan pushed back his chair, which tumbled to the floor, and barged his way out of the bar. Charlotte gave me a much-needed hug and tried to brush the episode off as alcohol-induced only. I could not help but hear alarm bells ringing. I wondered, had I instigated the event through my perving over the hot metrosexuals? Was I struggling to play the part of the dutiful boyfriend?

I decided to walk the thirty-minute journey home alone so that I could reflect on Ryan's behaviour. He had appeared less patient in recent weeks. I wondered if it was the lack of marijuana in his system since he had apparently given this up since dating me. Did he resent this sacrifice?

As I slipped into bed alongside Ryan later that evening he turned his back on me. Maria and I always had the motto that we should not let the sun go down on an argument, but clearly Ryan was prepared to let the sun implode before he was willing to talk. I knew he was emotionally inept and this was a part of him. I snuggled up next to him and slowly drifted off to sleep.

'I'm sorry,' were the words Ryan whispered in my ear as the daylight blazed into our bedroom.

'It's okay Ryan. I'm sorry too.'

I was not really sorry. I was not sure what mistakes I had made, but I saw little point in dragging the event out.

He had apologised and that was good enough. That day was going to be incredibly difficult for me and the last thing I needed was to be worrying about Ryan's bad behaviour.

After talking at great length with Aunt Jess, I had decided it was time I revealed my story to my grandfather. I was numb with fear and totally unable to complete the task alone. I had assumed my parents did not approve of me burdening my grandfather with my sordid issues as there had been no real offer of accompanying me. Maybe they thought this was something I needed to do alone. More likely they were still in denial and the fewer people we shared this with, the less real it would seem. I only wish they could have felt a fraction of my anguish. My grandfather was so incredibly important to me. I respected this man *so* much and would be unable to survive if he turned his back on me. He had been so instrumental in my life; he was my world. Aunt Jess knew I needed support without me even saying the words. I was certainly in no fit state to drive on account of my legs shaking profusely!

I never spoke a single word to Aunt Jess for the entire twenty-minute journey. I was unable to. My mouth was incredibly dry and my mind vacant. I was just drowning in fear, struggling to catch my breath. Escorted by Aunt Jess, I walked up the ten steep steps to the front door that was unlocked as usual. Before entering the lounge I paused suddenly, temporarily paralysed by the choking anxiety of my grandfather's rejection. Aunt Jess placed a gentle hand upon my shoulder and gave the slightest, yet most tender, squeeze. No words needed. I knew that no matter what happened in the next hour, Aunt Jess would always be there for me.

A ribbon of tobacco smoke danced out of the lounge and circled us, a signal that the old man was at home. Turning the corner into the living room I saw him sitting in his usual corner chair looking a little sombre. He appeared deep in thought and I was unsure if he had heard us arriving. The emotionally charged classical music playing quietly in the background was apt. The creaking floorboard I stood on brought my grandfather back from his place. His charming smile was welcoming as I leant down to kiss him on either cheek. He wrapped his strong hands around the back of my head and held me close to his head.

'Okay son?' he asked gently.

I just wanted to savour the hug in case it was my last.

'How have you been? Why the long face?' he enquired.

I knew he sensed my pain. Of course he did. We were incredibly connected and my pain was his too. Only this time the root of my pain would surely bring us into conflict. He slowly lifted himself up from his chair. Although almost eighty, he was the fittest, strongest and for sure the most handsome pensioner I knew. His full head of silvery hair never ceased to amaze me and I continually prayed that I had his genetic make-up for this characteristic. Even at this age his arms were impressive and I imagined how in awe the ladies would have been when he was in his early twenties. This Italian looker had turned many a girl's head and even now his charisma still oozed. An incredibly intelligent guy, he sensed my torment.

'Soooo?'

He seemed different. No humour. No teasing. He just stood there and waited. I was silent. No words could be generated. My lips refused to open. I glanced at him and then at Aunt Jess and then back to my grandfather again, never looking into his eyes. I could not. I felt too ashamed. This man had done so much for me and I was about to disappoint him beyond belief. He never lost his patience.

He just stood and waited. Aunt Jess resisted the temptation to break the silence and remained silent herself.

'Tell me son. What's up?' he asked once more. Equally patient. Equally loving. My lips quivered slightly and a few faint sounds escaped, but nothing audible or cohesive. I pulled on the lobes of my ears and folded the tops over (always symbolic of my nervous tension). My senses were heightened for some reason. The melody of the music was deafening. The smell of Marlboros intoxicating. Palms sweating; fingers dancing.

'I... I... um... I um... '

I looked over at Aunt Jess who was now sitting on the edge of her chair, eyes wide open, silently chanting for me to finish the line. Time was not passing. We were in freeze frame and only I could bring back the tick tock of time. Why was it so difficult to say the words? I took one long glance at the wooden floor, noting every imperfection in the wood and then looked up at my grandfather, straight into his eyes, longing for him to take away this burden. I saw the passage of pain transfer to his eyes and his half smile and subtle nod signalled this was my moment. One final confirming nod from Aunt Jess and I was good to go. The single tear that clung to her lower eyelashes showed her alliance.

'Grampy... I... I... um... I'm... gggg... gay.' The volume tailed off at the end and I broke my gaze. It was barely noticeable but for sure I saw it. Disappointment? It must have been and it hurt more than any rant or cutting words.

'Thank God for that! I thought you were about to tell me you had frigging cancer or something. Come here you soft sod!' Maybe it was not disappointment but rather relief, or maybe it was disappointment for a split second but love conquered and rose above this.

I threw my arms around him and cried. I squeezed him so tightly and let all my emotion run free. The relief was incredible and I knew now that I could finally move forward. Aunt Jess was silently sobbing in the corner, desperately trying to prevent her mascara from running. At this moment I knew that she had never doubted my grandfather's reaction. She would never have knowingly brought me into a lion's den. This was her father and she knew him so well. She knew his acceptance would provide so much healing power to me. She was right. Immediately I was in remission.

Returning from the kitchen with a hot cup of tea for me I caught Aunt Jess mouth the words, *'Thank you!'* to my grandfather. Her support meant the world to me. She loved and protected me like I was one of her own children. For many years I was. It took a long time for the miracle that was my cousin Jasmine to arrive. I had always considered myself so fortunate to have the parents that I did, but to have a second mother in an aunt and a second father in my grandfather meant I was truly spoilt.

'Look son, you can't help who you are but I can't deal with knowing about it. But I don't love you any less, remember that!'

He had already given me enough so this request was okay by me. We talked for thirty minutes about why I had never shared this information before and I saw him wince when I referred to my fear because of his homophobic comments in the past.

'I bloody warned your grandmother about all that baking with you!'

The three of us broke out into laughter which lifted the heavy atmosphere. 'Or was it the musicals she took you to?' he bantered.

'I was born gay. Nan didn't turn me gay. I just didn't realise I was gay until now,' I replied.

'So is there a Mary Two then?' Mary had always been his nickname for me on account of my 'sensitive' disposition. Maybe deep down he had always known and so his name for me was so apt.

'Yes, there is a guy...'

'Well don't bloody expect me to meet him. I don't like puffters!' he interrupted. Only my grandfather could get away with this comment and it just made me giggle even more. As the conversation changed to other topics, I sat back and reflected on how lucky I was to have been born into this amazing family and spared a thought for all those guys who were not as lucky as me and faced either a life of rejection or on-going denial. For me, the ability to rise above your own prejudices and views for a loved one is the definition of true love and I was now fully immersed in this.

CHAPTER THIRTY-TWO

It was a long time coming but my parents were finally ready to meet Ryan. I think they finally realised time was running out as I had now secured a job in Thailand for the next academic year. Ryan and I had always joked about running away to Jamaica from the first night we shared together. I am not sure why we picked Jamaica, though maybe it was because of Ryan's previous love of the country's plant life! It was incredibly difficult living in the same city now I had changed sexual preference, with many an awkward moment when I bumped into old friends who would invariably ask about Maria, totally unaware I had transferred to a new team. I felt like I was hiding and this was not aiding my own acceptance of my new identity. I was still too concerned about the feelings of others: Maria, my parents, old friends, etc. I needed to focus on *me*. I needed the space to grow into my new-fangled skin. Working overseas seemed like a sensible way to achieve this and Ryan was equally excited by this prospect. After unsuccessful attempts to secure positions in the UAE we settled on the Land of Smiles. The house was now under offer which meant that that financial burden would soon be lifted and there would be one less tie to the UK. I had originally told Maria that I would support her with the mortgage for six months only but I knew she was struggling now on one salary and I could not further add to her anguish by also removing financial assistance. After all, this was my fault that she was in this situation.

The recent successful meeting with Adela and her boyfriend Karl had probably also been a contributing factor. Ryan had been a real hit with my sister and she had warmed to his humour instantly.

As we left the dinner that evening she had linked arms with me and whilst Ryan was engaged in a meaningful conversation with Karl, whispered, 'He is perfect for you. You look so happy together!'

Aunt Jess was in love with Ryan too. His charming smile and quick wit were a hit. They had talked like old friends whenever we met and no doubt all this information had filtered back to my parents. It had been over twelve months since the split and, now that Maria was also dating, the time seemed appropriate for them. I think they felt it would have been disloyal to Maria if they had met with Ryan too soon.

Why does it seem that time slows down when you are nervous or anticipating an event? The drive to my parents' house is no more than 12 km but it seemed to be double that. I was unable to sustain a dialogue with Ryan on account of the waves of nausea that were becoming overwhelming. Ryan seemed unaffected by the forthcoming event. He was more concerned with making himself look particularly dashing in his big eighties-style sunglasses. It was a really pleasant day and for the first time this year I was able to lower the roof of the Audi and pump up the music. In our heads we were two hot members of a new boy band. In reality we were a pair of middle-aged guys going through a mid-life crisis, well I was anyway! Yeah we were getting the looks from people but for totally the wrong reasons. I just kept rehearsing my lines like a nervous child in their first nativity play. How would I introduce Ryan? *Hi mum, this is Ryan my boyfriend, my lover, my friend...* And what would we talk about? And where should we sit? Next to each other, opposite? I was over-thinking everything as usual and Ryan would do whatever Ryan was going to do so it was difficult to predict the event. As we pulled up outside I noticed the blinds twitching and I imagined my father giving my mother his final wise words about how to handle the meeting. My mum wears her feelings on her face and there is no hiding her emotions. I knew this was so challenging for her and it meant the world to me that she had even reached this point. There were many times when I thought this moment would never come.

Opening the door into the lounge I knew there was no turning back. My father rose to his feet and gave me a welcoming hug that eased the pressure somewhat. He then greeted Ryan in the style of two drug lords from the Bronx. It was one of those really macho two step handshakes. Ryan seemed familiar with this move, although it still made him chuckle a little. I greeted my mother in our usual way, a kiss on either cheek and then the rubbing of heads like two alley cats. This had started off as a joke a few years back but had become an endearing greeting. Ryan looked particularly amused by this.

'Hiya luv, nice to meet you,' said my mother shyly. There was no real attempt at physical contact and Ryan sensed this.

'Tea? Coffee?' So predictable I thought. Nothing like a hot drink in times of stress or awkwardness. My father followed my mother to the kitchen pretending to tend to the dog's needs. I knew in reality he would be out there giving my mother a pat on the back for passing stage one. I sauntered out to the kitchen to try to gauge their first impressions. I didn't want to put any pressure on them so I simply gave a wide cheesy grin.

'What does your mate want to drink son?' asked my father.

'Dad, he's not my mate. He's my...'

My mother quickly interrupted, assertively pushing a coffee mug into my hand and inviting me to help myself to some cake. I sensed her discomfort with hearing me utter the words that defined mine and Ryan's relationship.

'He'll have a tea,' I replied as I wondered back into the lounge. Ryan looked unfazed by the whole event and was busy entertaining the dog.

We talked for an hour or so about this and that but always avoiding the topic of Ryan and I. I understood now that my parents' mechanism for coping was to think of us as friends and for now, this was okay with me. They had come a long way in a short amount of time. Ryan was charming and chatty and my parents were polite and receptive. I on the other hand was feeling less than comfortable. I had never been so observant of the decor in this room. I noticed every fine detail as I tried to subconsciously remove myself from the situation. Looking out through the large glass window that overlooked the well-maintained garden, I longed to be one of the sparrows flying free without a care in the world. I had sat in this very chair in this very room weekend after weekend making small talk with my parents. Only normally Maria was at my side and not my gay boyfriend. It was somewhat surreal. Why was I not feeling relaxed? Was it just because it was new and different? Did I sense my parents' own discomfort in the moment? Why did I always have to over-think every fucking situation? Two cups of tea, a round robin of every family member's life and we were good to go. I had never been so relieved to be saying goodbye to my parents. It was not them, it was me. It was all a little challenging, though I was not quite sure why.

The following three visits were no less relaxing and my mother's insistence on bringing Maria's name up at some point on each occasion did not exactly help!

CHAPTER THIRTY-THREE

Three months remained until the big move to Asia and life was pretty damn good as I turned thirty-two. My family was on-board and my friends, including my closest friend Michael, had given me their approval. Maria was still struggling despite fifteen months having passed, though she was accepting of the situation and was desperately trying to move forward and dating was helping to some extent. The house was finally sold and she had been making enquiries about a divorce and possible annulment. Her mother's anger was still elevated and although we had talked once on the phone she was unwilling to maintain any relationship. I knew she loved me but I had hurt her and her daughter *so* much and she was far from ready to forgive me. I had chosen to bury my head and avoiding the need to talk with her meant I did not need to hear about her unhappiness towards me. For now though I had decided that I was focusing on the positives and for once I felt I was experiencing true happiness. However, at 11 a.m. on a chilly April morning my happiness was shattered and my world truly rocked.

Sitting in the cold staffroom longing for the warmer spring days to come and trying to focus on completing some administration work, I felt my phone vibrating. The display showed my father's name and number and my heart sank. My father never called me and certainly never at work.

'Hello? Dad? What's wrong?' I gingerly asked not wanting to hear the response.

'It's your Uncle Sam. Heeee, ummm he's ummm, not good son. Everyone is here and Aunt Jess wants you here too.' I could not reply. I was totally choked up. My father was not the most articulate, but I still understood the seriousness from the uncharacteristic emotion in his voice. Having explained the situation to my boss I raced to my car cursing the forty-five minute drive ahead. I was totally confused. Last night Ryan and I had bantered with Uncle Sam for an hour at the hospital before he went in for routine surgery. Admittedly Uncle Sam was not in the greatest of health on account of three decades in a wheelchair, but the guy was like Troy. He was the ultimate fighter. My father's words replayed in my head. To be called from school signalled disaster surely, but the lack of clarity added to my confusion. I knew I needed to make a call. I could not face this alone. I turned on the hands free and dialled the number.

'Hello? Maria? Oh my God I think something terrible has happened.'

I explained my father's call to Maria and as expected she kept me calm for the entire drive to the hospital. As I hung up I questioned myself as to why I had turned to Maria for support and not Ryan. Parking the car I dialled Ryan's number, but was disturbed by my father knocking on the car window which startled me.

'Dad, what's going on?' I asked fearfully, as I clambered out of my car.

'He's not gonna make it son. Aunt Jess is in a terrible state and your mother. They both need you.' I did not have time to process the information as we hastily walked to the hospital entrance. My mother was standing there alone and even from this distance I could see how upset she was. I picked up the pace and grabbed her tightly, feeling her legs slightly buckle as I did. I was still not aware of what we were dealing with, desperately trying to piece the random comments together and interpret the emotions.

'Come and say your goodbyes son,' my mother whispered as she kissed my left cheek and squeezed the top of my arm tenderly. Her words resonated in my ears. *Goodbyes?* What the fuck was going on? No one was actually telling me. Somberly we stood in the elevator for five floors and walked the extremely long corridors to the ward. The smells were as distinctive as ever. As we passed the ICU Unit I figured that things could not be so bad otherwise surely that would be our final destination. How wrong I was. Turning into one of the shared rooms at the top of the ward my mother ushered me in through the curtains. The image will never escape me. There lying in the bed was Uncle Sam. My inspiration in life to succeed. My biggest supporter. Only Sam was barely there. His breathing was immensely shallow, his eyes fixed. He appeared to be struggling for every breath. Lying across his chest was his beautiful daughter Jasmine, silent, but clinging to him with every ounce of her will. To the left of Sam, my Aunt Jess. She held his gigantic hand in hers, their fingers crisscrossed like the first day they met. She rested her weary head upon the united hands and whimpered like an injured animal. Aunt Jess hid her face from the continually changing audience: nurses, doctors, family members and close friends. I was frozen to the spot. I was not reacting. I was *unable* to react. I had never experienced loss as an adult through death. My grandmother's death had been painful, but I was still a child. My emotions were undeveloped and my sense of the bigger picture was immature. Endless people came into the room, pushed past me and gave their condolences to my aunt and cousin. Yet I did not move and no one seemed to notice me.

The arrival of the priest to celebrate the final sacrament stirred further emotions from the crowd. Close family members crammed into the small space, some of whom I did not recognise. The priest was a friend of Uncle Sam's and his words were touching and poignant. I fought back my tears as one by one my family fell apart. I could not take my eyes away from Aunt Jess and Jasmine who had remained in the same position for the past three hours. I felt helpless. Here was the lady who had been my hero during the most difficult time of my life, suffering and experiencing incredible pain. I wanted to lift her agony in the way she had lifted mine. I stared at Sam as everyone once again vacated the room. The whispers outside provided the explanation I needed. The complications during surgery had led to his heart failing. How could the heart of a man with *so* much love fail? Why would God take an angel when we all needed him here? I took a few steps forward and slipped my hand under his and kissed his forehead. I longed to feel him squeeze my hand one last time or hear him say one last funny comment to me; but he was already packed up and was ready to go to a new destination. I imagined the place where he was heading to and thought of him walking around. No wheelchair. No pain or complications or prejudices. Only happiness. Aunt Jess stirred slightly. I placed my hand gently upon her head and whispered her name as I stroked her black hair. Immediately she turned and stared directly into my eyes, longing for me to now take away *her* pain. I wanted to say some words of comfort in the way she had done with me so effortlessly. I just held her close.

Sitting in the sterile corridor I stared blankly at the wall in front. I did not engage in any conversation. The clock was fast approaching midnight. I had explained the situation to

Ryan who was shocked and upset. His emotions turned to slight anger when I refused to allow him to come to the hospital. Of course I wanted him to be at my side, but my grandfather had already expressed his unwillingness to meet and today was not the time for a showdown. Of course I sympathised with Ryan too. Over the last few months he had become close to Aunt Jess and Uncle Sam, but my respect for my grandfather was more important right now. After much persuasion, Jasmine had moved to the family room to allow the nurses to examine Sam. She had laid upon his chest for hours. Fifteen minutes later Sam was gone. I only knew from the haunting wail that came belting from behind the curtain. My mother rushed to her sister, quickly followed by my grandfather. I lowered my head into my lap and cried. I could not bear the sound of my aunt's pain and so I rushed into the ward corridor and fell to the floor to cry alone. I did not want to see the face of my cousin when she was told her father had finally left. I knew he had held on until she had left the room. He would not have wanted her to see him slip away so when she briefly left, he had seized the moment. I was numb. I could not believe he was finally gone. For thirty-two years I had grown up listening to my family talking about Sam's health scares and how his existence was a miracle. I had become immune to it. I had stopped believing he was a miracle and instead considered him immortal.

An hour or so later my parents finally managed to pull my aunt away from Sam. It was the most moving scene I had ever witnessed and I could not begin to imagine for a second what she was experiencing. One by one people had left the hospital but I had refused. I could not leave Aunt Jess. I had no idea how I could possibly help her overcome the trials and tribulations that would unfold, but at least she needed to know I was standing beside her. My mother linked arms with her and slowly they sauntered down the long corridor. The sight was pitiful. My mother desperate to take away her little sister's agony. I kissed them both goodbye and drove back home, deep in thought about the day's events.

CHAPTER THIRTY-FOUR

The day of the funeral got off to a bad start. Ryan was less than pleased about me asking him to stay at home. My loyalties were divided. I did not want to face such an emotional day alone, but I respected my family and I needed Ryan to understand this. I knew he wanted to pay his respects although I also felt he was trying to force me into accepting my homosexuality by attending an important occasion as a couple. I also wondered if he was attempting to stamp his position in the family as a replacement to Maria. To some extent Ryan was very perceptive. Although I was respecting my grandfather's wishes, I was also afraid to be seen with my 'boyfriend' at the funeral. I was not even sure if all of my family were aware of my new disposition. A part of me also hoped that Maria would make an appearance. She had been incredibly fond of Uncle Sam and I knew his passing had really upset her. However, she had not attempted any contact with my family since the break-up and had failed to return any of my mother's text messages. The likelihood of Maria making an appearance was slim.

My endless attempts to explain the delicate nature of the situation to Ryan were futile. He was in his zone again. He was viewing this as another personal attack on him and was blind to the bigger picture. I sympathised yet despised him for stirring up an argument on what was already a difficult day. The phone rang as I finished putting on my sombre suit. It was my father.

'Son, your aunt wants Ryan to be there. She knows how fond Sam was of him and she knows you would welcome the support too.'

My father's voice was neutral and therefore gave no indication of what other family members were making of this. Even in her darkest hours, Aunt Jess was still thinking about others.

Returning the phone to its holder I pondered on the likelihood of Ryan declining the offer to attend and instead opting to cut his nose off to spite his face. I misjudged him, again. He was elated and rushed to get himself ready. I really hoped his intentions were just out of support and not about territory marking. I knew I was going to feel uncomfortable with a guy at my side, but I welcomed the support nonetheless as the ceremony would unquestionably be emotionally challenging. I am not sure anyone really noticed our presence. Why would they? This was not about me and my sordid love affairs but about the celebration of a great man. Aunt Jess and Jasmine were truly inspirational. They dealt with the tragic day with dignity and decorum and an inner strength that I envied. The sadness and despair was clear. It was in their eyes and eating away at their soul. Aunt Jess insisted we came back to the house afterwards and so I assumed my grandfather would be going straight home. He was struggling to see his daughter in so much pain and I knew he did not deal with these things well. You would think he would have become a little immune to the pain, having seen most of his twelve siblings pass away one by one. But can a person ever become immune to death? If they do are they not 'dead' themselves?

A post-funeral wake is uncomfortable at the best of times but when you are showcasing your gay lover for the first time to a predominantly Catholic audience, it's even more so. I felt selfish constantly fretting about myself on a day which was not about *me*. Ryan was great. He chatted away with anyone who was listening and lit up the room with his warm smile. The doorbell had continued to ring in the background for the past hour as mourners came to pay their respects one-by-one, some of whom Aunt Jess did not even know. The living room door suddenly sprung open and my grandfather stepped in. My heart sank. Showtime. It was impossible for Ryan and I to escape or hide and so I planned to make my excuses and exit quietly. Ryan did not flinch.

'What are these two faggots doing here?' he sniped. No expression. No emotion and certainly no humour. My heart sank.

'Well I can see where Jack gets his charm from!' said Ryan playfully. There was a long pause. There was no question that the timing of Ryan's wit was perfect, but the crowd were waiting to see how the Emperor himself responded to this challenge. The silence was deafening.

'Oh a bloody Taffy also!' snarled my grandfather. But this time there was a smirk. 'Give your grandfather a bloody kiss Mary!' he sniggered as he beckoned me.

I squeezed him so tightly and whispered, 'Thank you!' He walked across the room and pulled my nephew from the sofa to take his place as the head of the family. '*Soooo*, what's your name Taffy?' They were talking and I was once again breathing. In the event of tragedy there was still hope and I reflected once more on what a truly remarkable family I was blessed with.

It had been an incredibly challenging month for my family and I was constantly battling with myself about the shit timing of my move overseas. I felt so guilty leaving

Aunt Jess to face this battle alone. She was not doing so well and it was heartbreaking. For the past four weeks she had barely left her bedroom. She was broken. Lost. Through all the heartache over the years with Uncle Sam's endless medical scares, Aunt Jess had never lost her positive spirit. There was no questioning it was gone now. I think she felt her sense of purpose had been taken from her, having devoted her whole life to caring for Sam. I tried to call in to see her most evenings on the way home from work. My parents had also moved in for a few months to help. Aunt Jess was always in the same place; lying on her bed in the exact same spot where Sam had once lain. Maybe it was the closest possible spot to him that she had left. Despite her suffering she never failed to give me a smile. I knew she enjoyed my visits and my endless stories infused with drama. My repertoire of tales was an intentional ploy to distract her, even if only for thirty minutes, from her misery. There is always the fear of mentioning the name of a lost love but it is something that those in mourning desperately want to hear. When people stop saying the departed's name then they truly have gone. Speaking about them keeps their memory alive. I tried to drop Sam's name into my stories incidentally and I could see Aunt Jess thrived on this, despite the pain. Looking at her lying there, suddenly older in appearance, more fragile and damaged, I knew she would never be the same again.

CHAPTER THIRTY-FIVE

Maria seemed somewhat relieved about my impending move to Thailand. I think she welcomed the space the air miles would give us, space to heal and grow into our new lives. Of course she was teary about me leaving. We had been inseparable for thirteen years and although we had lived apart now for over a year, we always knew that the other was just around the corner. Now we would be divided by six thousand miles. It was not easy saying goodbye to her on the Friday evening before my Sunday flight. Ryan had encouraged me to spend the evening with Maria, whilst he quickly ran around saying his goodbyes to some of his friends that I had not even got around to meeting yet.

Maria and I reflected nonchalantly on our lives together. We laughed at various events over the years, normally at my expense, and we cried at the sadness we both felt for where we had ended up. My feelings for Maria now were the same as when we were together. I still loved her. I knew it was not in the way a husband was supposed to love his wife but it was love all the same. She was my soul mate, my best friend and the pain of leaving this person behind was intolerable. No one would understand these feelings – how could they? Even she found the words hard to hear. She felt abandoned, discarded and yet here I was telling her that I still loved her and thought about her every day. I chose to walk away in her eyes so why was I toying with her feelings? This was just something only I could understand. Before I left, I took one really long look at her porcelain face. Her thin red lips quivered as she anticipated the final hug.

'I'm sorry Maria. I'm going to really miss you!' Maria was unable to reply. She clung to me intensely and poured out every possible drop of sadness she had left. All I could do was simply hold her and wait for the moment to pass.

An emotional morning was followed by an emotional evening as we partied hard with our close friends at a local bar. The farewell party had been organised by Ryan, and his Facebook PR plug had brought in the crowds. It was great to be surrounded by so many of our good friends and have the opportunity to meet some new ones. The pre-party cocktails at Ryan's apartment had seemed like a good idea at the time but as I staggered to the toilet on arrival at the bar I figured I was mistaken. Ryan's close friend Mel had bought us Welsh flag boxer shorts which she is insisted we wore over our jeans and all attention was now clearly on the gay couple leaving for the tropics! Four hours of absolute fun. I had never felt so loved by so many people. Although emotional, I knew this was the beginning of an exciting new chapter.

Ryan was looking horrendously drunk and sounding particularly obnoxious as one of Charlotte's friends tried to help him up off the stool. 'Don't fucking touch me – dick!' Ryan snarled aggressively. He did not even know Mike, who was just trying to be friendly. Luckily Mike was a true gentleman and so took the comment in his stride. It was only by coincidence that he was at the bar and when Charlotte had spotted him with his new fiancé Chloe, she beckoned him over. I was sure he now wished he had remained with his original group! Ryan's outburst had only accrued a modest audience, all of whom were equally intoxicated. I had learnt to dodge Ryan during these times and so went about mingling for the final twenty minutes before closing time.

When the bar finally closed and everyone was ushered out into the midnight freeze, Ryan was nowhere to be found. His close friends were all familiar with his inability to drink and recalled the numerous times when Ryan had staggered home unaware of the need to wait for the group he had arrived with at the beginning of the evening.

'Jump in the taxi Jack and no doubt we will pass Ryan on the way,' hollered Mike, who for some reason was now joining us. Reluctantly I got into the cab, feeling disappointed by yet another spoilt evening courtesy of Ryan. Right on cue there he was staggering aimlessly along the pavement.

'Hey pull over mate!' said Mike. He was certainly a very helpful guy considering he did not even know me or Ryan. 'Ryan get in!' called Mike

'Fuck off, who do you think you are?' slurred Ryan, now barely able to keep vertical. Mike jumped out of the black cab and encouraged Ryan to get into the cab by applying a little pressure to his left shoulder. Ryan was enraged and threw his arms around in fury as if drowning in a rapidly flowing river.

'Get your fucking hands off me! Don't you touch me!' I was mortified and simply slumped my head into my palms and started to cry.

'Get into the taxi and stop being a dick!' retorted Mike, who was visibly losing patience. Whatever I thought of Ryan during these episodes I was not happy to hear someone else calling him names. I jumped out of the cab and signalled for them to go on ahead without us.

Lovingly, I wrapped my arms around Ryan in an attempt to calm him down.

'Ger off me! Why don't you just go off with your new sexy boyfriend?'

He pushed me hard and I fell to the ground. He did not even care as he turned and continued to zigzag off down the street. The Asian couple sitting on the bench waiting for the final bus were unsure of what to make of this behaviour and offered no helping hand. Ryan was in the zone and totally unaware of the upset and pain he was causing. There was no reasoning with him during these moments. The only thing I could do was walk slowly behind him, protecting him without him even knowing. How did we get to this point? Was I sure this was the kind of person I wanted to move to the other side of the world with? No truer saying than love is blind. You can justify every possible flaw in a loved one if you really want to.

Arriving at the front porch of Mel's plush apartment I was horrified to see the short, dark stranger in the tux still standing there. He was a persistent superhero if nothing else. Like a red rag to a bull, Ryan was quick to confront Mike with a heightened aggression. Mike was totally unfazed and simply stepped aside to allow for Ryan to fall in through the doorway. I walked off down the street, taking refuge on a low brick wall outside the exclusive coffee shop on the corner of the street. The cherry blossom trees looked so pretty now that the warmer July weather had finally arrived and encouraged a late bloom.

'How you doing?' whispered a mysterious voice approaching from behind. It was Mike, my knight in shining armour.

'I'm okay thanks, just embarrassed by how much of a cock my boyfriend can be sometimes.'

'Hey we've all been there. Don't worry about it. I hear you're off to Asia together. Wow big step, but pretty amazing, yeah?'

Mike was incredibly understanding and reasonable. His eloquent voice was soothing and his face so handsome. With him just sitting next to me my dick started to grow and as he leant in for a kiss I was totally unprepared. Why the hell was the hot, *straight* guy kissing someone like me? He was so gentle. He just softly pressed his lips upon mine and closed his eyes. He did not force his tongue into my mouth or grab at my body. He simply, gently, placed his left hand upon my right cheek and nestled into my neck.

'I'm sorry Jack. I don't know why I did that.' A little dumbfounded I didn't reply but gave a small grin. 'My God I'm desperate for a piss!' chuckled Mike as he proceeded to pull his dick out and urinate against the back of the wall on which I sat.

I could not help but take a few glances and part of me wondered if that was his intention. What he lacked in length he made up for in girth. As he pulled the foreskin back and forth to shake off the excess, it was noticeable that having an audience watching was exciting him a little. I wanted to reach out and grab his cock but I was still unsure of what his reaction might be. Plus we were on public display with the occasional car passing by. Returning his cock to its place of rest, Mike reached out and pulled me in for a hug. I wondered if he liked me or just felt sorry for me. After all he had a fiancé waiting back at the house. Hugging Mike felt so good. His strong frame made me feel safe. Protected. He was a classy guy with style and charisma.

'What are you two gay boys doing out here?' chuckled Mel who had come to look for me knowing how upset I would be following another outburst from Ryan. Mike did not seem bothered that we had been caught in an embrace and so I figured the whole evening could be justified by the large volumes of alcohol consumed. For the first time ever

I questioned my future with Ryan. I despised his behaviour at times and felt so frustrated by his inability to rationalise when under the influence. He was abusive and hurtful and this was not something I could tolerate in the long-term.

Returning to the apartment I sat on the edge of the bed and watched Ryan in his deep sleep, still fully clothed and oozing alcoholic fumes with every exhale. I stared at the flight tickets and considered the possibility of going alone. Starting completely again with no links to my mistakes or past. It was somewhat enticing yet I was petrified. I had never been alone and never even travelled solo on a train. I needed Ryan right now. He was the person who had given me the courage to change my life and for that he deserved another chance to change. Trying to sleep I thought about all the hurt and anguish I was leaving behind and the hopes I had for our new life in Asia. I thought about Maria. Was she lying in bed thinking about me? Was she hopeful for her future or totally despairing? I closed my eyes and whispered the words *'I'm sorry,'* in the hope she might hear them.

CHAPTER THIRTY-SIX

Two emotional family farewells, endless tears, hugs and promises to stay in touch with friends *and* a fourteen-hour flight and finally Ryan and I arrived in the heart of south-east Asia – Bangkok! I had never lived outside my home town so living almost 10,000 km away was going to be a challenge. Ryan had given me a new-found confidence and I felt I could face anything now. Despite the tiredness I was buzzing inside and could not wait to start our new amazing life together. The white sandy beaches, lush forests and fabulous culture were so enticing. So many times Ryan and I had stared at each other on the plane, so much hope in our eyes about what exciting adventures awaited us. The thought of space to grow as a couple, with no history or beady eyes watching our every move, no narrow-minded thugs shouting abuse on a Saturday night out and, best of all, the thought of endless sunshine.

My new boss, who I strongly suspected was gay himself, was waiting at the airport to meet us. I was not overly impressed about having to meet him for the first time after a long-haul journey wearing sweaty clothing and furry teeth! He appeared extremely friendly and was most welcoming towards Ryan. It was a little strange introducing someone as my boyfriend as it always made me feel like a ten-year-old schoolboy. Ryan did not have any employment lined up but planned to complete some further studies and then seek work teaching English as a second language. It was also a little overwhelming arriving at such a huge airport with bustling crowds from all four corners of the globe. The volume of everything seemed a few decibels higher.

As we stepped outside, the choking heat punched me straight in the face. It was incredible, like nothing I had ever experienced before. There was zero circulation of air. No wind whatsoever, which now explained why my new boss was sweating profusely. Despite being in the country for over five years, he had failed to truly acclimatise. Now I could understand why. Despite the heat, the sky was not the paradise blue I had imagined on account of the onset of monsoon season. The walk to the minibus was less than one hundred metres but already multiple beads of sweat were crawling around my face. I longed for just a sudden breeze of cooler air but it never came. The hot air hit the back of your throat, making it difficult to take deep breaths, as if someone had turned off the oxygen valve. Sure I had experienced extreme temperatures before in Kenya, Dubai and on one rare occasion in Europe, but this was different. The humidity was unreal and close to 90%. As we climbed into the minibus the ice-cold flow of air from the AC was like a gift from the gods. The stark contrast in temperature was numbing.

Driving to the hotel was extraordinary and fascinating. It felt as though we were viewing a travel programme on the Discovery Channel. It was an intriguing blend of modern western civilisation with eastern delight. The contrast was extraordinary between the state-of-the-art high rise buildings and the traditional temples, the familiar American food outlets and the local food stalls selling anything from sun-dried squid to an array of lush tropical fruits. It was a sensory overload. The insane traffic provided the time to absorb my new surroundings. Crowds of people bustled about like ants and the sound of countless whistles blowing was deafening as the traffic was beckoned from all directions. A tremendous number of motorcycles wove their way through the formation of colourful taxis, cars, buses and of course the signature tuk-tuk. The motorbikes formed a troop of taxis transporting goods, solo passengers and even whole families. I witnessed one woman breastfeeding on the back of a bike and one guy was carrying a set of ladders! Ryan and I were giggling and nudging each other as every new scene unfolded before us. It was so different from the city we had left behind.

Pulling up outside the hotel that would be our home for the next month it was clear that that was going to be very different too! Let's just say that website images can be a little deceiving. The two unattractive Thai girls at the reception desk had found it amusing that both Ryan and I would be sharing just one double bed when we checked in. This immature behaviour did not impress my boss, who appeared extremely uncomfortable. He had just spent the last twenty minutes of the journey explaining how it was so refreshing to live in such an accepting society. This was clearly not reflected in the attitude of our hosts. In fairness they were particularly young and the sight of two handsome white guys had flummoxed them somewhat. With my boss now on his way Ryan and I were alone and free to explore the hotel from hell! The room was dark and dreary with a horrendous shade of grey covering the walls. The plastic linoleum flooring was broken, or possibly chewed in multiple places, and the bathroom was reminiscent of the 70s. First thing needed was a hot shower to wash away the grime of the last twenty-four hours. No such luck. The water ran cold only, which although refreshing was still a shock to any weary body. There was the most incredible high-pitched clicking sound which was unfamiliar and yet curious. As Ryan and I moved the old and battered leather furniture around the room we caught sight of the smallest yet quickest moving lizard. It was not an intimidating creature, but being so unexpected it caused Ryan to throw down the heavy sofa suddenly, catching the tiny invertebrate's tail underneath. The poor gecko gave a little shrug to the side and ran scuttling off leaving his tail rooted to the floor. Ryan and I both screamed a little more before laughing hysterically. A three-inch harmless animal had caused so much drama! It was something we would have to learn to live with as the room was full of them.

What the hotel lacked in charm it made up for in an outdoor swimming pool. The pool was the perfect suntrap and the shimmering water that reflected an incredible blue haze was so seductive. The pool would have to wait, as the need for food was greater. Stepping out into the evening heat was no less surprising than our first encounter at the airport. Despite the departure of the sun the temperature remained elevated. Added to this was the choking pollution and additional heat from all the food stalls that lined the streets like soldiers. My senses were working overtime. The smells were incredible and rapidly changing with every few steps. From mouth-watering barbecuing meats to the sudden waves of nausea caused by the overwhelming stench from the drains that stood between the food sellers. It was one way to walk off an appetite! My eyes could not absorb my surroundings quick enough. So many unfamiliar food items hanging on hot grills, so many people muttering away in words I could not begin to comprehend. Cats, dogs, rats and cockroaches scurrying everywhere. Over-sized LCD screens hung on the tops of buildings, blaring adverts that competed in volume against the next one. It was bizarre yet thrilling.

An unexpected yet most welcoming cooler breeze danced through the streets briefly, a sign of the impending downfall apparently. Moments later the heavens opened and the heaviest downpour commenced. I had never witnessed rainfall of this magnitude. The water droplets were ginormous and menacing. The food sellers were accustomed to the season and within seconds yards of plastic sheeting was erected, providing little havens of protection from the rain. Umbrellas went up and life continued. Ryan and I took refuge in a shop doorway and watched silently as the water level in the street continued to rise. In less than twenty minutes the drains were gagging, overwhelmed by the excessive volume of water. Forty-five minutes later and the rain ceased with the same speed at which it arrived. However, it left behind a twenty-centimetre flood of water that Ryan and I had to wade through back to the hotel. It was a humorous highlight to an overwhelming day. Returning to our room from our first encounter with Bangkok we were exhausted.

'This is going to be insane!' joked Ryan excitedly. 'I hope you're ready for this!'

The jetlag was now taking its toll and although my mind was racing I was no longer able to fight my fate.

CHAPTER THIRTY-SEVEN

For one week we walked the busy streets all day every day in an attempt to familiarise ourselves with our new home. Ryan had not secured a job yet so it also provided the opportunity to look for potential employment. There was not much work for non-nationals and anything that was out there was so poorly paid it was not worth Ryan getting out of bed for. My salary was already considered impressive as the cost of living was so low, so we knew there was no pressure for Ryan to work. It was so refreshing to be able to eat out every night and yet pay less than a few pounds. And the food was incredible. My taste buds had never been so alive. The fusion of flavours was immense and the variety insatiable. The level of spiciness was overwhelming and I welcomed a few easy phrases from my pocket dictionary to help with placing my future orders! There were some food items that were totally off my menu: chicken feet, stewed squid and fried insects were just a few. The shopping was electrifying too. Bangkok had the full range, from top-end malls with designer brands to copy goods heaven. Every designer product, copied and marketed at pocket money prices. Handbags, sunglasses, jeans, DVDs etc, these malls had them all and *we* bought them all. Of course the quality was not always great but we did not care. The buzz of buying was incredible and using an unfamiliar currency made keeping track of the spending even more difficult to feel guilty about.

Adapting to the heat remained challenging but the skytrain or taxi rides provided a refreshing cool-down between destinations. The exhibit of culture was dazzling too. Endless temples sat nestled amongst the metropolis. Beautiful ornate masterpieces of architecture with intricate detail that housed an oasis of tranquillity. It was so easy to lose yourself for a few hours. I remained fascinated by the countless number of orange-robed Buddhist monks who moved silently about the city, collecting alms and effortlessly receiving the respect of others. The city was bustling yet moved at a slow pace. Cars sat patiently for hours in all-day traffic and the locals floated down the crowded streets in slow motion. I learnt over time that this was probably on account of the heat. The fast pace of the foreigners or *'farangs'* as they referred to us, made them smile. Some of us failed to leave behind our European ways and rushing about was still an inherent trait, often resulting in a sweaty and flummoxed demeanour.

Ten days later Ryan and I had decided we needed space from our reptilian friends so we began apartment hunting. I had a few more days before I started my new job so it provided the perfect opportunity for further explorations, though money was a little tight now as the final savings from the house sale were quickly evaporating. We stopped at every BTS or skytrain station and sampled the nearby living spaces. This was our first proper home together and so finding the perfect place was a priority. After one long weekend we finally agreed upon and secured a beautiful condo thirty minutes out of the city. The rooftop pool and gym had been the deciding factor. Leaving the condo building we decided to hop on the back of a motorcycle taxi. The thrill of racing through the streets with a speed generated wind was incredible. I hopped on the bike at the front and Ryan was following on a slower bike with an elderly gentleman as his chauffeur. My driver clearly had a need for speed and his brand new Honda bike fed his adrenaline addiction. I was grabbing on to his waist with both hands, my knuckles white as we flew over the brow of a small hill towards the train station. I glanced over my shoulder to check on Ryan's progress. A small blur could be seen in the distance and I wished I had chosen the grandpa as my driver now.

As we continued to race along the uneven road I noticed a car cruising alongside us. The driver was young and equally addicted to speed. The late night setting provided a quieter race track for the two of them. As the saloon took the slight edge he suddenly turned left unannounced. The bike frantically tried to brake but the close proximity resulted in a deafening collision. The sound of metal thrashing metal and glass shattering brought back shocking memories of my car accident nearly a decade ago as I flew through the air over the top of the now stationary car. The landing was painful and dramatic. The multiple log rolls resulted in an array of harsh cuts and slashes. My only thought was to protect my head that was not fortunate enough to have a helmet on it. As my final roll came to an end I lay splattered across the road only aware of the sound of shouting in a language I did not comprehend. I was petrified. I remained still, in dismay at how I could possibly be in this situation yet again. And then the pain struck me. My breathing was difficult and shallow and I felt sure I had broken a rib or two or worse still my back again. My immediate concern was my back but as I wiggled my toes I felt reassured. The sound of a scream that seemed familiar and comprehensible came rushing towards me. It was Ryan, or certainly a much whiter version of Ryan. He was panic-stricken but doing a damn fine job of appearing calm. We were in a foreign country, thousands of miles from home and unable to communicate with the countless people surrounding us. We did not even know the number for the emergency services or whether they even existed.

'Mr, Mr. You okay mai?' Thank God the young driver could speak English. He rushed to my assistance apologising profusely, quickly followed by the motorcyclist who appeared to be sporting a broken thumb only. They were incredible and so friendly. They avoided the temptation to blame each other and instead stood united in helping the poor white man sprawled across the roadside. As they lifted me to my feet the extent of my injuries became apparent. The blood was oozing from my knee and a fist-size flap of skin hung down. My right toe appeared broken and was bending out of shape to the side. A second flap of skin hung from the side of my foot and blood flowed continually from the wound. The sight of so much blood drained the colour from me and my sugar levels plummeted. As my knees buckled with the sudden drop in blood pressure, the young car driver beckoned Ryan and the motorcyclist to help me into his car.

'Ryan, Ryan! I can't breathe!' I exclaimed. The pain in my chest was unbearable and with every breath I felt the need to cry out. I was devastated. I imagined being flown home and that would be the end of our Asian dream.

'Mr, Mr! Okay na? I take you hospital,' shouted the young man from the driver's seat. He was equally panicked on account of the now damaged BMW that belonged to his parents. The motorcyclist, nicknamed Num, sat devastated with his head in his hands. His livelihood lay on the side of the road, broken and smashed. The fear in Ryan's eyes was not helping me to relax and as the level of pain rose I felt increasingly worried. The amount of blood pouring onto the luxurious mats below was also worrying and no attempt had been made to slow down the flow of blood. Waves of nausea consumed me and I began to cry. My sense of relief as we came to a stop was short-lived as I realised there was no hospital in sight. We were in the middle of a deserted side road. The shutters pulled down on the shop fronts indicated no one was at home.

'What the fuck are we doing here?' I screamed, as my ability to be patient had long since left.

'Mr, Mr no gas no gas!' You have got to be kidding me, I thought. I imagined bleeding to death in the back of this stranger's car. It was not the dramatic end to my life that I would have picked. Ryan briefly chuckled on account of the craziness of the situation but my scowl quickly wiped the humour from his face. A few phone calls later and a troop of fellow motorcyclists arrived and started siphoning off petrol from their bikes and into the car. The comradeship was extraordinary and uplifting. Here was me, an unknown foreigner bleeding in the back of a car and they were donating petrol to my escorts. Each gave me a beaming smile as they made their donation, totally fascinated by my western appearance. Finally we were on the move again, but as we turned the final bend I passed out to the sound of Ryan's faint hysteria.

An hour or so later and the nurse woke me as she changed the drip in my left arm that was replenishing my much-needed fluids and electrolytes. My vision was a little blurred but I could see Ryan beside me.

'Shit, you gave me a scare then Jack! Your parents would have fucking killed me if I'd let you die in Thailand.'

He grinned and stroked my face. I could feel the pressure of hands pressed on each of my arms and lifted my head slightly. There at either side of my bed were the speed demons themselves, Num and Jom. They had remained at my bedside for the entire hour and both gave a beaming smile as I acknowledged them both.

'So sorry krub. Okay mai?' asked Num, who was himself bandaged up to his elbow. Ryan had phoned my boss Mark and explained the situation. He had apologised profusely and seemed to feel personally responsible for our well-being. Ryan had needed to persuade him not to come to the hospital and that the broken toe and bruising was not life-threatening. Wearily I dropped my head back on the pillow and laughed at the prospect of arriving at work on the first day on crutches. Not quite how I had imagined it, I thought to myself. Although battered and bruised I felt uplifted by the wonderful faith in people I now had on account of my new-found Thai friends!

CHAPTER THIRTY-EIGHT

Now living in our new swanky pad and wallowing in a pampered life-style, life was pretty damn fine. Despite the challenge of being on crutches for the first few weeks, I was enjoying work. Ryan was enjoying the pool! He had not secured any work and I was not sure how hard he was really looking. I did not blame him at all. He had been working since he was sixteen and so this was a welcome change to the pace of life. Most days he would try to go out and explore new territory and give me a full breakdown when we met up later that day. I did feel a little pressure to get back home as quick as possible as I was conscious of how many hours Ryan was spending alone. This often meant turning down offers from my new colleagues to hang out. Of course, I could have invited Ryan but once again his drunken behaviour was sometimes compromising my position. The two occasions where I had invited him had not been successful from my point of view.

Admittedly the first night out at a local night spot was really good fun and gave me the opportunity to bond with some of my workmates. However, seeing Ryan and one of my staff falling over and rolling around on the floor was not a highlight. It was difficult to line manage someone the next day at work when the evening before they had been frolicking with your gay lover! The second occasion can only be described as painful, one of those moments when you wish the floor would open up and swallow you whole. A large crowd of my colleagues had arranged to meet for tapas and sangria. I was not really drinking which always made me hyper sensitive to the declining behaviour of others as their alcohol consumption rockets. I just could not comprehend why Ryan always had to guzzle his alcohol like a refreshing soft drink on a summer's day. Some of the younger girls had ordered a variety of cocktail concoctions and were eagerly badgering me to try. The mixture was lethal and quite simply disgusting!

'Ha, ha, your face was *so* funny when you drank that then!' giggled the girls.

'You should see his face when he cums!' retorted Ryan.

It was the single most embarrassing sentence that anyone had ever said about me. No one was quite sure how to react and for a moment the tumbleweed could be heard rolling past. Finally the crucifying silence was broken by the laughter of the intoxicated girls. That moment of inappropriateness had now marked Ryan's card and I preferred to isolate work from play – permanently!

I had become particularly close to a small group of new starters. We were probably attracted to each other by our Asian virginity. Luke and Gemma were both from England and were much younger than me. Luke had briefly been in Thailand previously and had returned to be with his Asian-Canadian girlfriend Chloe. They were the cutest couple and great fun to hang out with. Luke and I seemed to have more in common, probably because we worked together and both loved to work out in the gym, whereas Ryan and Chloe were bonded by their equally colourful pasts.

Chloe was also teaching but in a province just outside Bangkok. She was born to Thai parents, but raised in Canada. Her national identity changed depending on the context and we would often tease her for this. She was incredibly beautiful but did not truly realise it, turning heads whenever we were out. She was the fag hag that gay men dream about. Her caramel skin was flawless and her silky black hair framed her face to perfection. But she was a hippy at heart and her insistence on wearing oversized 'traditional' clothing and flip-flops always made me smile.

Gemma was here alone and very immature. I felt like an older brother, needing to look out for her all the time. Ryan was not fond of her but I figured this was more out of jealousy than about her personality. She continually made me laugh yet I do admit she was loud and a little over-powering at times. The funniest of her traits was how tight she was with money. She was incredible! Gemma once asked me for money for a packet of ten baht chewing gums and she was the only person I knew who insisted on waiting for two baht change from the economically challenged taxi drivers whenever we caught a taxi from work.

We had been in Bangkok for over two months and yet had failed to sample the seedier side of Bangkok's night life. My friendships with Luke, Chloe and Gemma were strong and despite working with two of them, we were able to separate work from pleasure. I was not too concerned about Ryan's behaviour in front of them, although his impatience with Gemma was sometimes irritating. She was an attractive young woman with luring bosoms, but had Ryan forgotten my homosexuality? Did he really have cause to be jealous?

Saturday night and we were in the Patpong area, notorious for prostitutes, happy ending massages, go-go shows and the infamous ping pong shows. We wanted to try it all, although Luke drew the line at the gay sex shows. He was a very tall, handsome young man who attracted a lot of attention from the gay guys and this often made him feel uncomfortable. Our first destination was the ping pong show. We paid our entrance fee to the mafia-style men standing outside, all three dressed in black suits and larger than any other Thai guys I had seen on the street. Their facial hair made them look particularly menacing so we declined the temptation to barter down the price. The room was dark and smelt of damp. The lighting was particularly poor and the blackened walls and floor added to the gloom. Rows of seats faced a small stage where two slim and very attractive naked females stood twirling around two metal poles. They wore only knee-length boots which were clearly exciting the crowd who were particularly old and generally white. We preferred to refer to them as dinosaurs or farangosauruses. Thailand is notorious for attracting middle-aged men experiencing some kind of mid-life crisis. Looking at the average age I figured this may even be an end of life crisis for some! Some of the elderly ex-pats and rich Singaporeans and Japanese men were being 'entertained' by some of the bar girls, the delight on their faces evident as the young girls rubbed their laps. It repulsed me at first but then I started thinking. Was it really so bad? Some of these men were probably widows, miserable from life's challenges. Was a moment or two of pleasure from a hot Asian babe really so bad? The clientele was also made up of groups of young men probably on a stag do or taking a year out after finishing university. Small pockets of females could also be seen and *heard* on account of their giggling.

We sat to the side in one long line along a worn leather bench. Clearly we were newbies and the bar girls sensed this. Ryan's charming smile never failed to attract attention and he was quick to be entertained by an eager bar girl named Fon. She was a little disappointed when Ryan explained she was barking up the wrong tree and Chloe's scowl gave enough warning for her to keep away from Luke. Despite not really liking the female form anymore I could not help but be impressed by the slender, sexy bodies of the two dancers and guessed that the show might actually be more erotic than I had anticipated. The lights went down and the disco balls started twirling. It was a poor attempt at retro. A few of the dinosaurs gave a roar of excitement and the women continued to giggle. I was quite looking forward to seeing the talent of these two hot females.

The onset of the upbeat music track indicated it was show time as the spotlights beamed on the... What the hell? The beauties were gone and had been mysteriously replaced by two plumper, far less attractive women wearing nothing but bed socks! This was to prevent them from slipping on the various fluids that were either used or excreted during the show. The first 'girl' was mid-forties and no taller than 5-feet. Her lady garden was more of a jungle and the way she swallowed those ping pong balls indicated that many a child had vacated that area at some point! I had to give credit to her though. She shot the balls out with enormous propulsion resulting in many an expat being struck on the face by the gooey projectiles! Her supporting act was a little younger but had definitely not discovered dental treatment as yet. I felt a little guilty for being so judgmental. These poor women probably had four or five youngsters at home to feed and this job probably barely paid for one meal. Was it entertainment or exploitation? There were no ping pongs used in act two. This talented mistress had raised the bar and was now firing darts across the room, bursting balloons that selected guests were eagerly holding up. Her encore was to pull a string of razor blades out from her vagina! Quite remarkable how entertaining one anatomical part can be. The sexy babes were back on stage for round two of their dancing routine as the stage was mopped down. When the girls returned and played a rendition of a vaguely familiar tune from small trumpets protruding from their vaginas, we knew it was time to move on.

Next stop, the gay sex shows! Luke and Chloe decided to call it a night. I am not sure if Luke was dreading the prospect of seeing the male form in an equally disturbing manner or whether the pussy acrobatics had been enough for one night. Gemma was more than keen to accompany the two gay boys. The men on the door were replicas of the previous security.

'Two hundred baht each. One free drink inside!' mumbled the largest of the three men. His body was like Thor, his voice like Tigger! The stark contrast made Gemma giggle which was not welcomed by the men who took a step forward.

'Must be the steroids playing havoc with his body,' I joked as I handed over my one thousand baht note. Escorted inside we felt privileged to be given front row seats. Thirty or more young Asian lads shuffled in rhythm to the music, each wearing rather revealing white speedos with a number tag attached. It was the first time I had ever appreciated the diversity of Asian men. There were some taller, muscular lads with beautiful artistic tattoos and very slight, effeminate 'boys'. Some of the boys were very dark and exotic, whilst others were pale with a fine covering of hair across their chests and down their abdomens. It was a moment of enlightenment and Ryan did not fail to notice. I figured he must have been as equally in awe but reluctant to admit it. Every twenty seconds or so the boys would rotate, enabling the horny hyenas sitting in the pulpit to view the full menu.

Two songs later and there was no sign of my change. Beckoning a rather impressive lady boy to the table I asked if she could return the four hundred baht change I was owed. Within seconds two burly guys and a 'queen' were in our faces.

'What's your fucking problem? You gotta fucking problem Mr?' squealed the sissy in a black suit with heels. I was somewhat distracted by the confusion in his appearance.

'You owe me four hundred baht that's all. You said two hundred baht each and I gave one thousand baht.'

'You gotta fucking problem Mr. You want me to kick your fucking arse out of here?' screamed the banshee. Ryan was crying with laughter on account of the high-pitched squeak that came with every reply and Gemma was clearly petrified.

'Ummm, no problem. My mistake. Sorry!' I grovelled, just as the pace of the music changed and the hotties left the stage leaving me puzzled as to the purpose of the little number tags on their briefs. Two incredibly built guys came out from behind the curtain wearing small leather pouches, black army boots and large silver-framed shades. It was incredibly horny and I was embarrassed to be enjoying the moment whilst sitting next to my young colleague. I attempted to look disinterested as the bald guy yanked the pouch from the waist of the second guy, who looked like a rock star, so revealing a rather intriguing, uncut cock that hung in a semi-erect state. His abs were beautifully defined and his hairless pale skin celebrated two fine pectoral muscles that I yearned to feel.

Suddenly, the bald guy was on his knees and pleasuring the other with his mouth. I was mortified that Gemma was seeing this yet too absorbed in my own viewing pleasures to overly care. She giggled and laughed hysterically as both took turns to suck on the other's *now* erect cock. I had not prepared myself for such a graphic display. I figured a few less than average looking men would dance around a pole naked or something similar. But this! This was heaven. We were sat so close I could have grabbed the pert cheeks of both guys. The bald guy flipped the cuter guy over and proceeded to rub his cock along the crack of his arse. Without warning, he was inside him and the two gyrated as the intensity of the music increased. With each push the guys edged forward, closer and closer towards us. Gemma was moving back and screaming possibly out of excitement or shock, but I felt as though I was leaning in. I wanted in on this action. The sex was angry and animalistic and we could see everything. There were no fancy camera tricks or clever angles, this was real live sex right before our eyes. The music came to a close and the lights went down as the audience applauded. I felt breathless and took the opportunity in the darkened room to adjust my crotch before Ryan noticed the extent to which I had enjoyed the show. It was now the return of the dancing angels as the lights shone bright once more.

'It's late. Let's go!' scowled Ryan. I sensed he had watched my reaction to the show and was not happy. What I did not foresee was his own level of interest and the guilt he felt for being somewhat tempted by the meat festival. That night, we had the best sex ever!

It was not long before Ryan and I instigated a repeat evening, this time minus Gemma. I am not really sure which of us made the suggestion, but either way we were both more than eager to go along. We stumbled upon a different area as we desperately tried to recall the location of the previous venue. Here was a whole street of gay delights! The flashing neon signs outside were not shy in advertising the boys on offer. Countless guys stood outside the dark panelled bars handing out fliers.

'Mr, Mr come see big cock show!'

'Handsome man, where you go? Come see fucking show upstairs!'

It was unreal. If the last place was heaven, was this hell? So sordid, so graphic and so tempting. We 'sampled' a few of the shows on offer as they offered a free one-minute viewing session. In one bar, sexy naked men swam like gay mermaids underwater. In another, boys in drag walked down runways in elaborate clothing with their over-sized cocks swinging with each step. Our carnal walk ended at 'Dreamboys – the big cock show!' I indicated for the waiter to sit us away from the front this time. Once again the stage, which was significantly bigger than the last, was crowded with an array of allurement, each wearing a red number tag. Number 32 was particularly attractive. His spiky, modern hairstyle and facial hair were most pleasing, together with the ripped, fit body. Number 11 was totally different but equally appealing. He was short and stocky and hairy. His peachy arse was beautifully framed in his tiny white speedos. His friend to the left, Number 25, was staring right at me. I had not noticed him previously but as he seductively rubbed his crotch I could not help but take note. Ryan seemed to be distracted by Number 3 and his impressive crotch, so I seized the moment to give a small cheeky smile to my admirer. He was trying to mouth some words and pointing repeatedly at his number tag. I tried to distract myself with another male beauty but every time I tried, Number 25 caught my eye.

Ryan stood up suddenly and wandered off to get a round of drinks and right before my eyes Number 25 flashed me his cock and mouthed, 'Pick me!' My eyes were fixated on his dark meat and I blushed like a naïve virgin. My reaction caused a giggle from him and a few of the numbers stood around him. A change in music track and a new batch of scantily clad guys took to the stage. As Ryan and I made a toast I felt someone squeeze in beside me. It was Number 25 himself.

'What your name handsome man. I go home with you?' I turned to Ryan and laughed.

'What the hell?'

'Only 500 baht Mr and then you give me special tip. I give good fuck fuck!'

'Jesus Christ Ryan is this for real? No, it's okay thanks. This is my boyfriend.'

'Mr, I can suck suck him and fuck fuck you. Come on. I go home with you please,' begged the now less attractive dancer.

'Up to him,' sniggered Ryan. 'I'm off for a piss!'

I could not understand why Ryan had left me with this guy. Was he testing my willpower or was he himself enticing me with a possible threesome? Did Ryan want to take this whore home with us? With Ryan now out of the room my lucky number grabbed my hand and placed it firmly and directly onto his crotch. I did not flinch. I just kept looking forward. The other punters were unable to see on account of the style of seating. I felt him move my hand a little more and as the temperature changed I knew my hand was now inside his pants. I wriggled my fingers a little and felt the soft folds of the skin of his balls and now rapidly enlarging penis. I turned my head and saw him grinning as his now fully erect cock sprung from his swimwear. There was still no sign of Ryan. The long slender dark skin was so tempting and I slowly retracted the skin back over the swollen gland. It felt amazing. This was my first ever Asian cock. Catching a glimpse of Ryan heading back towards us I quickly released my grip and signalled for my tempter to leave the booth. Ryan had a slight smirk on his face and I wondered if he had planned the whole episode. Either way I could not get the feeling out of my head as three well-hung lads masturbated in synch to the theme tune from *Titanic*! Three climaxes all over the stage and I knew that would be the last time I would ever listen to that song in the same way again!

CHAPTER THIRTY-NINE

Three long, yet exciting months, and it was finally the end of the first half semester. With the city life heavily explored over the past few months, it was time to venture to the paradise beaches we had eagerly awaited. I had organised a one-week adventure for Ryan's birthday around the islands of Thailand. It was going to be a dream. We were both incredibly excited as the plane touched down in Krabi, Southern Thailand. Wasting no time at all, we checked into the hotel, threw on our swimwear and headed for the port to rent a long-tail boat for the day. The sun was blazing, though the coastal breeze made it bearable. With the monsoon season now closing, the sky was picture perfect. Our guide for the day was Sprite, like the soft drink. He was incredibly lean with particularly dark skin, probably on account of being exposed to the intense sunlight all year round. I guessed he was around twenty. He spoke very little English but between the three of us we just about managed to communicate our needs through the random Thai words we had learnt, my iPhone translator and of course over-emphasised hand gestures!

Fifteen minutes later and we arrived at the first of our three island delights – Chicken Island. This oasis of beauty was of tiny proportions but beautifully formed. The single rock face remaining resembled the profile of a chicken's head, hence the name. Sprite anchored the boat and helped us ashore. It was magnificent. Never before had I witnessed such beauty in nature. The sand comprised of the tiniest beads of white pearls that felt like velvet underfoot. The water that kissed the sand shimmered between a jade green and a sapphire blue. The island itself was intensely green and unpopulated. There was not a single other person on the island. This was our very own desert island and it was perfect. Ryan and I threw off our T-shirts and flip-flops and bounded like two puppies around the circumference of the island. It was deceivingly bigger than expected. Less than one kilometre into our crazy trek and the sun had taken its hold on us. The rays burnt like naked flames and the incredible light made it difficult not to squint. We headed for the refreshing water. Clear like glass, cool like ice, the ocean bathed our frazzling skin. Shoals of tiny colourful fish swam between us, lighting up Ryan's eyes in awe. With no one around I leant in for a kiss. The salty water formed a glaze on his lips as we pressed our bodies up close. I could feel Ryan's excitement across my thigh. I felt comfortable in my own skin for the first time as I wrapped my arms around his neck. This was a remarkable step for me. I was engaging in public displays of affection – with a man! We bobbed up and down in the still, tranquil waters for what seemed like hours, never once letting go. The sudden sound of our long-tail boat gliding around the corner signalled it was time for our next stop.

Poda was the second of our idyllic stops, a significantly larger island that lacked the charisma and charm of the first, but was no less a 'Shangri-La'. The countless palm trees swaying ever so slightly in the soft breeze framed the picturesque island. Small wooden huts were scattered amongst the lush green landscape and island dwellers sat around resting and chatting. The inhabitants sat under trees away from the ball of fire that was now at its highest point. The holiday makers sat like uncooked meat on a pan. Fortunately the island was far from crowded. The sand was like a sheet of enamel and provided the perfect afternoon bed for tanning. Sun cream on, shades on, iPod turned up, I was ready for a few hours of R and R. The whisper of the waves in the slight distance was incredibly soothing and I felt myself drifting off. It felt unreal to be living in such a remarkable country and life was so different from the trials I had faced just a few months ago. I felt weightless and invincible. Ever since puberty I had been carrying a burdensome weight upon my shoulders. Now it was gone. There was no need to haul it around with me anymore.

'Sir, sir, eat eat. Have fish. Have fruit,' interrupted Sprite. He had barbecued some fish and vegetables and laid out a selection of tropical fruits for us. He looked so happy to oblige us and insisted we eat alone, as he watched and smiled only. His skeletal body looked under fed but I figured it was his genetic disposition. He had the cutest smile as he sat grinning whilst we finished our splendid seaside feast. Looking across at Ryan it was clear to understand why Sprite continued to grin. Both of us were sporting a pair of panda eyes and already our skin was glowing a shade of crimson.

Clearly it was time for the T-shirts to be back on and the SPF factor to be increased as we moved to our late afternoon spot – Maya Bay. The dramatic landscape was breathtaking and of epic proportions. Beautifully carved limestone formed iconic sculptures. It was most definitely the ultimate example of Mother Nature's work. Our resting spot was the first of two beaches to explore with a winding path that led through dense, low-lying grassland and into a pocket of heaven. Three walls of limestone formed a small arena with a lagoon sitting silently in the middle.

The spectrum of colours was captivating and both of us took a sudden gasp as we stumbled upon the sanctum. At the opposite end of the small lagoon was a bamboo ladder that took the climber to a small opening in the limestone. It was like a secret adventure from a land far far away. Had we been transported to the set of an exotic movie?

The outer perimeter of the lagoon was shallow with stepping stones strategically placed. A young couple were returning from the climb wearing the biggest smiles and a definite twinkle in their eye. This stimulated my own adrenaline and I began to negotiate the stones a little quicker.

'Slow down you idiot!' laughed Ryan as he grabbed my arm to stop me from falling when I stumbled. 'The opening will not close like a fairy tale time warp Jack!'

His grin indicated that he was happy to see my level of excitement. He had seen me so miserable and so troubled for such a long period of time. This new demeanour was most welcome I am sure. When we finally reached the opposite side of the lagoon we were faced with a three-metre stretch of sharp shale. Minus the flip-flops the journey was painful but our motivation to see the view gave us all the will we needed to continue as we giggled and screeched with every painful step. The climb up the bamboo ladder was far scarier and much steeper than I had first assessed. Ryan reached the top first and glanced back down at me and just grinned. It spoke a thousand words and I hurried up that last few rungs. Few words could describe the exquisiteness of what we were seeing.

'Whoa!' we both whispered simultaneously.

Standing on a small rock platform we were observing the second beach that was more impressive and breathtaking than all the other beaches combined. It was a jewel sitting in the privacy of its own colourful bay. Swirls of blues and greens provided a kaleidoscope of magical water that danced along the sun-kissed ribbon of sand. Every colour was exaggerated and piercing. The foliage of the plant life that nestled on the sand, the flowers that bloomed amongst that. The incredible glow of the white sand that reflected every ray of light and the colours of the sea were exquisite. An eagle circled a spot in the distance and I wondered what amazing creatures were hiding from our beady eyes and those of the predator above. A small family of monkeys could be seen in the lower trees and as a young guy dropped his water bottle, one of the larger males ran onto the beach to claim his prize! We stood frozen and speechless. The occasional song of a bird and the clicking of the cicadas were the only disturbers of peace. This was the definition of awe and wonder. I had never imagined that such beauty and tranquillity existed in the world and I wanted to savour every moment. I wrapped my hand inside Ryan's and simply smiled. We did not need words now. The beauty spoke for itself.

Stepping onto the baked sand below provided a soothing massage to our troubled feet. I simply sat in the centre of the beach and tried to absorb my surroundings. I closed my eyes and took three deep breaths, only opening my eyes to the sound of Ryan splashing about in the sea. Two young Italian guys were also on the beach, beautifully tanned and both wearing skimpy swimwear. My long board shorts looked a little conservative in comparison. They took turns to smother each other in sun cream and, from the gentle way that they massaged the cream into the skin, it confirmed my assumption that they were gay. The younger, bearded one caught me looking and gave a cheeky grin that revealed a cute dimple in his left cheek.

Knowing that he had an audience, he slowed down his massage technique, biting his bottom lip as he did so. Was he actually giving me the come-on? He seemed way out of my league but he was definitely enjoying the flirt. His muscular, hairy frame was difficult not to admire. It was time to cool down I thought. The water was cleansing and the waves non-existent. With the sun beginning its descent, the colours had changed. The transparency of the water was delightful as I scooped it over my body.

'Are you flirting with those hot Italians Jack?' enquired Ryan with a twinkle in his eye.

He was normally so jealous of others and I had learnt a number of subtle techniques to allow me to 'observe' sexy men discretely without upsetting him. For example, if a hot man was walking towards me I would turn my head so that *he* passed into my line of vision! But for some reason this time Ryan was actively encouraging me. The two hotties were now in the water with us and whilst 'appearing' to be swimming, they were certainly edging closer.

'Would you?' asked Ryan.

'Would I what?'

'Would you ever have a threesome or foursome?' Ryan gingerly enquired. The conversation both excited and petrified me. I had never considered the prospect and imagined it was something that only happened on the set of a porn movie.

'Have you before?' I questioned, not really sure I wanted to hear Ryan's answer.

'Yeah of course. When I was single I slept with this couple. It was hot!'

My stomach dropped a little and I felt myself judging Ryan unfairly, though at the same time I felt my crotch twitch with the slightest excitement. Ryan began to explain how his gay friends in Australia had been together for fifteen years but once a year on their annual trip to the UK, they would stop off in Amsterdam for a few nights of threesomes or foursomes. It was all very transparent and they would talk through every point before and after. They felt it took them to another level of trust. At all other times of the year they lived in an exclusive, closed relationship. I felt somewhat uneasy and wondered if Ryan was about to ask this of me. The conversation had distracted me from the sexy Europeans who were now drying off in the sun and touching up their tans.

'I'm not really sure I could do that Ryan. Not really me.'

'Nah, nor me! I'm only teasing you. Every couple is different. If it works for Max and Chris, good for them, but I couldn't share *you!*'

Ryan's words were comforting but the conversation unnerved me all the same. I had often wondered how couples ever bring up these kinds of conversations, when one or both has an unusual fetish. Had I just missed Ryan's attempt? Was this something I could consider in the future? It all just seemed wrong and inappropriate to me as I slowly meandered out of the ocean.

CHAPTER FORTY

We had decided to stay out of the sun for a few days whilst our skin took a much-needed rest from the intense rays. The main town provided enough places to explore. It was Ryan's birthday and the much-anticipated Apple product had already surpassed his expectations. I had arranged for a soothing Thai massage before an exciting night out. The massage shop was incredibly peaceful and the team of masseurs giggled as we took off our shoes and entered the room. Two Asian boys were quick to volunteer to help and as this was our first massage we had no idea what to expect. We were ushered to a small room on the first floor which provided two mattresses and two sets of traditional loose trousers. The room had dark-stained wooden floors and a number of ornate pieces were dotted around in the matching wood. A picture of the Thai King stood proud on the main wall, making me feel a little uncomfortable as I pulled off my shorts to the Royal audience! Panpipe music played effortlessly in the background and the single air-con unit maintained a bearable temperature.

Lying down on our mattresses side my side Ryan squeezed my hand. 'Thank you for a great day already!'

My masseur was the first to enter the room. He gave a respectful *wai,* told me his name and proceeded to bend my toes and squeeze the soles of my feet. Tum was gentle and attentive. His slight frame was not to be under-estimated as he certainly did not lack strength. Ryan's masseur entered and was incredibly handsome. Pax was taller and stockier than your average Thai guy. His hair was styled and trendy and his skinny jeans emphasised the build of his upper torso. It was a little unnerving to observe a man of such beauty running his hands all over my boyfriend's body. It certainly did not help me to deal with my own insecurities about my body. Tum was now pressing firmly on my thighs and I closed my eyes to try to relax. I was sure I felt his hand cusp my balls as he massaged the top of my inner thigh. I opened my eyes slightly and found Tum grinning, his back forming a natural barrier from Ryan's line of vision. I closed my eyes again but felt my cock beginning to grow. I thought of every possible disgusting thought and image to force a flaccid state, but the more I thought about it the harder my cock felt. As Tum leant across my body to massage my right thigh, he pressed his forearm across my rigid shaft. Giggling, he spoke a few words of Thai to his colleague who proceeded to laugh in unison. I was mortified. The feeling was reminiscent of the days on the school bus when random erections would visit at the most inappropriate moments. But now I was in my thirties and this was not supposed to happen! Re-adjusting myself a little I closed my eyes and focused on the serene sounds of the ocean playing in the distance. Once again, Tum pressed his thumb on the top of my shaft causing a repeated number of twitches. He curled his hand around my balls and gently massaged them. It felt so good. I wondered if Ryan was enjoying the same and then I felt guilty. It did not seem appropriate and so I asked Tum to concentrate on my back which was continuing to cause me problems of late. Although a little disappointed that I could not enjoy the soothing hands of Tum on my crotch, I now felt relaxed as I drifted off to sleep. When we left the massage house I never spoke a word to Ryan about my experience. I was not sure how he would react. Would he accuse me of leading the masseur on? Would he ask if I enjoyed it and make a second attempt at the whole threesome idea again? Would he share his own experience with the sexy masseur attending to him? I decided it was better to focus on the evening's events and avoid *that* topic of conversation!

Three cocktails, two tequila shots and a tasty BBQ meal later, Ryan and I were enjoying some quality time together. His birthday had been a great success and both of us were feeling great. We had ended up in the Smile bar just before his birthday came to a close at midnight, for one final toast. The bar was empty except for the harem of bar whores who continually swarmed around it. I found them particularly irritating but Ryan soaked up the attention as usual. It was hard to get a look in whenever I was around him. His smile, perfect teeth and charisma overshadowed my insecure self. Each wore the smallest black dress that just about covered their dignity. I was impressed by their level of English, probably due to the number of men they had 'entertained' that holiday season. Each of the four 'ladies' was there to please and to encourage the intoxicated and foolish men to spend more money.

'Another drink, Mr!' was their catchphrase. Ryan was knocking them back and getting into the spirit of partying with the girls. Each took turns to sit on his lap or challenge him in a game of pool or Connect 4. I had become invisible. I did not feel jealous, just neglected. I had invested so much effort in the perfect birthday and now I was sitting alone drinking at a whore bar. It was clear just how different we both were. Ryan was now singing along to the track at the top of his voice and I was embarrassed. The group of young Russians who had come into the bar were also staring which was adding to my torture.

I wandered over to Ryan and whispered, 'Hey, can we go? I'm really tired.'

'Oh my fucking God. What's your problem? I'm enjoying my birthday with some friends,' he snapped back.

'It was your birthday yesterday Ryan and these are not your friends, they are fucking slags who just want your money!'

'Oh just fuck off Jack, you boring sod!'

His words struck my face with force. He was like someone possessed and staring into his eyes I didn't recognise my boyfriend. My eyes welled up and yet stirred no response from the man who supposedly loved me. I turned and walked out of the bar, unable to look at the group of European lads who had witnessed the lovers' tiff.

One hour later, Ryan stumbled into our villa. 'What's your problem? Is it too much to ask that you make an effort for my birthday? All I wanted was my boyfriend to buy me some flowers on my birthday. Is that too much to ask?'

He was now crying. The guy was fucking crazy, I thought as I resisted the temptation to point out the excessive costs of his fabulous birthday. As he passed out on the bed I stood in the mirror and cried at my reflection. How could one person be so hurtful and so ungrateful? Why did every night out have to end in this way? I did not get much sleep that night.

With only two days and one night remaining I was determined not to allow Ryan's outlandish behaviour to spoil the perfect trip. On cue, as always, he had apologised for his drunken misdemeanours and promised to reform. An unread email on my phone was waiting for me as I woke. It was from my solicitor explaining that the decree absolute had come through. It was official – I was no longer married. I instinctively wanted to rush to tell Ryan but my heart felt surprisingly heavy. It made everything so real. So final. I shed a tear for Maria and the pain she would no doubt feel when she opened the mail. I shed a tear for myself for the years of unhappiness that I dragged Maria and myself through. I also could not shake off the bitterness I felt towards Ryan for his ungrateful behaviour. For now, I chose to sit on my new marital status.

Following another day of relaxation on the beach, we took a walk around the town as the sun began to set. The array of reds and oranges sprawled across the horizon was beautiful. One coffee shop come bar that we passed looked particularly inviting – and there wasn't a whore in sight! The stark white walls and white leather couches were tasteful and different from the shacks we had been entertained in previously. A young British guy was quick to greet us and, although struggling to take his eyes off Ryan, he showed us to an empty sofa. He returned quickly with two iced lattes and invited himself to join us. My guard was up as usual, as I was always suspicious of such confident strangers. Ryan always rose to the occasion and instantly the two were heavily engaged in conversation. I desperately tried to participate but it was clear that Paul was not interested in what I had to offer. His eyes were fixated on Ryan. Despite Ryan's promise of less alcohol, we were sipping on our second vodka and still entertaining our surprise guest. He was now sprawled across the one sofa and leaning in towards Ryan. I failed to see why Ryan was remotely interested in this lanky young guy who spoke with the same intonation as Prince William. He was incredibly thin and plain in appearance and continually grabbed at the opportunity to point out all his successes, which basically revolved around the money accumulated by his rich Thai partner. They were the owners of this fine coffee house. Paul was particularly keen for us to join him at a local gay nightspot but Ryan was quick to point out that I was not into the gay scene and the two laughed.

'Come back to my house. We have plenty of drink!' suggested Paul eagerly.

'Up to him!' replied Ryan, pointing to me as if I was the geriatric partner who controlled him. I hated it when Ryan put me on the spot like that. He knew I would not want to go so why ask? I did not want to fuel their perception of me as old and boring so I agreed to join.

It was hard not to be impressed by the couple's house as we pulled up outside in his sporty BMW. It was a refreshing change to see a young white guy feeding off the wealth of an older Asian guy. The automatic gates that led us into a quaint courtyard, with a water fountain marking the centre point, opened. Two huge folding glass doors opened up into an excessive white living space. Every appliance was over-exaggerated in size and of the latest technology. The marble flooring felt cool underfoot and the artwork hanging throughout the room looked beyond my salary expectations.

Paul led us out into the garden space that framed a large swimming pool in the centre. The semi-naked figure in the water was his partner. He was not the elderly chap I had expected as he stepped out of the pool in his small blue aussieBum shorts to greet us. He was no older than thirty-five with a body to die for. Although small in height, he was packing an impressive muscular frame. He was a professional sportsman who had made a huge amount of money from endorsements. Tak was not the most talkative of people and he quickly fled the scene. Three more drinks and Paul was sharing the intimate details of his love life, or lack of it. Tak and Paul were apparently very much in love. They had been together for six years since Paul was eighteen and had both met each other's families. They planned to spend their entire lives together. The trouble was that they never had sex with each other. Sure, they fooled around a little but Tak would not have intercourse with Paul. He felt it was animalistic and, because it caused pain, it was not something that you did with a loved one. Bullshit, I thought! It was a bloody excuse to sleep around if you ask me. Ryan listened sympathetically but I was already preparing to leave.

'So Tak is happy for me to bring guys back and sleep with them. Sometimes he joins in,' explained Paul. I suddenly felt a little nervous and was now fully aware of exactly why we were enjoying drinks at *this* stranger's pool. Had we both been so naïve as to think this guy was *just* being friendly? Of course not. Ryan had known exactly what was going on. Whilst Paul went to check on Tak, I explained my unhappiness to Ryan.

'Okay we can leave now. No worries,' replied Ryan.

When I returned from the toilet, Ryan and Paul were both standing in the kitchen grinning. 'What would you think if I kissed your boyfriend Jack?' asked Paul.

'I am not sure,' I responded.

Part of me was intrigued and the other part petrified. With little time to process the question, Ryan and Paul were kissing. No peck on the cheek, like two school kids playing truth or dare, this was a full-blown snog, with tongues and so deep. My knees began to shake and I felt different. I did not feel disgust, jealousy or anger. I was excited. I wanted in on the action and so I wandered over, pulled on Paul's arm and took the place of Ryan like a game of tag. The kiss was not as good as I had hoped. Paul was a smoker and the taste of tobacco was unpleasant.

'Let's take this downstairs,' whispered Paul. We stepped past Tak who was engrossed in a Thai TV serial and proceeded down the winding stairs into the den. Tak had not appeared the least bit interested in our antics. The den was incredible. The single window looked into the pool and a projector sat on the ceiling with an impressive sound system surrounding the room. A leather couch and endless bean bags scattered the room. It was every guy's dream space. Paul pushed me and Ryan onto the sofa and proceeded to undo our belts, one at a time. I was already hard from the anticipation of the event. I looked at Ryan who gave a nod as he bit his bottom lip. As Paul pleasured me eagerly, Ryan kissed me more deeply and passionately. With every groan I gave, Ryan became more and more excited. I slipped my hands into his shorts and felt a covering of precum between my fingers. He was clearly aroused. The sound of footsteps came from behind and Tak appeared naked and eager to play. His cock was disappointing in size but his body no less impressive than when we first met. He took hold of Ryan's cock and sucked him slow and deep. Ryan and I sat side by side with two strangers pleasuring us. It was so horny and already I felt I could climax. The two switched positions and now Tak was on me. Before he took my dick he kissed me. His kiss was not as good as Paul's but he was more attentive. His technique in oral play was not to my liking. He sucked too hard and it hurt, so I lifted myself up to instigate a change. His arse was an incredible bubble and I needed to taste it. I bent him over and spread his cheeks slightly, revealing a perfectly smooth, hairless hole. Licking the outer rim he squealed in ecstasy and when my tongue gently teased the aperture he almost came. Ryan was mirroring my moves and Paul was now enjoying the same attention. The more I looked at Ryan, the more excited I felt. The jealousy or awkwardness I imagined feeling never came.

The room was incredibly hot and beads of sweat covered all four of our bodies. The sight of our four naked bodies in the room was intense.

'Fuck me!' I heard Paul say to Ryan. At this point the line was crossed.

'No no. I'm not happy with this. Playing is okay, but no fucking,' I replied sharply. I was not sure if Ryan was disappointed or not. I did not care. This was going to be on my terms.

With Paul now sitting on the sofa I switched partners and now straddled Paul, kissing him so deep. I did not find him attractive in the slightest and his skinny penis was of no interest to me. What was electrifying was the feeling of knowing that Ryan was watching my every move. With Paul playing with my arse and slipping his fingers inside, I could not contain myself and I shot an impressive load across his chest and stomach. Paul could not help but laugh at the amount released. Watching Ryan cum shortly afterwards was equally exciting. Strangely enough, Paul and Tak declined the offer to finish. Maybe they had another rule about ejaculation.

The four of us scrambled to gather our clothes and spoke very few words. We exchanged Facebook contacts and promised to visit again soon. I knew I was lying when I made that agreement. If Ryan and I were going to go down this road again, we would be aiming higher and looking for two sex gods, I silently thought. Declining the offer for a lift back to the hotel, Ryan and I took to the streets for a long walk home. For half of the distance we walked in silence until Ryan finally broke the peace.

'So? What did you think? Are you okay?'

'Umm, yeah I'm okay. It was ummm hot I guess,' I replied.

'Are you worried about anything?'

'No not really. I guess it brings us closer together. Involves a greater level of trust,' I suggested.

'I agree!' said Ryan with a huge grin and a wink of his eye.

I was lying of course. I was far from okay. My mind was racing and I did not know what to say to Ryan or where to begin. I had felt the build up to this moment and clearly it was something Ryan wanted. I had wanted it too when caught up in the moment. But now? Now my sexual tension was out, I felt only scared and anxious about the future. We had crossed a line so would things ever be the same? Where was the line now and what would be acceptable or unacceptable in the future?

CHAPTER FORTY-ONE

I had every reason to question myself so intensely that night. This occasion marked the turning point in our relationship. Before this event I had been so obsessed with Ryan. I loved him dearly and tolerated all his drunken antics because of this love. Now I had lost a level of respect for him. I did not blame him for the event; after all I was a willing participant. Nonetheless my feelings were different. The rules had changed and it confused my understanding of boundaries. Ryan had always been intolerably jealous of me even looking at guys and yet on that night he had observed my intimate moments with two random strangers. I was addled. If we could do this when together, was it also okay to play around as individuals? I had also still not told him about the divorce which puzzled me somewhat. Why was I choosing to sit on this important information?

With Ryan still not working, things had become a little tense at home. He had taken a few language teaching jobs but quit each time after a day or two. On some days he refused to leave the apartment and would spend endless hours playing on his Xbox. This did not overly bother me but when I came home from work to find a pile of dishes or laundry, it was difficult not to be a little annoyed. I was also paying for a cleaner twice a week and wondered why Ryan had not offered to save the money and do the household chores himself. I felt I had created a spoilt child who did very little yet still expected a lot. I was paying for all the exotic holidays, luxurious weekends of pampering and shopping. At first it had been very difficult to get Ryan to accept that my money was also his money. We were a couple after all. But now he had high expectations and when I paid for a personal trainer at the gym, he expected the same. This clearly added to the tension. He was bored and his pride was hurt.

Ryan had also formed a friendship with a Thai guy that he had met at the gym whilst I was away on business. Apparently they had started talking as they both worked out and decided to grab some food afterwards. Chate was a very friendly guy but there was no denying he was a white man hunter. I had expressed my unhappiness with Ryan about the way the friendship had been formed and, as always, he had managed to turn it around on me and made me feel possessive. Of course we both needed to make new friends, but exchanging mobile numbers with someone you have met once at the gym was crossing the line I felt. One week later they were going out for a meal together and I was not even invited. I found the whole situation very upsetting which added further to my paranoia. Ryan did a good job of reassuring me but with so many issues already at home I felt this was just another problem. As they wined and dined I sat at home imagining all possible scenarios. I had not met Chate at this point but had imagined him as a very attractive, confident guy with a firm, muscular frame. I still trusted Ryan though, even with all the rule changing that had recently taken place, yet I wondered if we had different opinions on what behaviour was acceptable. When Ryan came home later that evening and jumped straight in the shower, I could not resist the temptation to check his phone. Unfortunately, there was no message from Chate but there was a message from Ryan to him. It read: *Thank you for a great evening. You are the sweetest guy I have ever met x.* I was furious and stormed into the bathroom screaming and wailing.

'What the fuck is going on Ryan?'

'What the hell? Nothing, you psycho!' snapped Ryan.

'I just read your message to Chate. *You're the sweetest guy I ever met.* What the fuck? *I'm* supposed to be the sweetest guy you have ever met. Not a fucking stranger!'

Without waiting for a response I slammed the door and threw myself onto the bed. Ryan did not rush out to comfort me which only added to my pain. When he finally made an appearance he was very attentive and gentle.

'Hey, why don't we all hang out this Friday. Then you will see we are just friends and that you have nothing to worry about. Okay?'

Having met Chate later that week I accepted that I had no reason to be insecure about myself but still every reason to be suspicious of his interest in Ryan. After he had shown us a picture of his ex-boyfriend, the resemblance to Ryan was chilling. The way he looked at Ryan signalled trouble to me but Ryan refused to accept my concerns and again chose to mock me as being paranoid. It was difficult not to be insecure. Ryan rarely complimented me or said sweet things. Sure, he made me laugh and the sex was still good but the relationship lacked the intimacy I so desperately craved. It was incredibly difficult dealing with the inconsistencies in our relationship.

After a session at the gym alone I was confronted by a guy asking for my number. We had caught each other's eye a number of times. I was not particularly attracted to him but his incredible muscles and height somewhat bewitched me. I was flattered that he was so keen to ask for my number. Sadly, he was a 'butter' face – great body, well-dressed, good personality. Everything is great *BUT* the face! His name was Sek and he had informed me that he was a model but inside I chuckled wondering if it was for underwear or gloves only! He was not ugly but he had definitely had a lot of surgery and Botox and the result was... unusual! However, there was no denying the incredible body and I guess a part of me was somewhat tempted. Needless to say, Ryan was less than impressed when I explained about Sek, forbidding me to make contact with him. The hypocrisy of his argument was laughable. When I tried to make comparisons to the situation with Chate he refused to engage. It was a rule of Ryan's. Whenever having an argument about one matter, you were not allowed to bring other issues or previous arguments into the discussion. To a large extent I admired this rule. It helped to keep you focused on the immediate problem. However, there were occasions when drawing comparisons to past events would help to illustrate the point. Ryan was having none of this and the argument continued to spiral out of control. We were barely speaking by the time it came for him to fly back to the UK to renew his visa. I was looking forward to the space between us.

Despite hanging around the gym at the same time each day for the five days that Ryan had been away, I had failed to encounter my model admirer. I am not sure why I was so keen to see him again and I am certainly unsure of what I planned to do. Having deleted his number at Ryan's request, I had no means of flirting. I felt low in myself and needed attention to make me feel better. Sitting at home watching TV late one evening a message appeared on my Facebook chat. It was Chate. He had added my name via Ryan.

Jack, how r u krub? he asked casually.

Good thanks. Just back from the gym and now watching crap TV.

Awwww you seem down. Missing Ryan hey? Want me to keep you company? he asked.

I paused for a moment to re-read his message. On first impression it seemed innocent enough but the emoticon on the end of the message suggested something more.

What did you have in mind? I asked.

Well I could keep you warm tonight! Hahaha.

I think you are joking with me. You couldn't handle me anyway! I teased.

I knew I was crossing the line at this point but feeling so low I was vulnerable to the possible attention of others. My phone beeped and startled me somewhat. Strangely enough it was a message from Chate. A picture message. Opening the file I was excited and yet nervous. The image was provocative and suggestive. He was lying on his bed in only a pair of gym shorts that he had pulled down slightly to reveal the start of his pubic hair. His body was as I suspected – lean and ripped. I still felt no attraction to his face. His nose was overly large and flat and his chin was quite pronounced. The smooth, hairless caramel skin was tempting.

Why did you just send me that pic? I enquired.

You don't like? Chate asked.

It's nice. But you are our friend. We need to behave! I suggested.

Similar conversations took place for the following few days, each time instigated by Chate. Granted, I willingly engaged. After all it was exciting and the positive attention was much needed. It seemed like harmless fun.

Three days later and Ryan had returned. Sadly, although I had missed him, the tension between us remained. It was not like me to be so stubborn. I had even forgotten what had caused the tension in the first place. Each time we tried to engage in a meaningful conversation, it became tense. We seemed to have little patience for each other. Unfortunately I was now expected to fly to New Zealand for training so Ryan and I were parted once more, having failed to resolve the issues that appeared to be surrounding us. The night before I flew out we arranged to go for dinner but sat for the entire time in silence.

Of course, Chate wasted little time in confiding in Ryan about my advances. Unable to either deny or defend, I stood guilty as charged. Any attempt to blame Chate or explain his involvement seemed pathetic. Being a fourteen-hour flight away *this* conversation was not easy over the phone, especially when I was aware that Chate had spent the night at our apartment, although in the guest room Ryan insisted.

Ryan and I did not talk for the remainder of my eight-day trip. Clearly we both needed the space to reflect. I was so angry with Chate for setting me up and leading me on. But I was also disappointed in myself. I had allowed my need for attention from others to become a potential threat to my relationship with Ryan. I felt so alone once again. In my head I was so confused. Ryan was the guy I had changed my life for. He was the man I had finally left my wife for. Two years and now it all seemed to be over. Or was it? It was always so complicated. A part of me was tired of Ryan's behaviour and mind games and another part still longed for him.

Returning to Bangkok to find that the only bed sheets that had been changed were on the bed that I shared with Ryan took my paranoia to another level. The guest bed was still covered in the same quilt cover as before I had left. I knew this meant that they had spent the night together but I could not face challenging Ryan. I was done. I was handing in the towel and letting go. However, with one of our friends transiting in Bangkok for the weekend on her way to New Zealand, it was going to be difficult to face up to the situation right now. We would simply have to play happy families.

Ryan had arranged to take our friend Mel to one of the local islands, only a three-hour bus ride away. Mel seemed unaware of any issues between Ryan and I and things seemed less tense as we sat drinking on the beach. The hotel was near the main party spot and it was not long before Ryan insisted we joined. He was drinking at an incredible rate and dancing with random guys. The bar was infamous for its gay clientele and clearly Ryan was popular. Mel had long since passed out in the corner and once again I found myself drinking solo at the bar. A couple sat alongside sensed my loneliness and the English guy started to chat. I assumed the Thai girl he was with was his girlfriend though he was quick to explain that they were friends only. He was no looker himself, but his stocky frame and height made him quite attractive.

'You have a great chest. Very sexy!' he said. I was quick to blush and looked down at my feet, smiling coyly. 'I'm serious man, I would love to get my hands on that!'

'Get your hands on what?' questioned a voice from behind me.

It was Ryan looking possessed from the level of alcohol in his blood. My admirer just laughed and walked off to the toilet.

'What the fuck did he say to you? What are you up to?' snapped Ryan.

'I don't know what he was saying Ryan. Calm down. He's just some random guy like the ones you have been dancing with all night! But I'm not trying to sleep with *him* Ryan!'

I snapped back. A part of me was lying. A night of passion and attention from this guy would be a welcome relief from the misery that Ryan and I had found ourselves in lately.

'You are a fucking liar Jack. You always fucking flirt with guys behind my back. If you wanna fuck him – go and do it!'

He was shouting at maximum volume and right into my face. I did not recognise this man. I pushed past him and returned to my hotel room, surprisingly calm. In my mind the relationship was over.

One hour later Ryan fell through the hotel room door swearing and cursing. He was such a poor drunk. Initially I pretended to sleep but I needed on outlet for the rising frustration and resentment I was feeling towards Ryan.

'You were wrong about that guy Ryan. He was just a nobody trying to flirt with me. Nothing more.' I spoke quietly and calmly hoping that this approach would trigger Ryan into following suit.

'Fuck off!' he snarled. He leant in close to my face. He was unable to focus and his sense of balance was wavering. 'You are a fucking slut! You probably fucked him already.'

This angered me and I now stepped into his personal space and shouted, 'Get real you idiot!'

'Fuuuuuckkk oooooofffff!' he yelled, emphasising each phoneme.

I could not tolerate his abuse any further and so pushed his chest with both my hands to move him away from him. Without warning Ryan took a swing and punched me in the face. Thankfully his drunken state had removed his ability to hit with any damaging force. My face may not have been hurt but my heart was shattered. It was the single most hurtful act that anyone had ever imposed on me. If someone you love so deeply could do *that* to you, what hope was there? Both now equally angry we were engaged in a physical battle. We repeatedly struck at each other. There was no force or intention to inflict pain. It was only a representation of the inner pain we were both experiencing. The tears flowed from us both and suddenly Ryan was out of the door. He did not return that night and I did not care. When we got back to Bangkok I planned to ask him to leave. I assumed Ryan had spent the night with Mel when I saw them both having breakfast the following morning. We never spoke a single word that day or during the journey back that evening. I felt total despair.

Three nights, four days and not a single word exchanged between Ryan and myself. The atmosphere at home was soul destroying. I felt so alone and abandoned. But my own anger was preventing me from calling a truce.

'I'm going to X-Club!' he barked at me as he finished pampering himself in the bedroom.

I had already heard that some of my colleagues were celebrating a birthday so I assumed he was joining them. I did not have any interest in hanging out in gay bars and instead planned to talk through my personal problems with Aunt Jess in the UK. For three hours my aunt listened so patiently. She really helped me to understand the situation from both points of view. I told her everything. Aunt Jess' anger at hearing Ryan had struck me was clear. Despite this, I still believed I loved Ryan and by the end of the conversation I was ready to forgive Ryan and try to work at things. I sat eagerly waiting for his return so we could start our discussion. Midnight came and went and no sign. Three a.m., four a.m. and still no word from Ryan. His phone was switched off and now I was beginning to worry. Exhausted, I fell asleep briefly, before suddenly waking up to the sound of Ryan staggering through the front door. It was six a.m. and he was visibly upset. A part of me knew what was coming.

'Ryan? What's wrong?'

'I'm sorry. I'm a terrible person. I'm sorry!' he sobbed. It was so difficult to understand him as he was crying so much. I felt a little excited about what Ryan was about to admit to as I knew this would be my ticket out.

'Is this about Chate? You slept together when I was in New Zealand right?'

'No! I told you, we are just friends Jack. Why are you so paranoid about that guy?'

'Well then just tell me. Nothing can be that bad,' I replied.

'I kissed someone tonight! I'm sorry. I hate myself. I'm a typical dirty gay who will never find true happiness,' he wailed. It was hard to remain so cold towards him seeing such emotion. Although I knew this would give me just cause to leave, I suddenly found myself not wanting to.

'It's okay Ryan,' I said sympathetically. 'We can work this out.'

Ryan's own confessions made me reflect on my own behaviour. I had somewhat neglected Ryan and given up on our relationship. I had flirted with friends and instigated inappropriate conversations. Maybe I had driven Ryan to this crime? I knew at that point I wanted to work at things. What I had not accounted for was the upcoming attack from Ryan. Not satisfied with my reaction, he embarked on a self-crucifixion of character before finally turning his attack to me. He repeatedly swore and cursed. His upset and anger was disturbing. It was impossible to reason with him and this time he was almost sober.

'You are still in fucking denial Jack and you always will be. You make false promises of marriage and children and yet you are still trying to be a straight guy who is in love with his wife!'

'Ex-wife actually Ryan! We are fucking divorced though I never did get the chance to share that with you!'

After attacking his own character and mine, he went on a rampage against gay men in general. 'Gays are all the same. We can't be trusted. I hate myself. I don't want to be gay!' he yelled.

I had never witnessed Ryan like this. Every possible frustration was oozing out of him and it was painful to see. I wanted to reach out, hug and reassure him. But as Ryan attacked with a second string of profanities, I knew it was time to let him go and walk away. I stood up and walked out. I never looked back once. Eight a.m. and nowhere to go, I wandered the streets wondering where it had all gone wrong. So much hope, so many dreams. Gone. Once again I was alone, only this time I was six thousand miles from home. I took my mobile from my pocket.

'I need to see you. It's over,' I cried.

CHAPTER FORTY-TWO

Chloe was standing waiting for me in her lobby. It was a little awkward on account of her being such good friends with Ryan *and* me, but I figured she understood us better than anyone. Luke was still in bed although he was quick to rise when he heard my tears. I explained the most recent episode which appeared to shock Chloe. She tactfully tried to point out to me that Ryan had been feeling a little neglected over the past few months.

'That's no excuse to cheat on someone is it? You talk to your partner if there are problems. But Ryan doesn't *do* talking does he? Cos he's fucking emotionally inept!' I wailed, dropping my heavy head into my palms.

Neither Chloe or Luke were particularly comfortable with public displays of emotion and so neither were quick to comfort me. Chloe tried patting my back like a dog which made me spontaneously laugh. We all laughed hysterically at the awkwardness I had created.

'Hey you'll work things out mate!' said Luke.

'And what if I don't want to?' I replied. 'What if I am fed up of all his shit?'

'It's just 'cos you are upset now. Give it a day or two and everything will be back to the way it was. You just need to talk things through. I know he needs to talk to you too,' answered Chloe.

'Either way mate you are welcome to stay here for as long as you need to!' offered Luke.

I had spoken with Luke in greater detail about the problems I was facing with Ryan and I suspected he had not shared this information with Chloe on account of her closeness to Ryan.

Six hours later and not a single word from Ryan. Chloe had kindly offered to go around to my apartment to collect some clothes for work and to make sure that Ryan had not done anything stupid. She was gone for nearly two hours and on returning she was not particularly forthcoming. I guess her loyalties were torn. Chloe explained that Ryan was sorry for what he had done and that it was no more than a kiss. She could read my mind and knew I had been pondering on the prospect of Ryan's infidelity being much greater.

'You just need to talk to him Jack,' repeated Chloe for the third time.

'I don't want to!' I snapped back. As the hours passed the hurt was growing and all the past events were rearing up for my consideration.

Facing my colleagues two days later was the next challenge. Most had witnessed my partner publicly cheating on me and word had spread to the others. I resented Ryan for compromising me professionally. I had always prided myself on my professional integrity and now it felt damaged. Holding my head up high, I faced the week ahead despite the gossip and rumours, unsure myself of what the future would hold. No one asked how I was but all displayed the same sympathetic face that was far worse than any spoken word.

Three days passed and Ryan had failed to make any effort to contact me. No text, phone call or spontaneous visit. I guessed this was a sign that he was happy to end the relationship in this way, although Chloe insisted he was just trying to give me space. I tried to believe this but as *he* was in the wrong, was it not for him to be making the first move? Sleeping on Luke and Chloe's sofa was not exactly comfortable, though I welcomed their company all the same. On day four I decided to be assertive and message Ryan. After all, I was the one paying for that apartment, yet it was me being inconvenienced. The text message read:

Ryan, I need you to find somewhere else to stay so that I can come back home.

I knew the message was cold. There was no indication of wanting to work at things but I was still too angry for that. At least *I* was breaking the ice. Part of me hoped he would not reply, the other part wished it would make him come running. My phone beeped as his reply came through:

Fine! I will move out today or tomorrow.

It was not the reply I secretly hoped for. No apology; no loving words; no begging for forgiveness. Nothing. Cold and concise. Ryan was the type who fought fire with fire. He would respond in the way he was spoken to. He was not man enough to rise above this. I had hoped that Ryan and I would simply swap living arrangements. I would move back to the apartment and he would stay with Luke and Chloe until he was ready to talk and ask for my forgiveness, but when Chloe informed me that he was signing for a new lease agreement I figured we were well and truly over. Having recently secured quite a well paid teaching position at a language school he was now able to stand on his own two feet. I was stunned and hurt. How could he give up on us so easily? I thought about Maria and how much I had hurt her in order to be with this guy. Was that hurt now all pointless?

With Ryan out of the apartment the following day I faced my first night alone in Bangkok as a single guy. Still numb at just how easily he had given up on us, I analysed every moment of our time together, looking for clues and answers as to why it had failed. I looked deep within myself at my own behaviour and tried to figure out why I was still seeking attention from others. Who was to blame? It seemed to be a vicious circle. Ryan felt neglected and so went into emotional shut down. I craved his attention yet he could not give it so I looked elsewhere, which only further added to his issues. The questions in my head were endless. Did I still love and want Ryan or was it just out of habit? Clearly all of this suggested we were just not *right* for each other. As the tear-jerking music played in the background I released my emotions in a splendid display of endless tears.

Desperate to break my cycle of self-pity, Chloe had messaged me the name of a phone app that she had stumbled upon. It was a social networking site for gay men, aka 'meet and fuck' site. You register your name and location, upload a profile picture and then you can 'cruise' for gay men sniffing around your neighbourhood. It all seemed a bit seedy yet enticing. I downloaded the application but was not ready to upload any pictures or profiles just yet. It was all still too raw and early I thought. It was a shame that Ryan was on a different page in this thinking! As the profiles loaded I was confronted by a familiar image: Ryan's naked chest. Twenty million people in Bangkok, half of whom are men, most of which are gay and I stumble upon Ryan's profile! Extremely erotic pictures, an enticing and outright slutty message and a profile creation date of six months ago. The guy was a fucking liar. I thought of all the names I could call him, the abusive message I could post on his profile, but I knew it was futile. I needed to deal with this silently and accept that men can be manipulative and complicated. There was no face, but having lain across that chest for two years, I knew it was him. The distinctive dragon tattoo also blew his cover. I was livid. Clearly he was looking for a quick fuck so what further signs did I need to know it was all over. I was also angry with Chloe for convincing me that Ryan was so keen to talk. The best way for me to deal with it was in the arms of an even sexier guy.

I loaded the social network application, uploaded a moderately sexy picture and profile and I was cruising. The array of men was mesmerising: young, old, Asian, white, gay, bisexual and even transsexual! Each stated the distance from your current location. It was like online shopping, but for cock! One click and a guy would come running over for a fuck. It was just what I needed. You can tell a lot about the personality of a guy from his picture and profile. Some of the guys uploaded semi-naked pictures or photos of their abs only. Clearly these guys would be shallow, self-obsessed and inattentive. A message suddenly popped up from a rather striking guy named Max.

'Top or bottom?' he asked. Well nothing like being direct, I thought. It was not the romantic opener I had hoped for but it certainly made me smile for the first time in a while. He was very exotic looking with incredible bone structure. Twenty minutes later and I had agreed to meet him at a coffee shop in Silom, a neighbourhood populated with gays of every kind. I was incredibly nervous as I sat waiting for Max. I had never really dated a guy before and was unsure what topics of conversation we would have in common or even if he could communicate effectively in English. With Ryan and I it had been different. We didn't really date because of my fear of being discovered. Apart from the Valentine's meal it had all been secret rendezvous at his home.

When Max walked into the coffee shop it was hard not to be impressed. He was unusually tall for a Thai guy and that bone structure was even more incredible in person. His skin was dark and his frame slim but noticeably defined. The slight bent legs were also endearing.

'Hi. Jack? Nice to meet you. I'm Max.' His English was near perfect and his accent a little American. He was polite and respectful in every way. We sat chatting for hours and the conversation never ran dry. I felt so young and carefree as Max thought nothing of holding my hand in public. As he talked to me he rubbed his index finger playfully along my forearm. He leant in and whispered answers to my questions and he would breathe a little deeper as he did so. It was making me so horny and clearly I was excited. Max took a quick glance around the coffee shop and then grabbed my crotch.

'Wow, someone's excited!' he smiled. 'Let's get a taxi back to your place.'

There was a sexy glint in his eye as he bit his bottom lip seductively. I threw caution to the wind and jumped in the next available cab with him. I did not care if he was a psycho, mass murderer or any combination of the two. I just needed *him* so much.

'I only have one hour sorry,' he whispered into my left ear. The hastiness of it all made it seem even more horny.

The taxi finally arrived at my apartment building and the driver caught sight of us fumbling in the back seat. Max had done a great job of exciting me and I could not wait to get him inside. I felt a little paranoid as we passed the familiar security guard who appeared to be taking a mental note of my change of partner! Barely through the door and Max was pushing me up against the wall. The ornate table lamp toppled over as we fell into the side unit. The kissing was intense: deep and almost angry. His tongue swabbed every possible inch of my mouth. Between bouts of kissing he heightened my excitement further by gently licking and biting my lower lip. As I leant in for a deep kiss, unable to control myself for another second, he would pull back. His teasing was electrifying. It was difficult to catch my breath. Only when *he* was ready did the deep kissing recommence. He pushed me eagerly into the tall refrigerator and zealously grabbed at my belt. I knew I was being a little foolish but the level of excitement was better than any other I had experienced previously. With my jeans around my ankles, Max was licking and biting the firm shaft of my cock through my black Diesel pants. He groaned with pleasure and was quick to strip me completely naked. I felt a little self-conscious on account of Max still being fully dressed, but he was keen to focus all the attention on me.

He led me into the living room and pushed me assertively onto the sofa and started to pleasure me. He was meticulous in the detail. His tongue flicked and licked my entire groin area. It was a challenge not to cum in the first three minutes. His tongue was incredible. As he licked my inner thighs before attending to my balls my body shook with waves of delight. He was certainly talented in his oral skills. I needed to change the pace before cumming too soon and so I took a lead. I led Max into my bedroom and slowly undressed him. His skin was flawless from head to toe and the colour uniform – no blemishes, pimples or scars. He was a sculptor's perfect creation. His body was thinner than I had anticipated and the lack of muscular form disappointed me somewhat. His hairless brown nipples intrigued me. All my previous men had been Caucasians with pink nipples and blemished skin covered in hair. He was a stark contrast and maybe this was what excited me so much. As I ran my tongue across his nipples they were quick to stand to attention. They were infused with blood and clearly he enjoyed the attention they were receiving. I ran my tongue down the length of his torso as I fumbled with his belt and shorts. I reached inside his tight white briefs and felt his erect cock throbbing. It was long but incredibly thin and I was sure my disappointment was visible. I failed to remain excited as I tried to pleasure him with my mouth but the size did nothing to turn me on – it felt like I was sucking on a pencil! It was the briefest blow job I had given and I returned to kiss his sexy face in order to regain my erect form.

'I want to fuck you!' he demanded.

'Sure, do it!' I moaned, as he bit and licked the lobes of my ears. They were so sensitive and erogenous.

'On the balcony! I want to fuck you on your balcony!'

I had never had sex in the outdoors and the thought was amazing. It was dark outside and so I felt sure no one would see us. I gingerly stepped out onto the tiled balcony and lent over the metal railing to look down over the pool to see if we were on show. The coast was clear. I had not even stood up when I felt the moist sensation of Max's mouth pressing up against my tight cheeks. He bit and licked my cheeks and expressed his delight with my firm bubble butt. I grabbed the bars tight as he spread my cheeks and flicked his tongue against my hole. It was incredible and *he* could not get enough. His breath felt warm and as his tongue entered my hole slightly my cock throbbed intensely. With no warning he had now entered me. It was not an enjoyable sensation as his thin penis poked deep. I could feel no pleasure and I just wanted the moment to end. I considered how long it had been since he last fucked a guy as his eagerness was commendable. As he pushed himself up against me he ran his hands all over my hairy thighs which appeared to heighten his own pleasure. The sudden sound of someone diving into the pool signalled that we were not alone overlooking the courtyard so Max lowered himself down to the floor. I straddled him and ran my hands across his chest as he fumbled to reinsert himself once more. His black pearls stared intensely at me and his cheeks appeared a little flushed. My thighs were tiring from the position but I rode him hard and fast and for the first time I was now enjoying the moment. I had not cum for days and the display impressed him, causing him to cum only moments later. My hands pressed firmly on his chest, I could feel the intense beating of his heart. Tiny beads of sweat ran down his temples.

'I have to go!' Max said, as he coldly pushed me off and hastily ripped off the condom, spilling the contents onto the tiled floor below. I sat on the floor watching him dress with phenomenal speed and I felt used. I had been longing for the tender touch of a guy, some kind words or a soothing hug and instead all I got was a quick fuck.

'Shall I call you?' I asked.

'If I need a fuck I'll call you,' Max answered dismissively. 'Oh, by the way, how much do you earn? I only date guys who earn over a 100,000 baht a month.'

'Oh fuck off, you tosser!' I yelled, as he sadistically laughed when exiting the apartment.

I felt so stupid that I had allowed myself to be so easily seduced. I was in my thirties and completely clueless. I felt incredibly lonely as I lay on the bed thinking about where my life had all gone wrong. The downward spiral of depression was halted by the unexpected knocking at my door. I guessed Max had reflected on his bad behaviour and wanted to apologise. I jumped to my feet, ran to the door and flung it open angrily, ready to give Max a better piece of my mind. Only Max was not stood there – Ryan was.

CHAPTER FORTY-THREE

Returning from the shower, desperate to quickly remove the scent of Max from my body, I found Ryan looking at a photo of us that I had not had the strength to remove just yet. Neither of us spoke about it but he gave me a sympathetic look. I was not sure he would feel the same if he knew I had just been fucked by a stranger! It took only minutes before Ryan's humour and quick wit had me laughing. Although it had only been a couple of weeks I had missed his smile so much. I had missed everything about him.

'I want us to try again Jack. I know you are the one!' The words were incredible and the delivery perfect. I had prepared for closure only but this unexpected turn of events was most welcome. 'I'm sorry I hurt you. I've been an idiot.'

'I've missed you Ryan!' I beamed.

'But I'm not gonna lie to you Jack. I have been with other guys since we split up.'

'Me too Ryan. It's okay.'

We both sat smiling at each other. His hair looked longer and blonder than I remembered. His tanned skin gave him a healthy glow. I could not believe we were actually going to do this.

'There is one other thing I need to tell you Jack. If we are going to make it work I need to be honest with you so that we can start again.' He appeared a little nervous at this point and my own anxiety started to rise.

'Okay,' I replied.

'I did sleep with Chate and I am sorry!'

My heart stopped. I was mortified. It was not because of the crime itself but the deceit around the crime. I had known that something more had happened between them but both Ryan and Chloe had convinced me otherwise. All the times I'd been accused of being paranoid and I had even started to believe it myself. I started to cry before anger and rage took a greater hold.

'You are a fucking cunt! How could you?' I wailed. 'You bastard!'

I hoped Ryan would give some comforting words of explanation or at least hug me and hold me tight. But he had not changed. He gave what he was given – an attack.

'Oh don't play the fucking martyr card with me. It was just a race to see who could get to Chate first. You are only upset because you didn't get him first.'

Tears streaming down my face I took one long look at Ryan and felt nothing but pity. I knew he would never change and I knew I could never be happy with him. I did not want to fight with him. I had made too much progress for that. I simply stood up, walked to the door and asked him to get out of my house.

Every night I searched the profiles of every possible gay guy in Bangkok and there was certainly no shortage. For weeks I met a string of guys who were only too happy to satisfy my needs and now *I* was the player. I took on the role of the timid, naïve newbie and flirted my way into bed with countless fools. I fucked. I left. I felt like the king of the fucking world. My gaydar was working overtime and the attention was incredible and for a moment I believed I was God. On more than one occasion a cute guy would flash his cock at me in the urinal alongside me and before you knew it we were sucking in the cubicle. It was seedy, wrong and yet so good. My massages were also so much more enjoyable now that I had taken on a new persona. Now whenever the massage guys brushed their hands across my crotch I would smile and press their hand a little firmer indicating for the guy to take my cock in his hand and wank me to completion. And all for a little tip! I was on the dark side for sure but I did not care. All of my life had been spent pleasing others, doing the right thing and ignoring who I really was. And even when I had finally admitted my true self I was still being controlled by others or worrying myself over their feelings and thoughts and not my own. Now that had changed. Now I was being the selfish prick for once, using guys to satisfy urges and fantasies. I pretended I was looking for relationships or friends because that increased the pool of men, but really I was looking for just a no-strings fuck.

One guy named Tan had been messaging me for weeks after being hooked on a naked picture I stupidly sent him one night when I was lying in bed, horny and alone. On first impressions the guy seemed pretty cool. He was a doctor, smart and intelligent with a sexy geek chic about him. However, his behaviour was quick to alarm me. Every day he insisted on messaging me asking me to meet and questioning me about my whereabouts. On one occasion he even copied and pasted a previous conversation we had had in order to try to catch me out. When he referred to me as 'messing him around' and 'breaking his trust', despite having never met him, I knew it was time to block his profile. I never spoke to anyone about my behaviour. My friends knew I was 'active' but I only told them a fraction of the stories. I did not want to be judged, though when Chloe and Luke caught me creeping out of room 213 in their building one morning, my cover was blown a little.

I never stopped to consider the possible consequences of my actions or the risks I was putting myself in. Not until my encounter with Aun and his partner. They had messaged me a number of times after I had responded to their request for a threesome. They looked pretty hot in the picture and the thought of doing something more daring was exciting. When Aun met me in his lobby it was hard not to bolt. Judging from the grey hair and additional kilos he was carrying it was clear that the profile picture used was at least ten years old. He was charming and friendly and I was horny and foolish. It was quite intimidating walking along the corridor with a stranger knowing that in just a few moments he and his boyfriend would be fucking you simultaneously. The boyfriend, whose name I forget, was a little cuter but more distant. They sat me down on the bed and fussed around me. We tried to maintain in-depth conversations about life in general but they were clearly keen to start the action as soon as possible. I was less reassured when they informed me that the threesome was a regular Thursday night treat for each other. My sudden reluctance must have been apparent.

'Just relax Jack. We can take it nice and slow. Aun, get Jack a drink.'

When Aun returned with a glass of orange juice he was topless. The sight of his podgy torso was not exactly doing the trick to relax me. Sipping on my juice I watched as the couple started to kiss whilst both gazing at me from the corner of their eyes. They slowly undressed each other and started running their hands along my thighs. I found it difficult to focus and my vision seemed somewhat blurred. The room was beginning to spin a little as they both undressed me whilst both taking turns to kiss me. When we moved to the shower room my legs felt heavy and my actions clumsy. I was sandwiched between the two Asians as they vigorously rubbed their soapy bodies up against mine. My head felt *so* heavy and I longed for my bed. The concept of time had left me. I remember lying on their bed and feeling Aun climb up behind me as his boyfriend stood eagerly beside him masturbating. I was still aware and still choosing to partake, but my judgement seemed impaired. I remember Aun appearing to cum and changing places with his boyfriend but that was the last thing I remembered. My next memory was of me staggering along Sukhumvit Road. I knew how to get home but when I finally arrived at my place I could not remember *how* I had got back. My legs just about held my weight until I fell onto my bed.

The following morning I was woken by my colleague's sharp phone call wondering why I had not shown up for work. I had slept through my alarm. Rushing to the school my colleague called me to his office.

'What the hell has happened to you? You look like bloody shit!'

'I'm fine,' I replied. It had all been so sudden, I'd had little time to consider my feelings.

'You look like shit. What's going on with your eyes? Are you on fucking drugs?' he asked.

My head was pounding and his intense questioning was freaking me out. It all made sense now. Clearly Aun had spiked my drink last night. I knew they had not raped me because I was actively taking part but to what extent I was capable of giving my consent I was not sure. I was too embarrassed to share and made my excuses to return home on account of an upset stomach. This encounter with the predator couple had scared me and I started to reflect on my actions.

I had already planned to meet up with a guy called Win later that week and, although I was still feeling a little down, I decided the positive attention would do me good. We had been chatting on the web for a few weeks and the mystery that surrounded him had captured my interest. He was very reluctant to send any pictures and the one I did see seemed very familiar but I could not think why. His intense behaviour was also familiar. He was an accountant in Pattaya and was in Bangkok for the weekend. I invited him to my place for some drinks with the intention of eating locally. Seconds after walking into my apartment he was on me. He was so enthusiastic in his every movement as if he had been waiting for months to get his hands on me.

'Excuse me. I need to use your bathroom,' he explained.

I noticed the large rucksack that he took with him and when after ten minutes he had not re-appeared I started to consider the likelihood of him being a sadistic killer. When the lock finally clicked and the door opened I held my breath in anticipation of what would come and stand before me. He was wearing the smallest, silky sports shorts possible with a vest and long white football socks. Clearly there was some kind of fetish going on here and I did my best not to burst out in laughter. We had barely spoken so I was fascinated by his bold move. It excited me all the same. Win was desperate to fuck me but despite multiple attempts he could not stay hard. His desperation was hampering his performance. Just as we were about to give up he managed the task. It was rushed, awkward and anything but pleasurable. It also felt different. As I reached behind and felt the shaft of his cock I noticed he was not wearing the condom I had given him.

'What the fuck are you doing? Why are you not wearing the bloody condom! What's wrong with you Thai guys? No wonder there is a problem with sexual diseases here!'

My little rant passed quickly as did Win's orgasm. It was the worst sex I had ever had with the least attractive guy I had ever entertained. I have a theory that if a guy is less attractive than you then he will normally be a good fuck because he will be 'grateful' and therefore very attentive. Grateful or not this guy was dull! I sat waiting for him to change back into his normal civilian clothing and pack away his fetish outfit for another night. I felt a little under the weather. My throat was sore and my body ached a little. Win noticed and proceeded to take my temperature and pulse.

'Win, since when do accountants give out medical advice?'

He just smiled.

'You are not an accountant are you?' Win did not need to speak because I had already placed the pieces of this crazy jigsaw together. This was not Win the accountant, this was the psycho doctor Tan! I knew his face was familiar.

'What the fuck is going on your crazy idiot?' I yelled. 'Why did you lie to me and pretend you were someone else?'

'Because you would not meet me,' he innocently replied.

'Yes, because you are fucking mental. Get out of my house!'

I was furious with myself for being stupid once again, though took some comfort in being flattered by his insistence on meeting me. I felt a little uneasy in the condo that night and imagined him appearing on my balcony in the early hours. For weeks I heard nothing until he made his final mark in a phone call that put the fear of God in me and changed my promiscuous behaviour forever.

'Jack? It's Tan. Remember me?'

'I told you never to call me again. Fuck off!' I screamed.

'Are you positive?' he asked with an evil tone in his voice.

'Yes I'm positive! I don't want to ever hear from you again!'

'No. I mean ARE YOU POSITIVE?' Tan pronounced each word slowly and clearly.

'I don't know what you are talking about now fuck off!'

'Think about it Jack!'

His voice was menacing and slowly I was starting to realise what he was referring to, though I prayed to God he was wrong.

'What are you trying to say?'

'I'm HIV positive Jack and now so are you! I only slept with you to pass it on!' he laughed.

I was dumbstruck and speechless and simply pressed the end call button. I sat on the edge of the bed as the colour drained away from my cheeks. My hands started to shake and my mouth dried rapidly. I barely made it to the toilet as the vomit rushed from my gut. I dropped to the floor and screamed. I was petrified. It was 10.30 p.m. and no clinic would be open now. I stupidly had never been tested before and was unsure of the procedure. Reading online about the signs and symptoms of early onset HIV I convinced myself that I had it. I did not sleep for one minute that night. It was the longest night and the longest one-hour wait for the results at the clinic the next day.

'Congratulations you are negative!' smiled the nurse. The relief was tremendous though I knew it would be a further three months before I could finally move on. But I was now a reformed character. For six months I had risked my health and my life with random meets and poor judgement. I did not regret the mistakes I had made and

I felt it was something I needed to explore in order to grow as a person. I had always been too naïve and led too sheltered a life. In order to know what I really wanted in life and in a relationship I had to discover what I did not want! It may have been a long time coming and involved a lot of heartbreak along the way, but after thirty-five years my life was set to change forever. My white knight had finally arrived!

CHAPTER FORTY-FOUR

It would only be right that the place where I would finally meet my true love would be at the place I have spent most of my life – the gym! For three months I had been living my new life, focusing on health and fitness, friends and work. I was still a little lonely but I had found my inner peace and happiness for myself and not through another person. I had not had random sex or cruised seedy websites. I had 'dated' a few guys but there was never any chemistry.

It was the week before Valentine's and as usual I was at the gym after work. There was a large crowd there that evening and most of the equipment was occupied. I was standing around aimlessly, waiting for the opportunity to jump in.

'You can share,' said a voice from behind. His accent was unusual and I figured he was not Thai. I turned around and saw the most handsome, friendly face beaming back at me. He was extraordinary. I had never noticed him at the gym before, though I realised I was not normally here so late. He had a thick mop of black hair with the largest, sexiest smile I had ever seen. It extended from cheek to cheek and his teeth were perfect. He just kept smiling before breaking out into laughter on account of my staring.

'Ummm sure!' I responded eagerly. When he lifted himself up off the bench it was difficult not to be impressed by his incredible chest and back. He was the perfect V-shape. His back was so broad and his pecs would be the envy of many a girl let alone a guy! I was unable to take my eyes off his cheekbones. The definition was compelling and his skin was smooth and completely hairless. His name was Nino and he was from Indonesia. He was the single most friendly and handsome person I had ever encountered and it was not long before we were chatting and exchanging stories. I took my time with my reps because I did not want the moment to pass. I did not even know if he was gay or not.

'Well, I have to go now Jack,' he smiled. 'Was nice meeting you! Hope to see you around!'

I knew I could not let him walk away now. For two years I had visited this gym and never seen him once. What if I had to wait another two?

'Nino! Can I... can I umm, get your number? Maybe we could grab a coffee or see a movie?'

'Yeah sure!' The infectious smile was hard to resist.

I was so excited to meet Nino the following day. I was totally unable to focus at work and I watched the clock slowly ticking away to seven p.m. I arrived first and stood outside the coffee shop, my heart beating like a jungle drum. The anticipation was incredible. At 7.05 p.m. he arrived. As he walked towards me I found it hard to contain my excitement. The tremendous glint in his eye was captivating and spoke a thousand words. We had coffee before catching a movie and we talked continuously. I was fascinated by what he had to say. I could not stop staring at his perfectly formed lips and prayed he would lean in for a kiss at some point now that we had established we were both gay. I hung on to his every word and repeatedly asked questions so that I could learn even more about this intriguing man. He was perfection to me. His body looked even better in his tight blue Diesel T-shirt.

Constantly throughout the film I looked sideways to admire Nino and to convince myself that he really was sitting next to me, enjoying *my* company. A few times he turned simultaneously and just broke out into laughter.

'Sorry,' I whispered.

'It's cute. No worries,' he replied politely.

I am not sure I watched much of the film. I was just fixated on the incredible vibe I was feeling from Nino. I felt like we were old friends or lovers. He had an amazing gift or ability at making you feel so at ease and so content. There was absolutely nothing to dislike about him. I frequently closed my eyes during the film and enjoyed the tranquillity in my mind. I knew that Nino was just what I had always been searching for and this time I knew I was not being naïve. At the end of the night a part of me wanted him to ask me back to his place, but when he kissed my cheek and told me he would call I assumed that was the end of my dream.

I thought about Nino continually that night and battled with myself to avoid putting him under too much pressure to meet again. Before I had even picked up my phone to text him, Nino sent a sweet message. *I had a great time Jack. You are so sweet and I would love to get to know you more. Meet for lunch tomorrow?*

I fell back on my bed and smiled profusely. I was elated.

I knew *this* one was going to be different. I could just feel it. Something inside of me was confirming that Mr Right had finally arrived.

The second date was as exhilarating as the first. The sense of familiarity with each other was unreal. I just felt so comfortable in his presence and I sensed he felt the same way. Even if we were not talking, the silence was not awkward and from the way he looked back at me I was confident Nino liked me too. He had even done some research about my home country which made me smile so much as it showed an eagerness to know more about me. The conversation ranged from favourite films and countries visited, to family and education. We seemed to have the essentials in common, especially our love of Julia Roberts. In fact, it was hard not to make a comparison between her smile and Nino's!

It was impossible to make the lunch last longer than the three hours it already had. As the waiter paced up and down beside us we both sniggered and knew it was time to make a move. I didn't want things to be the same with Nino as they had been with all the other guys – a quick romp and then no further contact. But I wanted to take things further.

'Hey, you fancy watching a DVD at my place?' I asked as my heart froze with the fear of rejection.

'Sounds great Jack!'

We were like two virgins sat at opposite ends of the sofa. It was clear we both wanted something to happen but neither was forward enough to take the lead. I made every possible excuse to leave my seat and each time I returned I edged a little closer to Nino. I was like a hyena stalking my prey, though less subtle I felt. I caught a glimpse of Nino smirking and burst out laughing.

'What?' I moaned playfully.

'Nothing. You are just funny.'

I wasn't sure if being funny was my intention here. I was trying to be sexy, alluring even, but I guess funny would have to do for now. I could not hold off any longer.

'Can I kiss you?' I asked.

'You are asking permission to kiss me? How old fashioned,' he sniggered.

I lent in slowly and he giggled. It was not the response I wanted but it was endearing all the same. I tried a second time and this time Nino was moving towards me. His scent was fresh like an ocean breeze and as his lips touched mine I closed my eyes and wrapped myself up in the magical moment. His kiss was as polite as he was – no unexpected ramming of tongues or grabbing at my face. It was gentle. I placed my hand on his left cheek and was amazed at how soft his skin felt. His breathing intensified as he bit on my bottom lip ever so delicately. He kissed like a gentleman from a Jane Austin film and it was so romantic. It was then that I realised I had never experienced romance before. And, like a true gentleman, he didn't take it beyond kissing. We kissed for what seemed like hours and as we finally parted I was sure my lips were swollen and ruby red. My words came out slurred and I was all a flutter like an eighteenth-century damsel. We both fell about laughing again. Neither of us were familiar with behaving in this way and so both of us knew this seemed so different.

I didn't see Nino during the following week as he was busy at work preparing for an exhibition that he was involved with. A part of me wondered if he was changing his mind about us and giving me the cold shoulder. Maybe he has found someone else I kept telling myself. I found it impossible to focus in work and the only topic I talked to Chloe and Luke about was Nino, so much so that on one occasion when we met up Chloe banned the name *Nino* for twenty minutes. I lasted three! I was absolutely besotted with him and was checking my phone every minute in the desperate hope of a message or call from him. When an invite to join him and his friend at the weekend came I could not help but sit there beaming, re-reading his message several times. Meeting his friends seemed serious. A good sign surely?

Friday night came around slowly and although I was reluctant to go to the local gay dance club I eagerly stood outside waiting for Nino to arrive. I had only been to this club once before. It was not really my scene. As a white man in Bangkok it was hard to blend in to the crowd and as flattered as I was with the amount of attention I could attract, I was uncomfortable. I was also dreading the prospect of encountering a few of my late night playthings in there!

Nino arrived five minutes after me, accompanied by Ed, one of his close friends from Jakarta. Ed was so quiet and mysterious looking but his charming smile made him instantly approachable. Inside the club I kept my eyes to the floor and grabbed on to the back of Nino's T-shirt as we made our way to the bar for the first of many drinks. The club was incredibly busy and dancing was an impossibility. Instead people moved only their heads and shoulders in rhythm to the music. When one guy caught my eye and gave a smile, Nino wrapped his arm around my waist and pulled me in. Admittedly it felt like a lion marking it's territory but it was also so gentlemanly. It was at that moment that I realised I no longer needed the attention or approval of others that I had so longed for. The attention of Nino was more than enough. I moved a little closer and kissed him. In public! I could not recall a time when I had kissed a guy in public in a room full of so many spectators. I was comfortable in my own skin for the first time and it was all because of Nino. I wanted to tell him I loved him at the moment but as we had been dating for only a week it seemed crazy so I resisted.

Two hours later and a short taxi ride home and we were back at my place, earlier than I had expected and minus Ed. He was staying at Nino's place, though clearly without

Nino. I was relieved that the night had not ended in a drunken mess. I did not want to end up in bed with Nino when intoxicated. I wanted to savour every passionate moment and not wake up alone in bed the following morning when he realised he had made a mistake.

We headed straight for my bedroom and slowly he undressed me. He was attentive and delicate as expected. I slowly pulled his T-shirt above his head and almost gasped at the beauty beneath. It was better than anticipated. Broad, defined and firm. The sight of his muscular, manly frame was so horny. He kissed my neck gently and bit my bottom lip seductively. My toes curled with each nibble. Slowly lowering ourselves to the bed, Nino and I embraced in a loving, beautiful hug that sent shivers throughout my entire body. It was better than any orgasm I had experienced previously. For the first time I knew this was what it felt like to be truly in love with someone. Nino was so gentle and as he entered me from behind I knew we were not fucking, we were making love, something I had not experienced before. We never once broke our embrace. Our fingers interlocked with our hands pressed into the pillows. His breath danced around my ear lobes and as he kissed my cheeks and neck by body spasmed. We fell asleep in the same position and eight hours later we woke from our peaceful slumber. The excitement of the whole event cancelled out any negative impact of the alcohol consumption the night before. I jumped out of bed with great excitement knowing that today was the start of something great in my life.

Leaving Nino peacefully resting under the soft white linen I ran to the coffee shop outside my apartment to buy some breakfast delights. The letter waiting in my post box distracted me somewhat and I returned to my room minus any edible pleasures.

'Hey Jack. What's wrong? You look really white,' said Nino.

'I am okay. Shit. I forgot breakfast.'

Nino was so intuitive. In just a short amount of time he had already developed an ability to decipher my behaviour. A man of few words at times, he simply wandered over and wrapped his arms around me until he knew I was ready to talk.

'It's my annulment document. I guess this officially marks the end of my life with Maria,' I sniffled.

'Jack,' Nino replied assertively. 'This is not the end of a life but merely the end of one chapter and the beginning of another.'

He was so right and I knew that whatever the next chapter would bring, what was certain was that this character would be staying for a very long time to come.

'I love you Nino,' I whispered

'I love you too Jack'. And with that he gave me his warmest signature smile.